APPLIED MATHEMATICS

APPLIED MATHEMATICS

MATHEMATICS

for Radio and Communication

Engineers

by CARL E. SMITH, B.S., M.S., E.E.

President, Cleveland Institute of Electronics
President, Smith Electronics

DOVER PUBLICATIONS, INC.

NEW YORK

Manufactured in the United States of America

Dover Publications, Inc.
180 Varick Street
New York 14, N.Y.

To

My Students

WHEREVER THEY ARE

PREFACE

THE material formerly presented by the author of this book as a practical home-study course is now offered as a series of radio and communication engineering books. These volumes may serve as a refresher course for persons already familiar with the subject, or as a study guide in correspondence[1] or residence school courses for those desiring a comprehensive treatment. The reader is more likely to learn correctly and rapidly if this material is used in a plan of directed study. However, for those who do not have time to take advantage of available courses, the books should prove valuable for reading and reference purposes.

This first commercial edition of "Applied Mathematics" has been preceded by four private editions used in a practical home-study course of the Smith Practical Radio Institute. The preparation of this course was started in 1934 to meet the needs of a group of radio broadcasting operators and engineers who had irregular working hours. The course is for the student who has a high-school education or the equivalent and is familiar with the popular terminology used in radio.

Chapters 9 and 10 cover the requirements of simultaneous equations in mesh circuits and quadratic equations in complex circuits having multiple resonance frequencies. The author is indebted to Mr. Daniel B. Hutton for assisting with the preparation of the material in these two chapters.

The advanced section, Chaps. 12 to 15 inclusive, presents a simplified treatment of calculus, series, and wave forms. Elementary calculus concepts assist in understanding the theory, such as that di/dt expresses the rate of current change with

[1] These books are a part of the general plan for a practical home study course offered by the Cleveland Institute of Radio Electronics Cleveland, Ohio. Further information is available upon request.

respect to time. Another illustration is the determination of impedance matching by maximizing the power transfer. The material on series is given because of their use in evaluating functions and making simple engineering approximations. The treatment of wave forms gives the underlying mathematics for analyzing and synthesizing wave shapes found in television and pulse techniques.

The section devoted to tables and formulas is included to make this mathematics handbook self-contained. The other books of this series will refer to this material whenever it is needed.

The author wishes to acknowledge the helpful cooperation which has been received from all sides. In particular, he wishes to thank the many students who by their constructive criticisms have helped to mold this course into its present form, and Beverly Dudley for his careful reading of the manuscript and for the suggestions that he has made for the improvement of the text in a number of places.

CARL E. SMITH.

THE PENTAGON,
WASHINGTON, D.C.,
July, 1945.

ACKNOWLEDGMENT

The table of Bessel functions on pages 285–293 has been taken from pages 171–179 of "Funktionentafeln mit Formeln und Kurven" by Jahnke and Emde, and the sine and cosine integral tables on pages 295–298 are from pages 6–9 of the same work. Copyright, 1933, by B. G. Teubner, in Leipzig. Copyright vested in the U. S. Alien Property Custodian, 1943, pursuant to law. Reproduced by permission of the Alien Property Custodian in the public interest, under license number A—963.

CONTENTS

APPLIED MATHEMATICS

APPLIED MATHEMATICS

CHAPTER 1

ARITHMETIC

Mathematics is one of the most valuable tools possessed by the engineer. This is especially true of the radio and communication engineer because the analysis of electric circuits is largely a study of linear equations. An example is the linear relation of Ohm's law,

$$E = IR \tag{1}$$

The simplicity of this law and its extensive use when working out electric problems have in a large measure been responsible for the rapid advance of the electrical industry.

Communication systems in general depend upon three things: (1) sending facilities; (2) transportation facilities in the form of telephone lines and radio links; and (3) receiving facilities. The study of the networks involved in such systems is nothing more than a study of alternating current at audio and radio frequencies. Such a study is materially clarified and simplified if one has the ability to apply the essential mathematics. The mathematics presented in this book is not difficult but must be thoroughly mastered if real progress is to be made through the rest of this series of books. Since many of the readers will have already had this mathematics it should not be a burden for them to answer the exercises at the end of each chapter as a matter of review.

Signless Numbers.—The child makes his first acquaintance with numbers in counting the objects of a group. These are simple signless numbers made up of arabic numerals or combinations of arabic numerals, thus

1, 2, 3, 4, 5, 6, 7, 8, 9, 10, 11, 12, 13, etc.

These signless numbers obey the arithmetic processes of addition and multiplication.

Example 1. Add 3 to 6.
Solution. 3 + 6 = 9. *Ans.*
Example 2. Multiply 2 by 6.
Solution. 2 × 6 = 12. *Ans.*

Real Numbers.—As the child's experience increases he will soon desire to use the arithmetic processes of subtraction and division. Occasionally the result cannot be expressed in the simple system of signless numbers. For instance, if the mercury in the thermometer drops below zero, or if he wishes to subtract a large number from a small number, the result is no longer in the simple system of signless numbers.

To expand the number system to take care of all four arithmetic processes, it is necessary to include a zero and negative numbers. The signless numbers will then be considered positive numbers even though no sign is used. This system of real numbers considered thus far is one of whole numbers called "integers" or "integral numbers." Whole numbers are called "even numbers" when exactly divisible by 2 and "odd numbers" when not exactly divisible by 2.

The real number system consists of *zero;* all *whole numbers;* all *rational numbers,* which can be expressed as whole numbers in fraction form; and all *irrational numbers,* which cannot be expressed as simple fractions. For instance, the diagonal of a square having sides one unit in length can be expressed as the square root of 2, thus; $\sqrt{2}$. The $\sqrt{2}$ is an irrational number which cannot be expressed as a simple fraction.

Example 3. Harry has $9 but owes Tom $12. What is Harry's financial status?
Solution. $9 − $12. = −$3. *Ans.*
This means that he is $3 in debt. Harry actually owns less than nothing.
Example 4. Divide 6 by 2 and state the kind of number that results.
Solution. 6 ÷ 2 = 3. *Ans.*
The answer is a rational odd integral number. In this example, 6 is the *dividend,* 2 is the *divisor,* and 3 is the *quotient.*
Example 5. Divide 4 by 6 and state the kind of number that results.

Solution. $\dfrac{\overset{2}{\cancel{4}}}{\underset{3}{\cancel{6}}} = \dfrac{2}{3}.$ *Ans.*

The answer is a rational number expressed in fraction form.

Graphical Representation of Real Numbers.—Real numbers can be considered as points along a straight line as shown in Fig. 1. These points are a measure of the distance from the reference point 0. The negative numbers are in the opposite direction to the positive numbers. For instance, if the numbers represent miles along a road that runs from west to east the positive numbers represent mileage east of the reference point and the negative numbers represent the mileage west of the reference point. A person starting at 0, the reference point, going 8 miles east, in the positive direction, and then turning around and going 18 miles west, in the negative direction, will be 10 miles west of the starting point, in the negative direction. In equation form, this is expressed

$$+8 \text{ miles} - 18 \text{ miles} = -10 \text{ miles} \quad Ans.$$

As another instance, consider a 4-volt and a 6-volt battery connected in series. If the positive terminal of the 4-volt battery

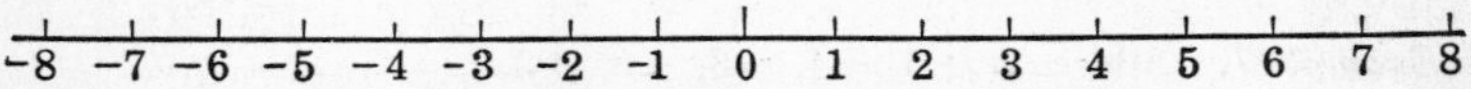

FIG. 1.—Graphical representation of real numbers.

is connected to the negative terminal of the 6-volt battery and the reference point 0 is considered at the negative end of the 4-volt battery, then the voltage at the positive end of the 6-volt battery is

$$+4 \text{ volts} + 6 \text{ volts} = 10 \text{ volts} \quad Ans.$$

which is with respect to the reference point 0. Now, if the 6-volt battery is turned around so that the positive terminals of the 4-volt and 6-volt batteries are connected together, the voltage at the negative end of the 6-volt battery, with respect to the reference point 0 at the negative end of the 4-volt battery, is

$$+4 \text{ volts} - 6 \text{ volts} = -2 \text{ volts} \quad Ans.$$

Smaller values will always be found to the left of the beginning point and larger values will always be found to the right of the beginning point, as shown in Fig. 1.

Example 6. Is the fraction $-\frac{1}{3}$ a larger number than the fraction $-\frac{2}{3}$? Illustrate graphically.

Solution. The fraction $-\frac{1}{3}$ is larger than the fraction $-\frac{2}{3}$ because it lies to the right as represented graphically in Fig. 2. *Ans.*

Rules for Addition and Subtraction.—Adding a negative number (-3) is equivalent to subtracting a positive number $(+3)$.

Thus $\qquad\qquad\qquad 2 + (-3) = -1$
or $\qquad\qquad\qquad 2 - (+3) = -1$

When two numbers of unlike sign are to be added, subtract the smaller from the larger and place the sign of the larger in front of the answer.

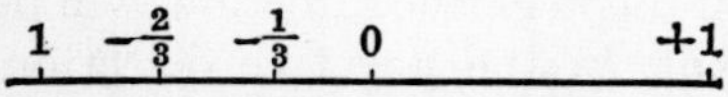

FIG. 2.—Position of negative fractions with respect to -1, 0, and $+1$.

If there are several numbers to be added, first, add all the positive numbers; second, add all the negative numbers; and third, subtract the smaller sum from the larger sum and place the sign of the larger in front of the answer.

Example 7. Add -1, -6, $+4$, -3, $+8$, $+2$.
Solution.

$$\begin{array}{rr} -1 & +4 \\ -6 & +8 \\ -3 & +2 \\ \hline -10 & +14 \end{array} \qquad 14 + (-10) = +4 \quad Ans.$$

Subtracting a negative number, such as -3, is equivalent to adding a positive number, such as 3. The rule for subtraction is to change the sign of the subtrahend and add.

Example 8. Subtract (-6) from 4.
Solution.

$$\begin{array}{l} 4 \text{ minuend} \\ \underline{-6 \text{ subtrahend}} \\ 10 \text{ remainder} \quad Ans. \end{array}$$

or, in equation form,

$$4 - (-6) = 10 \quad Check.$$

Addition can be performed in any order, but subtraction must be performed in the order given. For instance, in addition,

$$2 + 3 = 3 + 2 = 5$$

while, in subtraction,

$$2 - 3 \neq 3 - 2$$

In connection with the above rules, it is well to keep the following facts in mind:

1. Adding a positive number gives a larger value.
2. Subtracting a positive number gives a smaller value.
3. Adding a negative number gives a smaller value.
4. Subtracting a negative number gives a larger value.

Rules for Multiplication and Division.—1. The product or quotient of two positive numbers is always a positive number. For instance, in multiplication, $2 \times 4 = 8$, and, in division, $12 \div 3 = 4$.

2. The product or quotient of two negative numbers is always a positive number. For instance, in multiplication,

$$-2 \times -4 = 8,$$

and, in division, $-12 \div -3 = 4$.

3. The product or quotient of a positive and negative number is always a negative number. For instance, in multiplication, $-2 \times 4 = -8$, and, in division, $-12 \div 3 = -4$.

4. Multiplication can be performed in any order while division must be performed in the order written. For instance, in multiplication, $2 \times 4 = 4 \times 2 = 8$, but, in division,

$$12 \div 3 \neq 3 \div 12.$$

5. In a series of different operations, the multiplications are performed first, the divisions second, the additions third, and the subtractions fourth. Terms of a grouping, such as between parentheses, should be solved before performing the operation on the grouping.

Example 9. Solve: $12 \div 3 - 2 \times 9 \div 3 + 10 \times 2 - 2$.
Solution. Performing the multiplications, $12 \div 3 - 18 \div 3 + 20 - 2$
Performing the divisions, $\qquad\qquad\qquad 4 - 6 + 20 - 2$
Performing the additions, $\qquad\qquad\qquad 24 - 6 - 2$
Performing the subtractions, $\qquad\qquad\quad 16$ *Ans.*
Example 10. Solve: $[(2 \times 6) - (5 - 8)] \div (3 + 2)$.
Solution. Performing the operations within the parenthesis groupings,
$$[(12) - (-3)] \div (5)$$
Combining terms in the bracket, $\qquad\qquad 15 \div 5$
Performing the division, $\qquad\qquad\qquad 3$ *Ans.*

Cancellation.—Cancellation is a process used to shorten mathematical problems involving a series of multiplications and divisions. The following are rules for cancellation:

1. Any factor below the line can be divided into any factor above the line, or any factor above the line can be divided into any factor below the line.

2. Any factor common to factors of a term above and factors of a term below the line can be divided into each.

3. After canceling all factors possible, the answer is obtained by dividing the product of all the factors above the line by the product of all the factors below the line.

Example 11.   Solve $\dfrac{5 \times 3 \times 16 \times 8}{15 \times 8 \times 4 \times 3}$.

Solution.   Divide 5 into 15, 8 into 16, and 4 into 8, thus

$$\frac{\cancel{5} \times 3 \times \overset{2}{\cancel{16}} \times \overset{2}{\cancel{8}}}{\underset{3}{\cancel{15}} \times \cancel{8} \times \cancel{4} \times 3} = \frac{3 \times 2 \times 2}{3 \times 3}$$

Divide 3 into the 3 in the numerator and the 3 in the denominator, and, after multiplying the resulting terms in the numerator, perform the division to obtain

$$\frac{\overset{1}{\cancel{3}} \times 2 \times 2}{\underset{1}{\cancel{3}} \times 3} = \frac{2 \times 2}{3} = \frac{4}{3} = 1\frac{1}{3} \quad Ans.$$

With a little practice all the operations can be done without rewriting the fraction.

Fractions.—Fractions are valuable to represent numbers between consecutive whole numbers or a certain portion of a whole number. A fraction is an indicated division with the denominator below the line representing the number of equal parts into which the whole number is divided and the numerator above the line representing the number of these equally divided parts to be taken. A fraction that has a numerator smaller than the denominator is called a "proper fraction," while a fraction that has a numerator equal to or greater than the denominator is called an "improper fraction." A proper fraction, therefore, is less than 1 and an improper fraction is equal to or greater than 1. Equivalent fractions are fractions that have the same value.

If a whole number is associated with a fraction, the number is called a "mixed number." The answer to Example 11 is a mixed number and means $1 + \frac{1}{3}$. A mixed number can be converted into an improper fraction by multiplying the whole number by the denominator of the fraction and adding this number to the numerator, thus

$$1 + \frac{1}{3} = \frac{3 \times 1 + 1}{3} = \frac{3 + 1}{3} = \frac{4}{3} \quad Ans.$$

The following are some useful principles for fractions:

1. If the numerator and denominator are multiplied or divided by the same number, the value of the fraction does not change. Thus

$$\frac{6 \times 2}{8 \times 2} = \frac{12}{16} = \frac{6}{8} = \frac{3}{4} \quad Ans.$$

or $$\frac{6\!\!\!/2}{8\!\!\!/2} = \frac{3}{4} \quad Check.$$

2. If the numerator is multiplied by a number, or the denominator is divided by it, the fraction is multiplied by the number. Thus

$$\frac{6}{8} \times 2 = \frac{6 \times 2}{8} = \frac{12}{8} = \frac{3}{2} = 1\frac{1}{2} \quad Ans.$$

or $$\frac{6}{8} \times 2 = \frac{6}{8\!\!\!/2} = \frac{6}{4} = \frac{3}{2} = 1\frac{1}{2} \quad Check.$$

3. If the numerator is divided by a number, or the denominator is multiplied by it, the fraction is divided by the number.

$$\frac{6}{8} \div 2 = \frac{6\!\!\!/2}{8} = \frac{3}{8} \quad Ans.$$

or $$\frac{6}{8} \div 2 = \frac{6}{8 \times 2} = \frac{6}{16} = \frac{3}{8} \quad Check.$$

4. To add fractions, first, convert all the fractions to the same denominator; second, add all the numerators, and third, place this sum over the denominator. Thus

$$\frac{1}{7} + \frac{1}{3} + \frac{1}{2} = \frac{6}{42} + \frac{14}{42} + \frac{21}{42} = \frac{41}{42} \quad Ans.$$

Since 42 is the smallest denominator that can be used for these fractions, it is called the "L.C.D." (the least common denominator).

5. To subtract one fraction from another, first convert both fractions to the same denominator; second, subtract one numerator from the other numerator; and third, place the

remainder over the denominator. Thus

$$\frac{1}{5} - \frac{1}{6} = \frac{6}{30} - \frac{5}{30} = \frac{1}{30} \quad Ans.$$

6. To multiply fractions, multiply the numerators together for the new numerator and the denominators together for the new denominator. Thus

$$\frac{2}{3} \times \frac{3}{5} = \frac{2 \times 3}{3 \times 5} = \frac{2}{5} \quad Ans.$$

7. To divide fractions or to simplify complex fractions, invert the divisor and multiply, thus

$$\frac{\frac{2}{3}}{\frac{3}{5}} = \frac{2}{3} \div \frac{3}{5} = \frac{2}{3} \times \frac{5}{3} = \frac{10}{9} = 1\frac{1}{9} \quad Ans.$$

The *reciprocal* of a number is the fraction that has the number as the denominator and 1 as the numerator. Thus, the reciprocal of 3 is $\frac{1}{3}$. The reciprocal of a fraction is 1 over the fraction, or the fraction inverted, thus

The reciprocal of $\frac{2}{3}$ is $\frac{1}{\frac{2}{3}} = \frac{1}{1} \div \frac{2}{3} = \frac{1}{1} \times \frac{3}{2} = \frac{3}{2} \quad Ans.$

The sign of a fraction depends upon three signs, (1) the sign in front of the fraction, (2) the sign of the numerator, and (3) the sign of the denominator. The sign of the fraction is positive if the product of these three signs is positive and the sign of the fraction is negative if the product of these three signs is negative. Thus, for a positive fraction,

$$+ \frac{+3}{+5} = + \frac{-3}{-5} = - \frac{+3}{-5} = - \frac{-3}{+5}$$
$$+ = (+)(+)(+) = (+)(-)(-) = (-)(+)(-) = (-)(-)(+)$$

and for a negative fraction,

$$- \frac{-3}{-5} = - \frac{+3}{+5} = + \frac{-3}{+5} = + \frac{+3}{-5}$$
$$(-) = (-)(-)(-) = (-)(+)(+)$$
$$= (+)(-)(+) = (+)(+)(-)$$

Decimal Fractions.—Decimal fractions have denominators that are multiples of 10. Thus, $\frac{2}{10}$, $\frac{47}{100}$, and $\frac{63}{1000}$ are decimal fractions. For convenience, they can be written omitting the denominator if a decimal point is placed in the numerator so that there will be as many digits to the right of the decimal point as there are zeros in the denominator, thus

$$\frac{2}{10} = 0.2, \qquad \frac{47}{100} = 0.47, \qquad \frac{63}{1,000} = 0.063$$

The zero is written at the left of the decimal point for clearness. This is not necessary but is a very good practice to follow. When there are fewer figures in the numerator than there are zeros in the denominator, zeros are added to the left of the number figures to make the required number of digits.

Every time the decimal point is moved one place, the number changes by 10 times its value. If the decimal point is moved to the right, the number increases; if it is moved to the left, it decreases. The relative value of the digits on either side of the decimal point is illustrated in the following table:

TABLE 1.—RELATIVE VALUE OF DIGITS ON EITHER SIDE OF THE DECIMAL POINT

1,000,000,000.	Billions
100,000,000.	Hundreds of millions
10,000,000.	Tens of millions
1,000,000.	Millions
100,000.	Hundreds of thousands
10,000.	Tens of thousands
1,000.	Thousands
100.	Hundreds
10.	Tens
1.	Units
0.1	Tenths
0.01	Hundredths
0.001	Thousandths
0.0001	Ten thousandths
0.00001	Hundred thousandths
0.000001	Millionths
0.0000001	Ten millionths
0.00000001	Hundred millionths
0.000000001	Billionths

Engineers usually simplify the reading of decimal numbers. Instead of reading 342.79 as "three hundred and forty-two and seventy-nine one-hundredths," they usually read it "three, four, two, point, seven, nine." Another common practice is to express small numbers less than unity up to hundredths in per cent of unity by moving the decimal point to the right two digits, thus, 0.79 may be written 79 per cent of unity.

Exponents.—The exponent of a number is a small figure placed to the right and above the number and means that the number is to be taken that many times as a factor, hence the square of the number 10 is

$$10^2 = 10 \times 10 = 100$$

Similarly, $\qquad 10^3 = 10 \times 10 \times 10 = 1,000$

10^3 is read "10 cube," or "10 raised to the third power." When no exponent is written, it is understood to be 1; hence, $10^1 = 10$. Positive exponents give results greater than unity, if the number raised to the power is greater than unity.

A number raised to a negative power is equivalent to the reciprocal of the number (1 over the number) raised to a positive power, hence

$$10^{-3} = \frac{1}{10^3} = \frac{1}{10} \times \frac{1}{10} \times \frac{1}{10} = 0.1 \times 0.1 \times 0.1 = \frac{1}{1,000} = 0.001$$

Negative exponents give results between zero and unity when the number raised to the negative power is greater than unity.

Since positive exponents are for results greater than unity and negative exponents are for results less than unity, the system can be made complete if the exponent zero always gives unity. Hence, any number raised to the zero power is defined to be unity; thus, $10^0 = 1$.

In order to state general laws for exponents, it is convenient to substitute letters for the numbers as is done in algebra, thus

$$A^n = (A \text{ multiplied by itself } n \text{ times})$$

Hence, when $n = 4$, we have $A^4 = A \cdot A \cdot A \cdot A$. Using this notation, we can write the following laws of exponents:

1. *Addition of Exponents.*

$$A^m A^n = A^{m+n} \qquad (2)$$

This means that (A multiplied by itself m times) (A multiplied by itself n times) = (A multiplied by itself $m + n$ times).

Example 12. $\quad 2^3 \times 2^4 = 2^{3+4} = 2^7$. *Ans.*
Example 13. $\quad 6^{-3} \times 6^4 \times 6^{-8} \times 6^{-6} = 6^{-13}$. *Ans.*

It should be noted that this law is for like numbers raised to the same or different powers. If unlike numbers are raised to powers, it is necessary to raise the respective numbers to the power of their respective exponent before multiplying.

Example 14. $4^2 \times 2^3 = 4 \times 4 \times 2 \times 2 \times 2 = 16 \times 8 = 128.$ *Ans.*

2. *Subtraction of Exponents.*

$$\frac{A^m}{A^n} = A^{m-n} = \frac{1}{A^{n-m}} \tag{3}$$

when $m = n; \dfrac{A^n}{A^n} = A^{n-n} = A^0 = \dfrac{1}{A^0} = 1.$

Example 15. $\dfrac{2^3}{2^2} = 2^{3-2} = 2^1 = 2.$ *Ans.*

Example 16. $\dfrac{11^6}{11^{-7}} = 11^6 \times 11^7 = 11^{13}.$ *Ans.*

Example 17. $\dfrac{5^4}{5^6} = \dfrac{1}{5^6 \times 5^{-4}} = \dfrac{1}{5^2} = 5^{-2}.$ *Ans.*

These examples show that a number in the numerator can be moved to the denominator if the sign of the exponent is changed. Likewise, a number in the denominator can be moved to the numerator if the sign of the exponent is changed.

3. *Multiplication of Exponents.*   To find the power of a power, we multiply the exponents, thus

$$(A^m)^n = A^{mn} \tag{4}$$

Example 18. $(3^5)^3 = 3^5 \times 3^5 \times 3^5 = 3^{15}.$ *Ans.*
Example 19. $(2^{-3})^{-4} = 2^{12}.$ *Ans.*
Example 20. $(4^{-4})^2 = 4^{-8}.$ *Ans.*
Example 21. $(6^2)^{-7} = 6^{-14}.$ *Ans.*

4. *Power of a Product.*   The power of a product can be written as the product of the various factors raised to that power, thus

$$(ABC \cdot \cdot \cdot)^m = A^m B^m C^m \cdot \cdot \cdot \tag{5}$$

Example 22. $(3 \cdot 4 \cdot 5)^2 = 3^2 \cdot 4^2 \cdot 5^2 = 3600.$ *Ans.*

5. *Power of a Fraction.*   The power of a fraction can be written as the power of the numerator divided by the power of the denominator, thus

$$\left(\frac{A}{B}\right)^m = \frac{A^m}{B^m} \tag{6}$$

Example 23. $\left(\dfrac{3}{4}\right)^2 = \dfrac{3^2}{4^2} = \dfrac{9}{16}.$ *Ans.*

Scientific Notation.—Any number can be expressed by scientific notation if it is written as a decimal number between 1 and 10 multiplied by 10 raised to the proper exponent. The use of scientific notation materially simplifies the writing of many numbers used in electrical engineering. It is recommended that the student use scientific notation wherever it will simplify the numbers.

Example 24.   Write the following numbers in scientific notation:

$$6,000,000 \quad = 6 \times 10^6 \quad Ans.$$
$$0.000\,000\,34 = 3.4 \times 10^{-7} \quad Ans.$$

This example shows that the decimal point can be shifted as many places as necessary if the new quantity, or answer, is multiplied by 10 raised to a power equal to the number of places the decimal point is shifted. The power of 10 in the answer is positive if the decimal point is moved to the left and negative if the decimal point is moved to the right.

Example 25.   Simplify the following fraction and express the answer in scientific notation:

$$\frac{4,000 \times 5 \times 10^{-12} \times 2 \times 10^6}{0.0000005 \times 4 \times 10^{16}} = \frac{4 \times 5 \times 2 \times 10^{3-12+6}}{5 \times 4 \times 10^{16-7}}$$
$$\frac{2 \times 10^{-3}}{10^9} = 2 \times 10^{-3-9} = 2 \times 10^{-12} \quad Ans.$$

Conversion of Units.—In radio and communication engineering some quantities would be very small or very large if expressed in common units. The usual practice, therefore, is to use units that can be expressed in quantities of convenient size. For instance, a convenient expression for capacity is micromicrofarad, which is one-millionth of a millionth part of a farad, that is

$$1\mu\mu\text{f} = 0.000000000001 \text{ farad} = 10^{-12}\text{f or } 10^{-12} \text{ farad}$$

Here the Greek letter μ means "micro" and f means "farad." Likewise, one microfarad is one-millionth of a farad and is expressed

$$1 \ \mu\text{f} = 0.000001 \text{ farad} = 10^{-6}\text{f or } 10^{-6} \text{ farad}$$

the term millifarad is rarely used. The abbreviation mfd is used quite commonly on typewriters not having μ and even in printed matter to stand for microfarad.

Inductance values in radio and communication engineering are usually expressed in micromicrohenrys ($\mu\mu$h), microhenrys (μh), or millihenrys (mh). One millihenry is one thousandth of a henry, that is

$$1 \text{ mh} = 0.001\text{h} = 10^{-3}\text{h}$$

Resistance values are usually larger than unity and may be very large. $k\Omega$ is often used for kilohms, meaning "thousands of ohms," while $M\Omega$ is used for megohms, meaning "millions of ohms."

High voltage or wattage is ordinarily expressed as kilovolt (kv) or kilowatt (kw). A kilovolt or kilowatt is one thousand times greater than the volt or watt.

When changing from one size of unit to another, the conversion table on page 243 is very convenient to use. The table on page 239 gives other useful quantitative electrical abbreviations.

Radicals.—If a quantity is divided into n equal factors, then one of the factors is said to be the nth root of the quantity. In other words,

$$(A^{\frac{1}{n}} \text{ multiplied by itself } n \text{ times}) = A \tag{7}$$

The nth root of the quantity A can be written as a fractional exponent or as the nth root of the radical A, thus

$$A^{\frac{1}{n}} = \sqrt[n]{A} \tag{8}$$

Example 26. $9^{\frac{1}{2}} = \sqrt[2]{9} = 3$. *Ans.*

In Eq. (8), $A = 9$, $n = 2$; hence, by Eq. (7),

$$(9^{\frac{1}{2}} \times 9^{\frac{1}{2}}) = 9^{\frac{1+1}{2}} = 9 \qquad \text{or} \qquad 3 \times 3 = 9.$$

When expressing square root, the 2 is usually omitted; hence

$$\sqrt[2]{} = \sqrt{} \tag{9}$$

but for other roots it must be indicated.

The number under the radical sign is called the "radicand."

If a quantity is to have a root extracted and also be raised to a power, the following general form is applicable:

$$A^{\frac{m}{n}} = \sqrt[n]{A^m} \tag{10}$$

The numerator of the exponent indicates the power and the denominator of the exponent indicates the root.

Example 27. $A^{\frac{m}{n}} = 8^{\frac{2}{3}} = \sqrt[3]{8^2} = \sqrt[3]{64} = 4 = (\sqrt[3]{8})^2 = 2^2 = 4.$ *Ans*

Square Root of Numbers.—The extraction of the square root is a relatively simple process but that of higher roots is more complicated and calls for the use of logarithms. If the number is expressed in scientific notation, the root can be taken directly providing the exponent of 10 is even. However, if the exponent is odd the decimal point must be shifted one digit. When the exponent of 10 is even, the root of this part of the number is 10 raised to one half the value of the original exponent. If the exponent of 10 is odd, it cannot be divided by 2 to get a whole number. This is the reason for shifting the decimal point.

Example 28. $\sqrt{1.44 \times 10^4} = \sqrt{1.44} \times \sqrt{10^4} = 1.2 \times 10^2.$ *Ans.*
Example 29. $\sqrt{6.4 \times 10^3} = \sqrt{64 \times 10^2} = \sqrt{64} \sqrt{10^2} = 8 \times 10.$
Ans.

The extraction of the square root of a whole number will be explained in the following example:

Example 30. Extract the square root of 69,573.
Step 1. Start at the decimal point and divide the number into groups of two, thus

$$6'95'73'$$

Step 2. Find the largest squared number that will be less than the first group. In this case 2 square gives 4, which is the largest squared number less than 6. Place this 2 to the right as shown and subtract the square of this number from the first group, thus

$$\begin{array}{r} 6'95'73/2 \\ \underline{4} \\ 2 \end{array}$$

Step 3. The second group is brought down with the remainder, in this case giving 295.
Step 4. The number in the answer is doubled and brought down as a trial divisor.

Step 5. Another number is added to this trial divisor. This number is so selected that the product of it by the trial divisor will be the largest number that will go into the remainder, thus

$$6'95'73'/26$$
$$\underline{4}$$
$$46/\overline{295}$$
$$\underline{276}$$
$$19$$

Step 6. The process is now repeated, that is, the next group of figures is brought down with the remainder, the answer is doubled and one figure added to it of such a value that the product of the two numbers will be the largest number that will go into the remaider, thus

$$6'95'73/263$$
$$\underline{4}$$
$$46/\overline{295}$$
$$\underline{276}$$
$$523/\overline{1973}$$
$$\underline{1569}$$
$$404$$

The answer for this problem is 263 with a remainder of 404. If more accuracy is desired, it can be obtained by bringing down two ciphers and repeating the above process. *Ans.*

In the above example we had a whole number, but the process would not be changed if we had a decimal quantity to deal with. It is only necessary to keep in mind that the number must be pointed off in groups of two, starting at the decimal point. Examples of pointing off are

$$43'97'32'98'73 \qquad 0.00'07'56 \qquad 0.78'03$$

The student should work a considerable number of these problems to become familiar with the procedure.

Exercises

1. Add: 119, −34, 23, 56, −90, −43.
2. Add: −78, 89, 64, −34, 20, −85.
3. Add: 97, 44, −63, −56, −89.
4. Add: 45, −70, −54, 34, 24, −89, 865.
5. Subtract (−78, 87, −43) from −98.
6. Subtract (34, 67, −91, −52) from (45, −19, −65, −78).
7. Subtract −89 from (13, −76).
8. Multiply: 18 × −5 × 6 × −13.

9. Solve $\dfrac{18 \times 10^3}{6 \times 10^2}$.

10. Solve $\dfrac{8 \times -6 \times 10^{-11} \times 10^{-4}}{-4 \times 10^{16} \times 3^2}$.

11. Solve $\dfrac{6^{10} \times 6^{-9} \times 6^{-18}}{6^{54} \times 6^{-45}}$.

12. Express the following in scientific notation: 987,000; 76.456; 0.0007; 9,000.00; 8,976,500.01; 12,000,000,000,000,000,000.

13. Solve $\dfrac{0.0000006 \times 10^6 \times 100,000.00}{0.48 \times 10^{-1} \times 0.0000004}$.

14. Express each of the following in units, micro units and in micromicro units: 0.0000009 farad; 1,000 mh; 6μf; 67μμf; 104μh; 0.0003μf; 0.1μf; 0.008 farad.

15. Find the square root of the following numbers: 889,635; 9,976; 9,940.09; 5.890331; 0.0000000009; 0.00047; 0.004978.

CHAPTER 2

LOGARITHMS

Where four or more significant figures are required, logarithms may be used to advantage in all computations except addition and subtraction. Every engineer should be proficient in their use; hence the following notes and definitions are given to refresh the memory.[1]

A Logarithm is an exponent; therefore the same laws apply to logarithms as to exponents in general. This statement must be qualified slightly, because the base must be positive and other than 1.

To a person who thoroughly understand exponents, logarithms should be very easy to understand. Common logarithms are based upon the use of 10 raised to positive and negative powers. In Chap. 1, 10 was raised to positive and negative powers. This chapter goes one step further and introduces decimal powers. A table of logarithms is merely the systematic arrangement of the value of 10 raised to decimal powers. The base of common logarithms is 10.

$$\left.\begin{array}{l}\text{The } logarithm \\ \text{of } any \text{ number} \\ \text{to the base 10}\end{array}\right\} = \left\{\begin{array}{l}\text{the power to which} \\ \text{10 must be raised to} \\ \text{produce the number}\end{array}\right.$$

This may sound complicated, but it is really quite simple; for instance, $100 = 10^2$. Now the logarithm of 100 to the base 10 is 2, the power to which 10 must be raised to produce 100. Consider another illustration which is more general,

$$10^{2.457882} = 287$$

[1] Certain portions of this chapter have been taken with permission from Dana and Willmarth, "Engineering Problems Manual," published and copyrighted by McGraw-Hill Book Company, Inc., New York.

This equation says that the logarithm of 287 is written

$$\log 287 = 2.457882,$$

which means that 10 must be raised to the 2.457882 power to produce 287; this was obtained from the logarithm tables.

If 10 is raised to the third power, the result is 1,000. From this it is seen that the logarithm of any number between 100 and 1,000 will be a decimal number between 2 and 3. If 10 is raised to the first power, the answer is 10, so that $\log 10 = 1$, and the logarithm of any number from 10 to 100 will be decimal numbers between 1 and 2.

$10^0 = 1$; *not* 0, which is a common mistake. This says in terms of logarithms that $\log 1 = 0$, so numbers between 1 and 10 have logarithms between 0 and 1.

The discussion so far has dealt with positive exponents of 10. That is, all numbers greater than 1 have positive logarithms.

Now consider 10^{-1}. From the theory of exponents this can be written $10^{-1} = 1/10^1 = 0.1$. This says that $\log 0.1 = -1$. Likewise, $10^{-2} = 1/10^2 = 0.01$, or $\log 0.01 = -2$. A more general case is $10^{-1+.551450} = 0.356$, or $\log 0.356 = -1 + .551450$. This was taken from the logarithm table. It is seen from the above illustrations that any number between 0.1 and 1 will have a logarithm of $-1+$. decimal. Between 0.01 and 0.1 the logarithm will be $-2+$. decimal; between 0.001 and 0.01 the logarithm will be $-3+$. decimal.

The logarithm of a number is made up of two parts; a decimal, called the "mantissa," and a whole number (which may be positive, negative, or zero), called the "characteristic."

The *mantissa* determines the sequence of digits, and is all that is given in logarithm tables. It is always positive.

The *characteristic* determines the position of the decimal point.

Consider the illustration given above, $\log 287 = 2.457882$. Here 2 is the characteristic and 0.457882 is the mantissa. In the other illustration $\log 0.356 = -1 + .551450$ where -1 is the characteristic and $+.551450$ is the mantissa.

The following simple computations may serve to clear up some confusion regarding the meaning of logarithms and the characteristic numbers:

Base Raised to Exponent = Number	Logarithm of Number = Exponent
$(10)^3 = 1,000$	$\log 1,000 = 3.000$
$(10)^2 = 100$	$\log 100 = 2.000$
$(10)^1 = 10$	$\log 10 = 1.000$
$(10)^0 = 1$	$\log 1 = 0.000$
$(10)^{-1} = 1/10^1 = \frac{1}{10} = 0.1$	$\log 0.1 = -1.000$
$(10)^{-2} = 1/10^2 = \frac{1}{100}$ $= 0.01$	$\log 0.01 = -2.000$
$(10)^{-3} = 1/10^3 = 1/1,000$ $= 0.001$	$\log 0.001 = -3.000$

A brief study of this table of logarithms shows that the decimal point shifts as the characteristic changes. To illustrate this,

$$(10)^{0.5} = (10)^{\frac{1}{2}} = \sqrt{10^1} = 3.1623, \qquad \text{or} \qquad \log 3.1623 = 0.500$$
$$(10)^{1.5} = (10)^{\frac{3}{2}} = \sqrt{10^3} = 31.623, \qquad \text{or} \qquad \log 31.623 = 1.500$$
$$(10)^{2.5} = (10)^{\frac{5}{2}} = \sqrt{10^5} = 316.23, \qquad \text{or} \qquad \log 316.23 = 2.500$$

The characteristic of numbers from 1.0 to 9.99 is 0; from 10 to 99.99, 1; from 100 to 999.99, 2, etc. We can, therefore, make the following simple rule:

RULE FOR CHARACTERISTICS

Numbers	Characteristic
One or over..........	One less than the number of digits to the left of the decimal point
Less than one........	One greater than the number of ciphers between the decimal point and the left-hand digit; negative in sign

The characteristic of a number, written in scientific notation, is *the exponent of* 10. For instance, the characteristic of the number 8.394×10^9 is 9. Likewise, the characteristic of the number 1.743×10^{-3} is -3.

It will be noted in the above illustration that 3.1623, 31.623, and 316.23 all have the same mantissa of $+0.500$ but that the characteristic numbers of the logarithms of these numbers, according to the rule, are 0, 1, and 2, respectively. As the decimal point is shifted, the following result occurs:

Number	Log
316.23	2.500
31.623	1.500
3.1623	0.500
0.31623	$-1 + 0.500$
0.031623	$-2 + 0.500$

Example 1. Determine the logarithm of 2,873.

Solution. The desired portion of a logarithm table is found below.[1]

N		0	1	2	3	4	5	6	7	8	9	Diff.
285	45	4845										
6		6366										
7		7882	8033	8184	8336	8487	8638	8789	8940	9091	9242	151
8		9392	9543	9694	9845	9995	0146	0296	0447	0597	0748	151
9	46	0898										

The figure 287 is found in the left column under *N* and the figure 3 is found at the head of one of the columns. The mantissa of this number 2873 is then found across from 287 and down from 3, and is 0.458336. Always place a decimal point in front of the mantissa. The zero is placed to the left of the decimal point in front of the mantissa when there is no characteristic or when the characteristic is zero. The characteristic is always determined by inspection. From the rule for characteristics, since the number is greater than 1 the characteristic is 1 less than the number of digits to the left of the decimal point and in this case is 3. Then log 2873 = 3.458336. *Ans.*

The characteristic could also have been determined by taking the exponent of 10 when the number was written in scientific notation; thus $2,873 = 2.873 \times 10^3$, where the characteristic is 3.

By the above portion of logarithm table another point can be illustrated. It will be noted that the mantissa corresponding to 2,884 is $+0.459995$ and the one corresponding to the next number 2,885 is $+0.460146$. There has been a change from 0.459999 to $+0.460000$ between these two numbers. Now, for convenience of finding this place, there are dashes under the numbers across to this point, and then above the numbers on across. All numbers above this line must use $+0.45$, while all numbers below this line must affix $+0.46$.

Multiplication by Logarithms.—From Chap. 1 it was learned that to multiply the same numbers raised to various powers it was necessary merely to add their exponents. Since common logarithms are exponents of the same number (in this case, of 10)

[1] Allen's "Six-place Tables," McGraw-Hill Book Company, Inc., New York.

it is necessary only to add the logarithms of the numbers to multiply them. To find the product after the logarithms have been added, it is necessary to determine the number that has a logarithm equal to this sum. This reverse process is called "taking the antilogarithm." To take an antilogarithm, first look up the mantissa of the logarithm in the logarithm table and find the number that gives it. The characteristic of the logarithm merely tells where to place the decimal point.

Example 2.   Multiply 6 × 48.
Solution.   log 6 = 0.778151   mantissa from logarithm tables
         log 48 = 1.681241   characteristic by inspection
Adding, log (6 × 48) = 2.459392

Look up the mantissa + 0.459392 in the logarithm table (this mantissa can be found in the portion of logarithm table given above). The number having this mantissa is 2880. Since 2 is the characteristic, point the number off and get 288.0. *Ans.*

Logarithms are useful in multiplying large numbers, where accuracy to four or five places is sufficient.

Example 3.   Multiply 7,864,591 × 198,642.
Solution.   log 7,864,591 = 6.895644+   mantissa from table
      log   198,642 = 5.297979+   with characteristic affixed
log (7,864,591 × 198,642) = 12.193623+
        antilog 12.193623 = 1,562,000,000,000
                  = 1.562×10^{12} *Ans.*

The student should check all these examples to familiarize himself with the method of using the logarithm table. It will be noted in working the above problems that no interpolation was made. When looking up the antilogrithm, the number giving the nearest to the mantissa was used.

Logarithms are useful in multiplying very small numbers, as illustrated in Example 4.

Example 4.   Multiply 0.000000946 × 0.00087.
Solution.   log 0.000000946 = −7 + 0.975891 = 3.975891 − 10
      log 0.00087   = −4 + 0.939519 = 6.939519 − 10
    log (0.000000946 × 0.00087)
             = −11 + 1.915410 = 10.915410 − 20
                  =   0.915410 − 10
    antilog (0.915410 − 10) = 8.2302×10^{-10} *Ans.*

It will be noted in this example that instead of using a negative characteristic with the mantissa, it is more desirable to use a positive characteristic with the smallest available multiple of (−10) placed on the right-hand side. Since the mantissa is always positive, it is confusing to associate with it a negative characteristic and then always have to remember this detail.

If several numbers are to be multiplied, one addition of their logarithms is sufficient. The antilogarithm of this sum gives their product.

Example 5. Multiply 0.00004871 × 6497 × 1.984.
Solution. log 0.00004871 = 5.687618 − 10
log 6,497 = 3.812713
log 1.984 = 0.297542
$$\overline{9.797873 - 10}$$
antilog (9.797873 − 10) = 0.627875 *Ans.*

Raising numbers to higher powers is accomplished by multiplying the logarithm of the number by the power and taking the antilogarithm.

This operation would be quite a task to multiply out longhand, but by logarithms it is easily done as follows:

Example 6. Find the fifth power of 638, that is, 638⁵.
Solution.   log 638 = 2.804821
Multiplying by the power   5
$$\overline{\text{log } 638^5 = 14.024105}$$
antilog 14.024105 = 105,700,000,000,000 = 1.057 × 10¹⁴ *Ans.*

In this example the effect is the same as that of adding the logarithm of 638 five times and then taking the antilogarithm to obtain the fifth power of the number 638.

Division by Logarithms.—Division of numbers by logarithms is accomplished by subtracting the logarithm of the divisor from the logarithm of the dividend. The antilogarithm of this remainder is the quotient.

Example 7. Divide 8,964 by 479.
Solution.   log 8,964 = 3.952502
log   479 = 2.680336
Subtracting, log $\frac{8,964}{479}$ = 1.272166
antilog 1.272166 = 18.71+ the quotient *Ans.*

The plus sign means that the quotient is greater than indicated owing to not interpolating. Interpolation will be discussed later.

Example 8.   Divide 0.000371 by 791.
Solution.   log 0.000371 = 6.569374 − 10
               log 791   = 2.898176

Subtracting, $\log \dfrac{0.000371}{791} = 3.671198 - 10$

antilog (3.671198 − 10) = 4.69027 × 10⁻⁷   *Ans.*

Extracting the root of a number is accomplished by dividing the logarithm of the number by the root and taking the antilogarithm.

Example 9.   Solve $\sqrt[3]{976}$.
Solution.   log 976 = 2.989450
Dividing,
$$3)\overline{2.989450}$$
log $\sqrt[3]{976}$ = 0.996483
antilog 0.996483 = 9.919   *Ans.*

After the student thoroughly understands the use of positive and negative exponents, logarithms become a convenient tool in solving many problems. Only practice is then needed to make the solution of these problems rapid. Logarithms can be used to save considerable time in multiplying and dividing large numbers and the use of logarithms offers the only practical way to raise numbers to high powers and extract roots larger than 2.

Interpolation.—In order to increase the accuracy to more significant figures, beyond the values read directly from the table, resort is made to interpolation. Interpolation is used in many types of work and should be familiar to the student. Interpolation can be used with logarithm tables because the small difference between numbers is approximately proportional to the difference between their logarithms.

A practical illustration of interpolation is to find the capacity of a variable capacitor when set at 53 degrees. Since the capacity at 50 degrees is 278 micromicrofarad and at 55 degrees is 284 micromicrofarad, the capacity change from 50 degrees to 55 degrees is 284 − 278 = 6 micromicrofarad or ⁶⁄₅ = 1.2 micromicrofarad per degree change of the capacitor dial. Then the capacity for 3 degrees is 3.6 micromicrofarad and is added to the capacity 278 micromicrofarad at 50 degrees to get 281.6 micromicrofarad, the capacity at 53 degrees. This applies only to straight-line variable capacity capacitors.

Applying this principle of interpolation to logarithms, consider the log 78,634. The mantissa of 7863 from the logarithm table is 0.895588, but it is still necessary to obtain the 4 by interpolation. The figure 56 will be found as the "diff" in the right-hand column. At the bottom of the page will be found a table of proportional parts and going across from the "diff" 56 in the left-hand column to the column headed 4. Therefore 22.4 is the proportional part to be added to the above mantissa giving log 78,634 = 4.8956104.

Some logarithm tables do not have proportional parts, so in such cases it will have to be figured out each time. Considering the above illustration,

$$\log 78,630 = 4.895588 \quad \text{(from log tables)}$$
$$\log 78,634 = 4.8956104 \quad \text{(by interpolation)}$$
$$\log 78,640 = 4.895644 \quad \text{(from log tables)}$$

Here the logarithms of 30 and 40 are given in the last two digits of the number but it is desired to secure the logarithm of 34 in these last two digits. The corresponding mantissas for 30 and 40 are 0.895588 and 0.895644 respectively. The difference between 30 and 40 is 10, while the difference in the corresponding mantissa is 56. This is the way to secure the number in the right-hand column under "diff." Corresponding to 34 take 0.4 of 56, which is 22.4 and is the proportional part worked out at the bottom of the page.[1] The logarithm by interpolation is log 87,634 = 4.8956104.

To find the antilogarithm, the above process must be reversed. For illustration, find the antilogarithm of 3.657488. From the logarithm tables,

$$\text{antilog } 3.657438 = 4,544$$
$$\text{antilog } 3.657488 = 4,544.521 \quad \text{(by interpolation)}$$
$$\text{antilog } 3.657534 = 4,545$$

Subtract 3.657438 from 3.657488, giving 50, the proportional part. The difference in this case, as noted in the right-hand column, is 96. Across from 96 on the next page find under 5, not 50 but 48, the nearest number to 50, so the answer will not be exact. To make it exact, take the ratio

$$\frac{50}{96} = \frac{x}{10}$$

Solving for x,

$$x = \frac{500}{96} = 5.21$$

[1] See Allen's "Six-place Tables," McGraw-Hill Book Company, Inc., New York.

Now antilog 3.657488 = 4,544.521, while if the 48 from the table was used, the result would be 4,544.5. Ordinarily the accuracy of the proportional parts table is sufficient, but it can be seen that greater accuracy sometimes can be obtained by using exact proportion.

The student with a thorough understanding of exponents should find that what has been presented on logarithms here is sufficient to enable him to handle any ordinary problem in logarithms. However, it may be well to illustrate by example how to handle the characteristic in extracting the root of small numbers.

Example 10. Extract the fifth root of 0.0004466.
Solution. log 0.0004466 = 6.649919 − 10
Dividing by 5,   log $\sqrt[5]{0.0004466}$ = 1.3299838 − 2
                                    = 9.3299838 − 10
             antilog (9.3299838 − 10) = 0.213788 *Ans.*

It should be pointed out that the negative characteristic placed on the right-hand side (−10 in this case) should *always* be divisible by the root to be extracted. This number is usually made 10 for convenience in routine work.

Example 11. Extract the fourth root of 0.0004466.
Solution. log 0.0004466 = 0.649919 − 4
Dividing by 4,   log $\sqrt[4]{0.0004466}$ = 0.1624797 − 1
                                    = 9.1624797 − 10
             antilog (9.1624797 − 10) = 0.145372 *Ans.*

Operating the Slide Rule.—The slide rule is a graphic logarithm table. Many users of the instrument do not realize this and as a result are not able to make full use of its possibilities.

To multiply numbers, simply add their logarithms. To do it graphically on the slide rule, add the distances that are marked off proportional to the logarithm. To divide, subtract distance corresponding to the dividend. The resulting distance corresponds to the quotient.

The accuracy of a slide rule depends upon the precision with which it is made. A longer slide rule will give better accuracy than a short one, but the accuracy does not increase in direct proportion to the length of the scale. Common 10-inch slide rules will give an accuracy to three significant figures, and on the lower end of the scale it is possible to estimate to the fourth digit.

C and D Scales.—These are the most commonly used scales on the slide rule. An inspection of these scales shows that they start with 1 at the left end, known as "*the* initial index," and are marked off with consecutive numbers to 10 at the other end, which is marked with 1 and is the "right-hand, or final, index." This is a complete graphic logarithm table giving the mantissa which determines the sequence of digits in the number. The decimal point is determined by the characteristic, just as was explained earlier in this chapter. Usually it can be readily determined by inspection.

Rule for Multiplication on the Slide Rule.—1. Lay off the mantissa of the first number on scale *D* by setting the initial index of scale *C* over the graduation corresponding to the first number.

2. The mantissa of the second number is now added by shifting the runner so that its initial index comes over the graduation corresponding to the second number on scale *C*.

3. The mantissa of the product is the sum of the two distances and the answer is read on scale *D* under the hairline of the runner.

Example 12.   Multiply 2 × 4 on the slide rule.
Solution.   The answer 8 is indicated in Fig. 3 by following the above steps.

Rule for Division on the Slide Rule.—1. Lay off the mantissa of the numerator (dividend) on the fixed *D* scale by setting the hairline of the runner on its value.

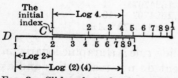

FIG. 3.—Slide-rule scales for multiplication and division.

2. The mantissa of the denominator (divisor) is subtracted by moving the slider so that the value of the divisor is under the hairline too.

3. The mantissa of the quotient is the difference and is found opposite the initial index of scale *C* on scale *D*.

Example 13.   Divide 8 by 4 on the slide rule.
Solution.   Figure 3 also illustrates this problem, which is the reverse of the multiplication. The answer 2 is obtained by following the above steps.

Square Root Rule.—If the characteristic of the number is 0 or an even number, then the square root is found under the left portion of scale *A* on scale *D*. Divide the characteristic by 2 and place the decimal point in the square root according to the result. If the number was originally written in scientific notation, then the exponent of 10 is divided by 2 and the answer is still in scientific notation.

Example 14. Find the square root of 97,969.
Solution. Since the characteristic 4 of this number is even, place the hairline over 97,969 to the left of the center on scale A and read 313 the answer on scale D. The characteristic of the answer is 2, just half that of the original number. Actually only the first three digits of the original number can be read on scale A of the slide rule.

If the characteristic of the number is an odd number, then the square root is found under the right-hand portion of the A scale on the D scale. Subtract 1 from the characteristic of the number and divide by 2 to find the characteristic of the root.

Example 15. Find the square root of 1.56816×10^5.
Solution. Below 1.56816 on the right-hand side of scale A find the answer 3.96×10^2. The characteristic 2 was found by subtracting 1 from 5 and dividing by 2.

Square Rule.—When the hairline is to the left of the middle of the A and B scales (roots less than 3.1623), the square of the number on the D scale is found on the A scale. The characteristic of the squared number is twice that of the original number. If the original number is written in scientific notation, then the answer will also be in scientific notation.

Example 16. Square 240.
Solution. Above 240 on scale D read the answer 57,600 on scale A. The characteristic doubled since the answer was on the left-hand side.

When the hairline is to the right of the middle on scale A and B, the characteristic is found by multiplying the characteristic of the original number by 2 and adding 1. Again, if the original number was in scientific notation, then the answer will also be in scientific notation.

Example 17. Square 6.2×10^3.
Solution. Above 6.2 on scale D read the answer 3.844×10^7 on scale A. The characteristic 7 was obtained by multiplying 3 by 2 and adding 1.

The student must use the slide rule at every opportunity if he wishes to become familiar with its operation and feel confidence in its results.

Folded Scales.—Sometimes when two numbers are being multiplied the second number appears beyond the right-hand index of scale D. Rather than sliding the other index of scale C over the first number and reading the answer at the other end, merely read opposite the second number on the CF scale the answer on the DF scale. For instance 2×6 permits the use of the folded scale to get 12 on scale DF opposite 6 on scale CF. This could have been obtained by placing the other index of scale C over 2 on scale D and reading the answer 12 on scale D opposite 6 on scale C.

It will be of interest to note that the CF and DF scales are folded at π, which is 3.1416. This permits the index to fall about the center of the rule and in addition permits rapid calculations which involve π. For instance, a circle has a diameter of 6 inches. What is its circumference? Set the hairline over 6 on scale D and read the answer ($6\pi = 18.85$) under the hairline on scale DF. In other words it is not necessary to use the slider.

Inverted Scales.—Labor may be saved in many problems through the use of reciprocals. A problem of division may be converted into a problem of multiplication by using the reciprocal of the denominator. (*Note:* The reciprocal of a number is a fraction with 1 over the number.) The CI and CIF scales, which are usually printed in red, are reciprocal scales.

Reciprocal Rule.—When moving a number from the numerator to the denominator of a fraction, or vice versa, write the reciprocal of the number in the position and change the sign of the characteristic of the number. When the initial index of the inverted scale (the CI to the right of the final index of D scale, and the CIF to the left of the DF index) projects, subtract 1 from the characteristic of the number causing the index to project.

Example 18. Multiply $6 \times 4 \times 3$.
Solution. Divide 6 on scale D by 4 on scale CI (which causes multiplication), then slide hairline to 3 on scale C and read the answer 72 on scale D. Since the initial index on the right-hand end of the CI scale is to the right of the final index on scale D, 1 must be added to the characteristic.

The student can get along without these inverted scales but if he is interested in short cuts he can read the instruction book with the slide rule for further information.

A and B Scales.—The *A* and *B* scales consist of two complete logarithm scales, each half as long as scale *D*. Since the values of the logarithm increase twice as fast on scale *A* as on scale *D*, the means of securing square roots and square powers is provided. Opposite a number on scale *D* the square is found on scale *A*. Conversely, a number on scale *A* will have its square root opposite it on the *D* scale.

K Scale.—The *K* scale consists of three complete logarithm scales, each one third as long as scale *D*. The *K* scale gives cubes and cube roots in the same manner as scale *A* gives squares and square roots.

L Scale.—This scale is a complete logarithm table. To take the logarithm of a number, place the hairline of the slider over the number on scale *D* and read the mantissa under the hairline on scale *L*.

The following facts are important to keep in mind when using a slide rule:

1. The slide rule is a graphic logarithm table.

2. The mantissa only is determined from any logarithm table, including the slide rule which is a graphic one.

3. The mantissa determines only the sequence of digits.

4. Characteristics are not given in any logarithm tables.

5. The characteristic is determined by inspection. It is the exponent of 10 when the number is written in scientific notation.

6. The characteristic determines the decimal point.

When multiplying very large or very small numbers on the slide rule, it is convenient to use 10 to some power and place the decimal point after the first digit.

Example 19.   Multiply 0.00000027 × 96000.
Rewrite $2.7 \times 10^{-7} \times 9.6 \times 10^{4}$
Rewrite and multiply $2.7 \times 9.6 \times 10^{-3} = 25.92 \times 10^{-3}$ *Ans.*

This makes it easy to keep track of the decimal point by inspection when scientific notation is employed.

Decimal Point and the Slide Rule.—The last example illustrates how the decimal point can be easily found by inspection. A definite procedure will now be given for keeping track of the decimal point when using the slide rule.

When using numerical logarithms the characteristic is added to the mantissa, but when using the slide rule this cannot be done. However, *keeping track of the characteristic* is the easiest way of determining the decimal point when using a slide rule.

When multiplying by means of numerical logarithms the sum of the mantissas is often more than 1.0 and so 1 must be carried over into the column of the characteristics. If this same problem is solved with a slide rule, it is found that there is an *exact parallel* between the numerical and graphic methods. The distances representing the mantissas will add to one full scale length or more. This corresponds to carrying 1 into the characteristic column; hence a note should be made each time this occurs.

There is a simple, quickly applied, and absolutely accurate rule for decimal points based upon the foregoing facts. This method completely does away with the need of longhand check-

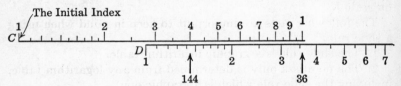

Fig. 4.—Slide-rule scale showing the initial index projecting.

ing, mental shifting of the decimal point, approximate calculations, or any other so-called "system" not based upon logarithms.

The Initial Index.—In the following rules for location of the decimal point, reference is made to "*the* initial index." There are many indexes on a rule; those at the beginning end of any scale are initial indexes, and those at the far end are final indexes. There is one initial index, however, which is so important that it is *the* initial index. When using the C and D scales, *the initial index is the left end of the C scale* for all operations. The graduations begin at the initial index and have increasing values as the final index is approached.

When the slide is in the position shown in Fig. 4, it is said that *the* initial index projects and *a change must be made in the characteristic*. The initial index never projects unless such a change should be made.

Rules for Locating the Decimal Point When Using the C and D Scales.—1. Note the position of *the* initial index as soon as each new term in the problem has been set on the rule

2. If *the* initial index projects, *add* 1 to the logarithmic characteristic of the term which caused the index to project. Thus, for multiplication, add 1 to the logarithmic characteristic of the multiplier which caused the index to project. The characteristic of the answer is the algebraic sum of the characteristics of the terms plus the "added characteristics." For division, add 1 to the logarithmic characteristic of the divisor which caused the index to project. The characteristic of the answer is the algebraic difference of the characteristics of the divisor and dividend.

3. When *the* initial index does not project, make no changes in the characteristics.

4. For continued operations, note the position of the initial index as soon as each new term is set on the rule, and record any necessary addition to the characteristics at once.

Sequence of Operations.—While becoming familiar with this method, the beginner should form the habit of going through the following steps in his slide-rule work:

1. Set the work up in a suitable form for a slide-rule computation. (See examples below.)

2. Indicate the logarithmic characteristic of each term somewhere close by. (Just above the multipliers and below the divisors is convenient.)

3. Note the position of the initial index as soon as each new factor is set on the rule.

4. Record the "added characteristic" if the initial index projects.

5. Determine the characteristic of the answer.

Multiplication.

Example 20. Multiply 36 by 0.0004.
1. Set the work up in a suitable form.
2. Indicate the logarithmic characteristic above each multiplier.

$$\begin{array}{cccc} & +1 & & \\ +1 & -4 & +1 - 4 + 1 = -2 \\ (36)(0.0004) = & 0.0144 & = 1.44 \times 10^{-2} \quad Ans. \end{array}$$

3. Referring to Fig. 4, it is seen that the initial index projects.
4. Hence 1 must be added to the characteristics.
5. Adding the characteristics gives $1 - 4 + 1 = -2$ as the characteristic of the answer. The answer is now pointed off according to this characteristic.

Division.

Example 21. Divide 0.512 by 800.

1. Set the work up in a suitable form.

2. Indicate the logarithmic characteristic above the dividend and below the divisor.

$$\frac{\overset{-1}{0.512}}{\underset{\substack{+2\\+1}}{800}} = \overset{-1\ -3\ =\ -4}{0.00064} = 6.4 \times 10^{-4} \quad Ans.$$

3. The initial index projects.

4. Hence 1 must be added to the characteristic of the divisor giving $2 + 1 = 3$.

5. The characteristics of the divisor are subtracted from the characteristics of the dividend giving $-1 - 3 = -4$ as the characteristic of the quotient. The answer is now pointed off according to this characteristic.

Multiplication and Division.

Example 22. Solve $\dfrac{\overset{-4}{(0.0003)}\overset{+3}{(1440)}}{\underset{\substack{0\\+1}}{6.0}} = 7.2 \times 10^{-2} \quad Ans.$

Place the characteristics above the respective numbers of the numerator and below the respective numbers of the denominator. Place the hairline over 3 on the *D* scale for the first number of the numerator. Slide the *C* scale until 6 is under the hairline to make the division. Since the initial index projects, add $+1$ below the 0 of the denominator. Next slide the hairline over 144 on the *C* scale. Since this cannot be done, the initial index is moved to the same point on the *D* scale that the final index was located. Now the hairline can be placed over 144 on the *C* scale. The initial index does not project, so no characteristic is added. The answer is now found on the *D* scale under the hairline and is 72. The characteristic of this answer is obtained by adding those of the numerator and subtracting those of the denominator, thus

$$(-4 + 3) - (0 + 1) = (-1) - (+1) = -2$$

The answer is then 0.072 or 7.2×10^{-2}

As another example, let us solve

$$\dfrac{\overset{+2}{(256)}\overset{\substack{+1\\-4}}{(0.0008)}\overset{-3}{(0.0012)}}{\underset{\substack{-3\\+1}}{(0.0048)}\underset{\substack{+3\\+1}}{(3200)}\underset{+1}{(96)}} = 1.666 \times 10^{-7} \quad Ans.$$

Place the characteristics above the respective numbers of the numerator and denominator. In this example place the hairline over 256 on the *D* scale and slide 48 of the C scale under the hairline to divide. The initial index projects; hence $+1$ must be added below the -3. Now slide the hairline to 8 on the C scale which is for the next number in the numerator. The initial index projects, so add $+1$ above -4. Next slide the C scale until 32 is under the hairline. This is for the next number in the denominator. Since the initial index does not project, no characteristic is added. Now slide the hairline to 12 on the C scale for the next number in the numerator. The initial index does not project, so no characteristic is added. Move the C scale until 96, the next number of the denominator, is under the hairline. The initial index projects, so add $+1$ to the 1 below 96. The final index of the C scale is over the answer on the D scale and is 1666. The characteristic is obtained by adding those of the numerator and subtracting those of the denominator, thus

$$(2 - 4 + 1 - 3) - (-3 + 1 + 3 + 1 + 1)$$
$$= (-4) - (+3) = -7$$

The answer is then

$$0.0000001666 \text{ or } 1.666 \times 10^{-7} \quad Ans.$$

The following problems are given to be worked on the slide rule, the accuracy of the answer then to be checked by the use of a logarithm table.

Multiply:

1. 296×265
2. 197×334
3. 486×361
4. 87.6×7.12
5. 1.91×0.629
6. 0.0534×0.00617
7. 967×0.000316
8. $41,900 \times 264,000$
9. 462×0.00091
10. $17,900 \times 264,000$
11. 0.49000×0.00017
12. 0.00042×0.0000084
13. $897,000 \times 0.000063$
14. $11,100 \times 99.9$
15. $191.00 \times 919,000$
16. 0.00000013×798

In each of the above problems, divide the first number by the second number. Then extract the square root of the second number. Then square the first number. See answers on page 317.

Suggestions in the Use and Care of the Slide Rule.—1. *Do not memorize special "trick" settings.* They are of value only in routine work where the same type of computation is used many times.

2. *Use fixed scales to read answers.* The slide is used only for adding or subtracting logarithms. Acquire the correct method and stick to it.

3. For continued operations, involving multiplication and division, *take a zigzag path through the problem.* Divide the

first number in the numerator by the first term in the denominator, then multiply by the second term in the numerator and divide by the second term in the denominator. This will save several settings and lessen chances to error.

4. *Avoid longhand checking,* as confidence cannot be gained in this way. If there are several numbers, take them in a different order as a check.

5. *Keep your slide rule clean* and away from dampness. Wipe off the face with a damp cloth occasionally, but never use alcohol or strong soap, as either of these may remove the markings.

6. *Keep scales and runner properly adjusted* as accurate results depend on this.

Exercises

1. 961×378

2. 14.7×7.917

3. $0.00049 \times 7,411$

4. $9,376 \times 1,375 \times 0.0006134$

5. $8,761 \div 1,942$

6. $\dfrac{1,918,000}{0.0002834}$

7. $\dfrac{0.0002978}{1,162}$

8. $\dfrac{962 \times 6,443}{248}$

9. $\dfrac{0.00092 \times 7,134}{345 \times 0.71}$

10. $\sqrt{96,432}$

11. $\sqrt{7658}$

12. $\sqrt[5]{29341}$

13. $\sqrt{0.0001392}$

14. $\sqrt[3]{0.0027965}$

15. $\sqrt[5]{0.00039 \times 6972}$

16. $8,967^5$

17. $492^2 \times 789^3$

18. $\dfrac{\sqrt{276^3}}{4,967^4}$

19. $\left[\sqrt{\dfrac{0.0067}{476}} \right]^3$

20. $\left[\dfrac{\sqrt[3]{0.0034}}{0.000496^2} \right]^5$

CHAPTER 3

ALGEBRA

We must study the fundamentals of algebra if we are to get anywhere with radio and communication principles. This review of algebra will consider only the fundamental principles met in everyday engineering work. Nearly all radio engineering involves algebra in some form. Enough of the subject will be treated here to enable the student to handle circuit theory and vacuum tube operation. The work presented will be as simple as ordinary arithmetic and should not baffle any student desiring to take the subject.

In this book algebra will be used to show derivations of useful radio equations. By this means, the student should be better prepared to use such equations than if he were simply given them to memorize. Equations can often be rearranged and solved for a desired term.

In arithmetic figures are used in equations, while in algebra letters are used in order to express more general conditions.

For instance, in algebra we can write Ohm's law by the expression

$$E = IR \tag{1}$$

By simple algebra this same law can be written in the fractional equations

$$I = \frac{E}{R} \tag{2}$$

$$R = \frac{E}{I} \tag{3}$$

In some problems one expression will be more desirable than the others.

When studying tuned circuits, we deal algebraically with $X_L = X_C$, where X_L is the inductive reactance and X_C is the capacitive reactance. The following equation is true for resonance no matter what the numerical values happen to be. It is

$$f = \frac{1}{2\pi \sqrt{LC}} \tag{4}$$

This is the familiar equation used to determine the frequency of resonance. If we know the inductance L and the capacity C, we can determine f, the frequency at which the circuit will freely oscillate.

Equations.—We have so far cited several equations, which are merely expressions of equality between two quantities. This equality is denoted by ($=$), the sign of equality. In Ohm's law $E = IR$ states that the voltage E has the same numerical value as the current multiplied by the resistance. *An equation is an expression having the same value on both sides of the sign of equality.* If this is not true, we do not have an equation but an inequality. *The value of one side of an equation may be changed or varied if the other side is changed the same amount.* Such quantities are called "variables." In this case we are changing the numerical value on both sides but maintaining equality; hence, we still have an equation. We can apply multiplication, division, addition, or subtraction to one side of the equation if we do the same thing to the other side.

Illustration of Addition.

Given $x + y = z$
Then $1 + x + y = 1 + z$

If $x = 4$, $y = 3$, and $z = 7$, the above equations read respectively, "Each side is equal to 7, or $(4 + 3 = 7)$," and, "Each side is equal to 8 or $(1 + 4 + 3 = 1 + 7)$."

Illustration of Subtraction.

Given $x + y - 3 = z - 3$
Substituting values $4 + 3 - 3 = 7 - 3$
Each side is equal to 4.

Illustration of Multiplication.

Given $2(x + y) = (z)2$
Substituting values, $2(4 + 3) = 7 \times 2$
Each side is equal to 14.

Illustration of Division.

Given

$$\frac{x + y}{7} = \frac{z}{7}$$

Substituting values,

$$\frac{4 + 3}{7} = \frac{7}{7}$$

Each side is equal to 1.

We see from these illustrations that if an operation is performed on one side, it must also be performed on the other, or the equality of the equation will be destroyed.

Equations usually can be written in several forms and still maintain equality. This often permits us to simplify a complicated expression. Before going farther we must learn how to write algebraic expressions properly.

Addition.—We may add *like* terms if we prefix the common term with the number of terms added.

Illustrations.

$$x + x = 2x$$
$$ab + ab + ab = 3ab$$
$$\frac{n}{m} + \frac{n}{m} = 2\frac{n}{m}$$
$$(a - b) + (a - b) + (a - b) = 3(a - b)$$

When no number is prefixed it is understood to be 1 of that quantity; thus, P means $1P$.

Unlike terms must be written out, thus

$$x + y + z$$

and cannot be simplified.

Subtraction.—We may subtract *like* terms if we prefix the common term to the remainder obtained.

Illustrations.

$$4a - a = 3a$$
$$9xy - 7xy = 2xy$$
$$\frac{m}{n} - \frac{8m}{n} = -\frac{7m}{n}$$

In the last illustration we have to subtract 8 from 1 which leaves -7.

Unlike terms cannot be handled this way. They must be written out; thus, $4x - y$ cannot be simplified. However, the expression can be rearranged, giving $- y + 4x$, without changing its value.

Positive and negative number rules, as already given, will always hold true in algebra. What is called "algebraic addition" takes into account all signs and may in some cases actually involve subtraction.

As an illustration, the impedance of a circuit can be expressed

$$Z^2 = R^2 + X^2 \tag{5}$$

where R is the resistance, X is the reactance, and Z is the impedance. Extracting the square root of both sides, we get

$$Z = \sqrt{R^2 + X^2} \tag{6}$$

In this form we can solve for the impedance, while in the original equation we had to deal with the square of the impedance.

If this circuit contained inductive reactance, X_L, and capacitive reactance X_C, this expression can be written

$$Z = \sqrt{R^2 + (X_L - X_C)^2} \tag{7}$$

In this case the capacitive reactance must be subtracted from the inductive reactance and then the quantity squared before being added to the square of the resistance to obtain the square of the impedance.

We see that the algebraic language in the above equation is very clear and simple in comparison with the expression of the relationship in a sentence. The exact and simple statement of relationships is one of the main objectives in mathematics.

Multiplication.—We may multiply *like* terms by raising the like term to the power corresponding to the number of terms multiplied.

Illustrations.

$$N \times N \times N = N^3$$
$$ab \times ab = (ab)^2$$

We may indicate the multiplication of *unlike* terms by simply writing the terms to be multiplied in succession with no sign between terms.

Illustrations.—To multiply I, the current, by R, the resistance, to obtain the voltage, E, we write

$$E = IR$$

As another illustration, for resonance,

$$X_L = X_C$$

but $X_L = \omega L$, where ω is the angular velocity in radians per second and L is the inductance in henrys, and $X_C = 1/\omega C$ where C is the capacity in farads. Since things equal to the same thing are equal to each other, we can write

$$\omega L = \frac{1}{\omega C}$$

or, multiplying both sides of the equation by ω, we get

$$\omega^2 L = \frac{1}{C}$$

Now, if we multiply both sides by $1/L$, we get

$$\omega^2 = \frac{1}{LC}$$

but

$$\omega = 2\pi f$$

so

$$(2\pi f)^2 = \frac{1}{LC}$$

Multiplying through by $\frac{1}{(2\pi)^2}$ we get

$$f^2 = \frac{1}{(2\pi)^2 LC}$$

Now, if we take the square root of both sides, we have

$$f = \frac{1}{2\pi \sqrt{LC}}$$

which is the familiar equation to determine the resonant frequency of a circuit.

In this development we have had several occasions to multiply unlike terms such as $\omega \times L$, written simply ωL. Several times we have multiplied both sides of the equation by the same thing so the equation must still hold true. Then in the last step we took the square root of both sides to get the answer in a familiar form.

Let us now apply the above rules to some more problems. As an illustration,

$$2adc \times 3abc = 6a^2bdc^2$$

Here we note that the numerical coefficients 2 and 3 are multiplied to get 6. Then we have $a \times a = a^2$ and $c \times c = c^2$. The d and b must appear in the answer because they are unlike terms, and hence the multiplication can only be indicated.

This same type of reasoning is applied to the following illustration:

$$(4x^2y^3z)(5xyz) = 20xxxyyyyzz$$
$$= 20x^3y^4z^2$$

It will be noted that the theory of exponents comes into play here; that is, when like terms are multiplied their exponents are added.

A pair of parentheses indicates one quantity. If we should have $(4a^2b)^3$ it would mean that every unlike term in the quantity must be raised to the third power, thus getting

$$4^3(a^2)^3b^3 = 64a^6b^3$$

An exponent following a letter refers to that letter only. For example, xy^2 means that only the y is raised to the second power. If we want the x also raised to second power we must write x^2y^2 or $(xy)^2$, which are the same and mean $xxyy$.

So far we have dealt with single terms. We must learn how to deal with quantities with more than one term.

Illustrations.

abc	(single term)
$a - bc$	(two terms)
$a + b - c$	(three terms)

This illustration shows that several terms in a quantity are grouped together by plus and minus signs. One quantity multiplied by another quantity, as $(a + b)$ multiplied by c, can be expressed $c(a + b)$ and if multiplied out gives $ca + cb$. This shows that *each term in the quantity must be multiplied individually.* To multiply more complicated quantities where the answer is not so evident, the following method is suggested:

$$a + b$$
$$\underline{\;\;c} \quad \text{multiplier}$$
$$ac + bc \quad \text{answer}$$

As another illustration,

$$c(ab + cd - e^2) = abc + c^2d - ce^2$$

To show this
$$ab + cd - e^2$$
$$\underline{\;c}$$
$$abc + c^2d - ce^2$$

After the multiplication has been performed there are still three terms, but the parentheses have been removed, and the multiplication by c has been indicated in each term.

Careful attention must be given to the signs when multiplying. The following rules are, therefore, important to keep in mind.

1. Multiplication of terms with *like* signs gives a *plus* product.
2. Terms with *unlike* signs give a *minus* product.

Illustrations.

$$z(x + y) = xz + yz \qquad z(x - y) = xz - yz$$
$$-z(x + y) = -xz - yz \qquad -z(x - y) = -xz + yz$$

The application of these rules can be extended to expressions having more than one term, as illustrated by the following:

$$(x + y)(x + y) = x^2 + 2xy + y^2$$

To show this
$$x + y$$
$$\underline{x + y}$$
$(x + y)$ multiplied by $x \quad x^2 + xy$
$(x + y)$ multiplied by $y \quad \underline{ + xy + y^2}$
Adding $\quad x^2 + 2xy + y^2 \quad$ total product

$$(x + y)(x - y) = x^2 - y^2$$

To show this
$$x + y$$
$$\underline{x - y}$$
$(x + y)$ multiplied by $x \quad x^2 + xy$
$(x + y)$ multiplied by $-y \quad \underline{ - xy - y^2}$
Adding $\quad x^2 - y^2 \quad$ total product

$$(x - y)(x - y) = x^2 - 2xy + y^2$$

To show this $\qquad\qquad x - y$

$\underline{\qquad\qquad\qquad\qquad x - y}$

$(x - y)$ multiplied by $x \qquad x^2 - xy$

$(x - y)$ multiplied by $-y \qquad\quad -xy + y^2$

Adding $\qquad\qquad\qquad \overline{x^2 - 2xy + y^2}$ total product

$$(a - c)(d + f) = ad - cd + af - cf$$

To show this $\qquad\qquad a - c$

$\underline{\qquad\qquad\qquad\qquad d + f}$

$(a - c)$ multiplied by $d \qquad ad - cd$

$(a - c)$ multiplied by $f \qquad\qquad + af - cf$

Adding $\qquad\qquad\qquad \overline{ad - cd + af - cf}$ total product

In the first three examples common terms were placed in the same column and added, but in the last example there were no common terms, so the complete expression had to be written out.

Particular care must be taken to keep the signs of the individual terms correct. If the student follows this procedure, very little trouble should be experienced, because each step in itself is very simple.

Division.—To reverse the above process, the law of exponents is readily applied.

Illustrations.

$$\frac{C}{C} = C^0 = 1$$

$$\frac{C^4}{C^2} = \frac{CCCC}{CC} = C^2 \qquad \text{(by cancellation)}$$

$$\frac{abc^2}{bc} = \frac{abcc}{bc} = ac \qquad \text{(by cancellation)}$$

The first illustration is an important one to remember. As mentioned in the previous lessons, any quantity raised to the zero power gives 1. In the second example the two C's in the denominator canceled the two C's in the numerator, giving 1 to be multiplied by C^2, but to simplify, the 1 is dropped in the answer and it is understood that the coefficient of C^2 is 1. The 1 is used only when there are no other factors in the product.

The division of unlike terms must be indicated because they cannot be further simplified.

Illustrations.

$$\frac{X}{R} \qquad \frac{1}{4\pi^2 LC} \qquad \frac{E}{I}$$

As in multiplication, if a quantity is to be divided by a term, each term in that quantity must be divided by that term. As an illustration,

$$\frac{x^2 + xy + x^3z}{x} = x + y + x^2z$$

In this illustration the division could actually be performed, but when there are unlike terms the division must be indicated. To illustrate,

$$\frac{ab + cd}{a} = b + \frac{cd}{a}$$

The second term in the numerator did not contain a, so the division was indicated.

Reciprocals.—Reciprocals are very convenient in problems involving fractions. As shown before, the reciprocal of 10 is $\frac{1}{10} = 0.1$.

Extending this principle, we get illustrations like the following:

The reciprocal of y is $\frac{1}{y}$; that of $\frac{1}{10}$ is $\frac{1}{\frac{1}{10}} = 10$, of $\frac{1}{x}$ is $\frac{1}{1/x} = x$

Instead of dividing by a number, multiply by its reciprocal. To illustrate,

1. $$\frac{y}{1/x} = y\frac{x}{1} = yx$$

2. $$\frac{I}{100} = I\left(\frac{1}{100}\right) = 0.01I$$

3. $$\frac{xy + zy}{y/(x + z)} = \frac{(xy + zy)(x + z)}{y}$$
$$= (x + z)(x + z)$$
$$= x^2 + 2xz + z^2$$

Removal of Parentheses.—A single pair of parentheses can always be removed from an algebraic expression. In case the sign before it is plus, no change is necessary; but if a minus is before it, the sign of all the terms within it must be changed.

Illustrations.

$$a + (b - cd) = a + b - cd$$
$$a - (-b + cd) = a + b - cd$$

It will be noted that no signs were changed in the first illustration, but because of the negative sign in the second illustration before the parentheses, the signs between them had to be changed when they were removed.

Factoring.—Already, in division, some factoring in effect has been done. For example, we wish to remove x from within the following parenthesis without changing the value of the quantity.

$$(ax + b^2x^2 - cxy)$$

Since x appears in each term, we can divide each term by x; thus

$$\frac{ax}{x} = a$$

is the way the first term is handled. Applying this to each term, we have

$$\frac{ax + b^2xx - cxy}{x} = a + b^2x - cy$$

Since x is now divided out,

$$ax + b^2x^2 - cxy \neq a + b^2x - cy$$

This unequal sign, $\neq$, means that one side is not equal to the other side. To make it equal we must multiply the right-hand side by x, thus

$$ax + b^2x^2 - cxy = x(a + b^2x - cy)$$

From multiplication we see that if x is multiplied by the quantities in the parenthesis, the left-hand side of the equation is obtained. So, factoring is really the reverse of multiplication. It is usually done to obtain a desired result which will be illustrated later.

Substituting Terms.—Terms may be substituted in an equation provided each term substituted has the same value as the term it replaces. To illustrate, the formula for the velocity of light is

$$\lambda f = c$$
$$f = \frac{c}{\lambda}$$

Now in the equation, $f = \dfrac{1}{2\pi \sqrt{LC}}$ we can substitute for f and have

$$\frac{c}{\lambda} = \frac{1}{2\pi \sqrt{LC}}$$

Complex expressions are often simplified by substitution when several operations are to be performed, thus saving the labor of writing the whole expression out each time. The impedance of an alternating current circuit can be expressed

$$Z = \sqrt{R^2 + \left(2\pi fL - \frac{1}{2\pi fC}\right)^2}$$

This can be simplified by making the following substitutions:

$$X_L = 2\pi fL$$

and

$$X_C = \frac{1}{2\pi fC}$$

which give

$$Z = \sqrt{R^2 + (X_L - X_C)^2}$$

Now if we let $X = X_L - X_C$ we can simplify still further and have

$$Z = \sqrt{R^2 + X^2}$$

In this case we assume X_L larger than X_C. If X_L were smaller than X_C, the value of X would be negative, but X multiplied by itself, X^2, would be positive. This means that the assumption is not necessary to get the correct answer.

Solving Equations.—All the necessary theory has now been covered to solve equations. Summarizing, these *rules* are

1. The same quantity can be *added* to both sides of an equation, without destroying the equality of the equation.

2. The same quantity can be *subtracted* from both sides of an equation, without destroying the equality of the equation.

3. A term can be transposed from one side of an equation to the other, *if the sign is changed*, without destroying the equality of the equation. (This is a result of Rules 1 and 2.)

4. If *all the signs* in an equation are changed, the equality of the equation will not be destroyed.

5. Both sides of an equation can be *multiplied* by the same quantity without destroying the equality of the equation.

6. The same quantity can be *divided* into both sides of an equation, without destroying the equality of the equation. In other words, terms can be canceled.

7. Both sides of an equation can be *raised to the same power* without destroying the equality of the equation.

8. The *reciprocal* of one side of an equation is equal to the reciprocal of the other side.

9. Both sides of an equation can have *the same root extracted*, without destroying the equality of the equation.

10. Terms in an equation can be replaced by *terms that are equal* in value.

To solve or evaluate an equation we use the above rules in order that the term for which we are solving can be placed on only *one side of the equation*. With all other terms of known value on the opposite side, we have a solution and thus know the value of the unknown quantity in terms of known quantities. The usual practice is to arrange unknown terms on the left-hand side of the equation and all known terms on the right-hand side.

For example, $E = IR$ is an expression of Ohm's law. If $I = 8$ and $R = 6$, we can replace I and R by the values they equal and then solve for the unknown value of E, thus

$$E = (8)(6) = 48$$

Sometimes an algebraic equation is indeterminate; that is, it cannot be solved as explained above. To illustrate,

$$IX_L = 2\pi fLI$$

where $L = 30.$
$\qquad f = 60.$
$\quad 2\pi = 6.28.$
$\quad X_L = 11,300.$

Substituting
$$11,300I = (6.28)(60)(30)I$$
$$11,300I = 11,300I$$
$$I = I$$
$$1 = 1$$

In such cases as this it is not possible to place the unknowns on one side of the equation and the knowns on the other side; therefore, no solution is possible.

Illustrations of the Use of Above Ten Rules.

Given $\qquad x - y = z$
add $\qquad\quad \dfrac{+y = \quad +y}{x \quad\;\; = z + y}$ (Rules 1 and 3)

To make this perfectly clear, let $x = 10$, $y = 8$, and $z = 2$. Then, substituting,

$$10 - 8 = 2$$
or $\qquad\qquad 10 = 2 + 8$

Now, use Rule 2 and subtract x from each side of the equation.

Given $\qquad\qquad x - y = z$
Subtract $\qquad\quad +x = +x$
giving $\qquad\qquad -y = z - x$
Substituting, $\qquad -8 = 2 - 10$

This is seen to be true.
Changing all signs,

$$y = -z + x \qquad \text{(Rule 4)}$$
or $\qquad\qquad 8 = -2 + 10$

This also is true.

Even though the value of both sides of the equation is changed in each of these cases, the equality is not destroyed.

For an example in multiplication and division we have the general form of Ohm's law,

$$I = \frac{E}{Z}$$

It is desired to solve for the voltage E. Multiply both sides by Z, giving

$$IZ = \frac{E}{Z}(Z) \qquad \text{(Rule 5)}$$

On the right-hand side, $\dfrac{E}{Z}(Z) = \dfrac{EZ}{Z} = E$

But we want E on the left-hand side so we turn the equation around and have

$$E = IZ \qquad \text{(the solution)}$$

Now let us solve this equation for Z.   Dividing both sides by I gives

$$\frac{E}{I} = \frac{IZ}{I} \qquad \text{(Rule 6)}$$

By canceling I,

$$\frac{E}{I} = Z$$

As above, turning the equation around gives

$$Z = \frac{E}{I} \qquad \text{(the solution)}$$

As another illustration, the Q of a circuit is given by the equation

$$Q = \frac{2\pi fL}{R}$$

If we know the figure of merit Q, the frequency f, and the resistance R, we can solve for the inductance L as follows:

$$Q = \frac{2\pi fL}{R}$$

Multiplying both sides by R removes the denominator on the right-hand side, thus

$$RQ = 2\pi fL$$

Dividing both sides by $2\pi f$ transfers the $2\pi f$ from the right side of the equation to the left.   Thus

$$\frac{RQ}{2\pi f} = L$$

Then, by turning the equation around,

$$L = \frac{RQ}{2\pi f} \qquad \text{(the solution)}$$

Suppose we wish to find the plate resistance (R_p) in a vacuum tube from the following equation:

$$A = \frac{\mu R}{R + R_p}$$

Clearing of fractions, by multiplying both sides by the denominator on the right side, gives

$$A(R + R_p) = \mu R$$

Removing the parentheses and multiplying each term inside them by A, we get

$$AR + AR_p = \mu R$$

Subtracting AR from both sides,

$$AR_p = \mu R - AR$$

Dividing both sides by A,

$$R_p = \frac{\mu R - AR}{A}$$

This is the required solution for R_p.

The procedure of removing the denominator and clearing of fractions, shown above, is one of the most useful in solving equations. When any equation with fractions is to be solved they should be removed by this means.

The last step is also important, for the desired term is often multiplied by other known factors. In such cases dividing both sides of the equation by this known term will leave the unknown alone on the left-hand side and give the desired answer.

Solve the above equation for R.

$$A = \frac{\mu R}{R + R_p}$$

Clearing of fractions,

$$A(R + R_p) = \mu R$$

Removing the parentheses,

$$AR + AR_p = \mu R$$

Subtracting AR from both sides,

$$AR_p = \mu R - AR$$

Factoring the right-hand side by dividing through by R and multiplying by R,

$$AR_p = \frac{R(\mu\cancel{R} - A\cancel{R})}{\cancel{R}} = R(\mu - A)$$

Turning the equation around to get R on the left-hand side,

$$R(\mu - A) = AR_p$$

Dividing both sides by $(\mu - A)$,

$$R = \frac{A R_p}{\mu - A}$$

Solving for R was slightly more complicated but each step in itself was quite simple. The student should write out each step when solving problems until the procedure is thoroughly understood. If the steps are written out in detail, mistakes will be less likely to occur.

In an alternating current circuit,

$$I = \frac{E}{\sqrt{R^2 + X^2}}$$

To solve this equation for X, proceed as follows:
Clearing of fractions and turning the equation around,

$$E = I \sqrt{R^2 + X^2}$$

Dividing by I,

$$\frac{E}{I} = \sqrt{R^2 + X^2}$$

Squaring both sides (Rule 7) and turning the equation around,

$$R^2 + X^2 = \left(\frac{E}{I}\right)^2$$

Transposing R^2 (subtracting R^2 from both sides),

$$X^2 = \frac{E^2}{I^2} - R^2$$

Reducing to a common denominator,

$$X^2 = \frac{E^2}{I^2} - \frac{R^2 I^2}{I^2} = \frac{E^2 - R^2 I^2}{I^2}$$

Extracting the square root of both sides (Rule 8),

$$X = \sqrt{\frac{E^2 - R^2 I^2}{I^2}} \quad \text{or} \quad X = \frac{\sqrt{E^2 - R^2 I^2}}{\sqrt{I^2}} = \frac{\sqrt{E^2 - R^2 I^2}}{I}$$

The student should become familiar with these processes and be able to prove such problems. To prove this problem, take the answer and solve for I.

$$X = \frac{\sqrt{E^2 - R^2I^2}}{I}$$

Clearing of fractions,

$$IX = \sqrt{E^2 - R^2I^2}$$

Squaring both sides to remove the radical,

$$I^2X^2 = E^2 - R^2I^2$$

Transposing I^2R^2,

$$I^2X^2 + I^2R^2 = E^2$$

Factoring I^2,

$$I^2(X^2 + R^2) = E^2$$

Dividing by $(X^2 + R^2)$,

$$I^2 = \frac{E^2}{X^2 + R^2}$$

Extracting the square root of both sides by rule 9,

$$I = \sqrt{\frac{E^2}{R^2 + X^2}} = \frac{\sqrt{E^2}}{\sqrt{R^2 + X^2}} = \frac{E}{\sqrt{R^2 + X^2}}$$

Which is the original equation and indicates that the solution is correct.

Another help is to substitute known values in the equation and prove the answer is correct for a particular case. If it is true for a particular case, it will likely hold in the general solution. Thus, let $E = 100$ volts, $R = 8$ ohms resistance, and $X = 6$ ohms reactance.

Then

$$I = \frac{E}{\sqrt{R^2 + X^2}} = \frac{100}{\sqrt{8^2 + 6^2}} = \frac{100}{\sqrt{64 + 36}} = \frac{100}{10} = 10 \text{ amp}$$

Substituting these values in the answer and solving for X give

$$X = \frac{\sqrt{E^2 - I^2R^2}}{I} = \frac{\sqrt{100^2 - (10)^2(8)^2}}{10} = \frac{\sqrt{10,000 - 6,400}}{10}$$

$$= \frac{\sqrt{3,600}}{10} = \frac{60}{10} = 6 \text{ ohms reactance}$$

This checks the value given above.

In case the student may not know when to square or when to extract a square root, it may be helpful to remember that $X = (\sqrt{X})^2$, so if X^2 is given, extract the square root to get X and if $\sqrt{X}$ is given, square the quantity to get X. Of course rules 7 and 8 must be remembered when performing these operations on equations. Both sides of the equation must be treated alike.

In the equation,

$$X_l = X_c$$

we know that

$$X_l = 2\pi fL \quad \text{and} \quad X_c = \frac{1}{2\pi fC}$$

Therefore, by substituting as pointed out in rule 10, we can write

$$2\pi fL = \frac{1}{2\pi fC}$$

Exercises

1. $x + y = a - b$. Find y, b.

2. $ax + by - cz = R$. Find b, z.

3. $RST = XY - JQ$. Find S, Q.

4. $\dfrac{xy}{z} = ab$. Find z, y.

5. $\dfrac{x + y}{z} = a + bz$. Find x, b.

6. $\dfrac{z}{x - y} = az + c$. Find y, a.

7. $\dfrac{X + Y}{M - N} = PQ$. Find M, Y.

8. $\dfrac{O + P}{X} = \dfrac{R - S}{T}$. Find T, S.

9. $\dfrac{T^2}{X + Y} = \dfrac{R - SP}{T}$. Find T, P.

10. $xy^2 + z = \sqrt{a + b}$. Find a, y.

11. $I = \dfrac{E}{R + jX}$. Find R.

12. $\dfrac{1}{C} = \dfrac{1}{C_1} + \dfrac{1}{C_2}$. Find C, C_1.

13. $L = \dfrac{a^2 n^2}{9a + 10b}$. Find a, n.

14. $e = \dfrac{N}{t \times 10^8}$. Find t.

15. $W = \dfrac{I^2 Rt}{4.187}$. Find I.

16. $F = 2\pi r \dfrac{m}{r^2}$. Find r.

17. $T = 2\pi \sqrt{\dfrac{I}{mH}}$. Find H.

18. $K = \dfrac{M}{\sqrt{L_1 L_2}}$. Find L_1.

19. $R_t = R_0(1 + at)$. Find t.

20. $\lambda = 1884\sqrt{LC}$. Find C.

CHAPTER 4

GEOMETRY

This lesson will be concerned with the study of the right triangle. Conventional geometry as given in high school is not touched upon in this lesson. All the student need remember from high-school geometry is how to find the hypotenuse of a right triangle if the two legs are given.

In studying electrical engineering, it is often desirable to add voltages and currents that are not always in phase. These voltages and currents can be represented by means of vectors and added by means of geometric addition.

Arithmetic addition concerns itself with adding positive numbers only. Graphically, this means that only numbers from the origin out along a positive axis can be considered. This permits the addition of vectors in only one direction.

Algebraic addition concerns itself with adding both positive and negative numbers. Graphically, this means that all numbers on a straight line through the origin can be handled. This number system is twice as large as that of arithmetic addition. This permits the addition of vectors acting in the same direction or in exact opposition.

Geometric addition concerns itself with adding vectors in a plane and hence has generalized algebraic addition much as algebraic addition has generalized arithmetic addition.

A vector is a quantity which has both *magnitude and direction*. Quantities such as dimensions, weight, and temperature have magnitude only. Quantities with magnitude only are called "scalar quantities." Quantities such as displacement, velocity, force, voltage, current, and impedance have direction in addition to magnitude. These quantities are called "vector quantities"; they are represented by directed lines called "vectors." The length of the line represents the magnitude, and the line is drawn in the direction of the vector. An arrow on the end of the line indicates its sense.

Arithmetic Addition.—Let us consider a force vector $A = 6$ pounds, and another force vector $B = 8$ pounds, acting in the same direction on point O (the origin), as illustrated in Fig. 5.

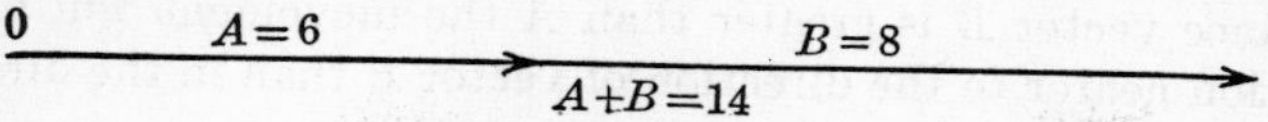

0   $A=6$ $B=8$
$A+B=14$

Fig. 5.—Arithmetic addition of vectors.

In this case arithmetic, algebraic, and geometric addition are the same. The point O is acted on by the total force,

$$A + B = 6 + 8 = 14 \text{ pounds } \quad Ans.$$

Example 1.   An automobile going east is stuck in the mud. A tractor coupled to the front of the automobile exerts a pull of 400 lb. If the car is able to exert an aiding force of 300 lb., what is the total force, acting in an easterly direction moving it out of the mud?

Solution.   Let A = 400 lb., the tractor force.
  B = 300 lb., the auto force.
  C = A + B = 400 + 300 = 700 lb.   *Ans.*

Algebraic Addition.—Now let the force A act in the opposite direction as shown in Fig. 6. The resultant force is in the direction of vector B. That is, $A + B = -6 + 8 = 2$ pounds. *Ans.*

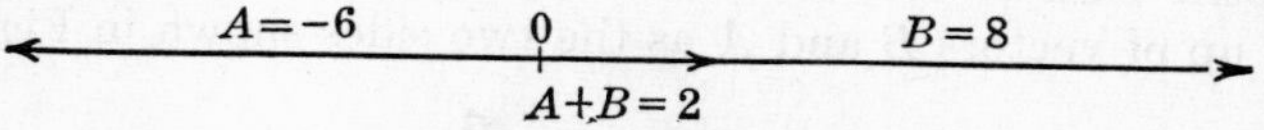

$A=-6$ 0 $B=8$
$A+B=2$

Fig. 6.—Algebraic addition of vectors.

Since A in this case is a negative quantity, arithmetic addition does not apply in this case, but algebraic and geometric addition do apply.

Example 2.   If the tractor is connected to the back of the auto in Example 1, determine the total force acting on the auto in a westerly direction.
Solution.   C = A + B = -400 + 300 = -100 lb.   *Ans.*

Geometric Addition.—Now let the force $A = 6$ act at right angles to the force $B = 8$ as shown in Fig. 7.[1]

Since vectors A and B are not in the same straight line, neither arithmetic nor algebraic addition applies, so we must rely upon geometric addition in this case. Our common sense tells us that with these forces acting on the point O it will tend to move in the direction of both forces A and B and the resulting movement

[1] The complete expression for a vector will be given later, see p. 80.

will be in a direction somewhere between vectors A and B. If vectors A and B were of the same magnitude, the resulting movement would take place halfway between the two vectors, but since vector B is greater than A the movement will be in a direction nearer to the direction of vector B than in the direction of vector A.

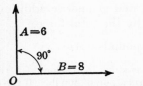

FIG. 7.—Geometric addition of vectors.   FIG. 8.—Geometric addition of vectors by completing the rectangle.

The geometric sum of vectors A and B is obtained by completing the parallelogram (rectangle, in this case) and drawing the diagonal from the origin O to the opposite corner. This diagonal of the parallelogram is in the correct direction and has the correct length to represent the geometric sum of vectors A and B. Figure 8 illustrates this geometric addition. The geometric sum of $A + B$ is the hypotenuse of a right triangle made up of vectors B and A as the two sides shown in Fig. 9.

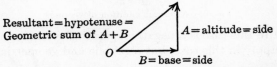

FIG. 9.—Geometric addition of vectors by using the right triangle.

Figure 8 gives the same result as Fig. 9, but Fig. 9 gives the true vector triangle for addition geometrically. Vector A can be moved from its position in Fig. 8 to its position in Fig. 9 without altering its magnitude or direction and therefore is the same vector.

The hypotenuse of a right triangle is equal to the square root of the sum of the squares of the other two sides.

If C is the hypotenuse with A and B the two sides, then

$$C = \sqrt{A^2 + B^2} \tag{1}$$

Applying this basic principle of geometric addition to the above illustration we find that the magnitude of the resultant in terms of the magnitude of the sides is[1]

$$\text{Resultant} = \sqrt{|A|^2 + |B|^2} = \sqrt{6^2 + 8^2} = \sqrt{36 + 64}$$
$$= \sqrt{100} = 10 \quad Ans.$$

Then the total force acting on the point O is 10 pounds and will be in the direction of the resultant vector $A + B$ as shown in Fig. 9. *Note:* "$A + B$" in this case means geometric addition and is equal to 10 instead of 14, the algebraic sum of the magnitude of $A = 6$ and $B = 8$.

The hypotenuse of a right triangle must always be longer than either of the other two sides. It is always the side opposite the right angle (90 degrees) in the triangle.

Example 3. If the tractor is connected to the side of the automobile of Example 1 and pulls due north, determine the magnitude of the force acting on the automobile in a northeasterly direction.

Solution.

$$|C| = \sqrt{|A|^2 + |B|^2} = \sqrt{400^2 + 300^2}$$
$$= \sqrt{160,000 + 90,000} = \sqrt{250,000}$$
$$= 500 \text{ lb.} \quad Ans.$$

Parallelogram Law.—This law is the fundamental principle on which it is possible to determine the effect of a group of vectors

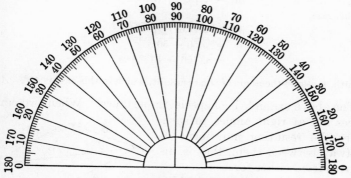

Fig. 10.—Semicircular protractor.

(forces). The law states that *the resultant of two vectors (forces) which act at any angle upon a rigid body, or point, is represented in magnitude and direction by the diagonal of a parallelogram, the*

[1] The vertical bars placed on both sides of A and B are used to denote *magnitude only* of the quantity between them.

sides of which represent the magnitude and direction of the two vectors (forces). The diagonal representing the resultant starts from the corner where the two vectors start and extends to the opposite corner. The parallelogram is constructed by drawing lines through the end of each vector parallel to the other vector. Usually dotted lines are employed. The end of the resultant will then be at the point where the dotted lines intersect. The angle of the resultant can be determined by means of a protractor as shown in Fig. 10.

Example 4. The magnitude of vectors A and B is 7.07 and the angle

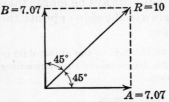

between them is 90 degrees as shown in Fig. 11. Determine the direction and magnitude of the resultant.

Solution. First, always draw a vector diagram, to scale, of the given relations, in this case vectors A and B.

Second, complete the parallelogram by means of dotted lines as shown in Fig. 11.

Fig. 11.—Geometric addition of vectors by completing the square.

Third, draw the resultant vector, R, from the intersection of the two vectors to the intersection of the two dotted lines. This is the desired diagonal of the parallelogram.

Fourth, calculate the magnitude of the resultant, thus

$$|R| = \sqrt{|A|^2 + |B|^2}$$

In this case,

$$|R| = \sqrt{(7.07)^2 + (7.07)^2}$$
$$= \sqrt{50 + 50}$$
$$= \sqrt{100} = 10 \quad Ans.$$

Fifth, measure the angle of the resultant, which in this case is 45°. *Ans.*

The above example is of special importance. When two equal forces act at right angles to each other the resulting movement is halfway between them, that is, 45 degrees from either force.

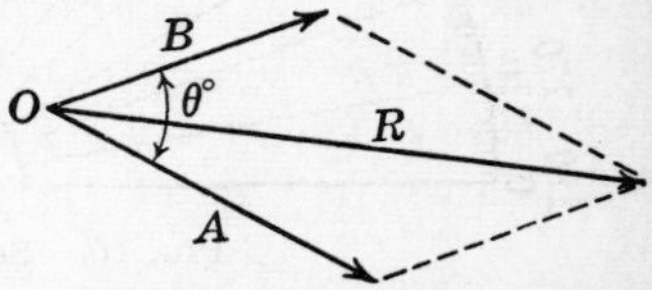

For a general case, let us consider vector A and vector B with an angle of θ degrees between A and B as shown in Fig. 12.

Fig. 12.—Geometric addition of vectors by completing the parallelogram.

From the parallelogram law, the resultant vector R in Fig. 12 is the geometric sum of vectors $A + B$. But A and B cannot be added as in the above example, since they are not at right angles. Such problems can always be worked graphically but, since it is seldom convenient to do so, the necessary mathematics will be given to handle them analytically. Since geometric addition depends upon right triangles, this problem must be broken up into right triangles.

Resolution of a Vector.—So far it has been shown that two vectors can be added to get the resultant vector. The reverse of this process—namely, the resolution of a vector—is also of great importance. Taking a horizontal line, called the x-axis, and cutting it at right angles by a vertical bisector, called the y-axis, gives us a basis on which to work to resolve the vectors into other vectors at right angles to each other. In Fig. 12 the vector A is drawn acting on the point O, called the origin, where the y-axis intersects the x-axis. Dotted perpendicular lines are drawn from the extreme end of vector A to the two axes. The dotted lines that are perpendicular to one axis are parallel to the other. The dotted perpendicular to the x-axis in Fig. 13 marks off the vector A_x on this axis and the dotted perpendicular to the y-axis marks off A_y on this axis. It can

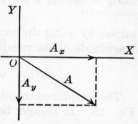

FIG. 13.—Resolution of vector A into its x and y components.

be seen that A_x and A_y, being at right angles, can be added geometrically to obtain the diagonal vector A which is the resultant of their sum. That is, the magnitude of[1]

$$|A| = \sqrt{A_x^2 + A_y^2} \qquad (2)$$

These vector forces A_x and A_y are known as the "vertical" or "y-component" and "horizontal" or "x-component" of A. The vector A can then be replaced by vectors A_x and A_y acting at right angles to each other.[2]

Similarly, vector B of Fig. 12 can be drawn from the origin O as shown in Fig. 14 and be resolved into its components B_x

[1] The components A_x and A_y are also vectors; hence, by rights, they should be expressed as magnitudes $|A_x|$ and $|A_y|$ in this equation. For the sake of simplicity, however, and where it will not cause confusion, these components which have their direction specified by the subscript will be written without vertical bars to designate magnitude.

[2] The subscripts are used here to designate the direction of the vectors.

along the horizontal or x-axis and B_y along the vertical or y-axis. Now we have in place of B its components B_x and B_y which are at right angles and can be handled in geometric addition. In this case, the magnitude of vector B is

$$|B| = \sqrt{B_x^2 + B_y^2} \tag{3}$$

To solve the general case as illustrated in Fig. 12 we can com-

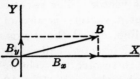

FIG. 14.—Resolution of vector B into its x and y components.

bine the results of Fig. 13 and Fig. 14. We add algebraically the vertical or y-axis components to get the total y-component and the horizontal or x-axis components to get the total x-component. The geometric sum of the total y-component and the total x-component gives the same resultant as was obtained by using the parallelogram law graphically. That is, the magnitude of the resultant

$$|R| = \sqrt{(A_x + B_x)^2 + (A_y + B_y)^2} \tag{4}$$

The combined results of Fig. 13 and Fig. 14 are shown in Fig. 15. It should be noted that these components must be

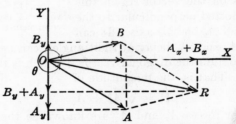

FIG. 15.—Geometric addition of the A and B components to determine the resultant vector R.

added *algebraically*. For instance, in Fig. 15, A_y must be actually subtracted arithmetically from B_y to obtain their algebraic sum, $A_y + B_y$ because A_y is a negative number. Distances measured to the right of the origin O on the x-axis are positive and those measured to the left are negative. Distances measured up from the origin O on the y-axis are positive while those measured down are negative. The resultant vector R forms the hypotenuse of a right triangle with sides of length $A_x + B_x$ and $A_y + B_y$.

By using the x-axis and y-axis as a framework or reference system, it is possible to determine accurately not only the magnitude of the resultant but also its direction. The direction is usually expressed in degrees measured from the positive x-axis in a counterclockwise direction. Figure 16 plainly illustrates four examples.

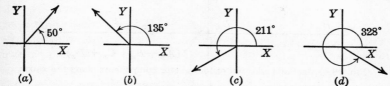

FIG. 16.—Vectors in the first, second, third, and fourth quadrants.

Since the resultant of two vectors can be added to another vector geometrically, it is possible to add any number of vectors geometrically by the above scheme. Let us consider vectors A, B, and C, as shown in Fig. 17. Resolving these vectors into their respective components gives A_x, A_y, B_x, B_y, C_x, and C_y along the two axes. A_x and C_y are the only negative components, and hence they must be subtracted from the others when added algebraically. The horizontal components along the x-axis give $A_x + B_x + C_x$ and the vertical components along the y-axis gives $A_y + B_y + C_y$. In writing the algebraic expression all signs are positive but, as in this example,

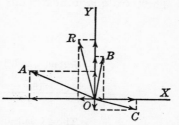

FIG. 17.—Geometric addition of three vectors.

when numerical values are substituted some of these terms (A_x and C_y) will be negative. The geometric sum of vectors A, B, and C is given by the resultant magnitude of vector R, thus

$$|R| = \sqrt{(A_x + B_x + C_x)^2 + (A_y + B_y + C_y)^2} \qquad (5)$$

This scheme can be extended to add geometrically any number of vectors. We must remember that *each vector must be resolved into its two components* along the x-axis and the y-axis. Vectors along the axis in the same direction are added arithmetically and those in the opposite direction are subtracted. To illustrate, if the magnitude of $A_x = 6$, $B_x = -8$, $C_x = 4$, and $D_x = -1$ are the components of A, B, C, and D along the x-axis, the algebraic sum gives the magnitude

$$A_x + B_x + C_x + D_x = 6 - 8 + 4 - 1 = 1$$

These vectors are shown in Fig. 18.

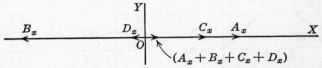

Fig. 18.—Algebraic addition of four vector components along the x-axis.

In order to classify the directions of vectors acting on a point the circle is divided into *four quadrants* as shown in Fig. 19. This is easier than stating the angle in degrees between the vector and the base line (positive x-axis). The first quadrant extends from 0 to 90 degrees, between the positive y-axis and the positive x-axis. The second quadrant extends from 90 to 180 degrees between the positive y-axis and the negative x-axis. The third quadrant extends from 180 to 270 degrees between the

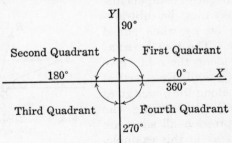

Fig. 19.—The four quadrants of a circle.

negative x-axis and the negative y-axis. The fourth quadrant extends from 270 to 360 degrees between the negative y-axis and the positive x-axis. The 360 degree line coincides with the 0 degree line or the positive x-axis; the 90 degree line coincides with the positive y-axis; the 180 degree line coincides with the negative x-axis and the 270 degree line coincides with the negative y-axis.

In Fig. 16, diagram *a* illustrates a vector in the first quadrant, diagram *b* illustrates a vector in the second quadrant, diagram *c* illustrates a vector in the third quadrant, and diagram *d* illustrates a vector in the fourth quadrant.

Example 5. Vectors *A*, *B*, and *C* have the following components:

$$A_x = 10, \ A_y = 26, \ B_x = -20, \ B_y = -20, \ C_x = 6, \ C_y = -3.$$

Determine:

1. The components of the resultant vector *R*.
2. The quadrant of each vector.
3. The magnitude of each vector. (four-place accuracy)

Solution.

1. $R_x = A_x + B_x + C_x$
   $= 10 - 20 + 6 = -4$
   $R_y = A_y + B_y + C_y$
   $= 26 - 20 - 3 = 3$

2. *A* is in the first quadrant.
   B is in the third quadrant.
   C is in the fourth quadrant.
   R is in the second quadrant.

3. $|A| = \sqrt{A_x^2 + A_y^2} = \sqrt{10^2 + 26^2} = 27.86$
   $|B| = \sqrt{B_x^2 + B_y^2} = \sqrt{(-20)^2 + (-20)^2} = 28.28$
   $|C| = \sqrt{C_x^2 + C_y^2} = \sqrt{6^2 + (-3)^2} = 6.04$
   $|R| = \sqrt{R_x^2 + R_y^2} = \sqrt{(-4)^2 + 3^2} = 5$

Summary.—The resultant of a group of vectors (forces, voltages, impedances, etc.) is obtained by the following procedure:

First, draw a diagram showing the vectors to be added geometrically, drawn from a common point *O*, the origin. This diagram should represent the magnitude of these vectors to a convenient scale and the actual direction with their angle designated.

Second, draw perpendiculars from the extreme end of each vector to the *x*-axis and the *y*-axis. Mark these components with the vector subscribed with *x* or *y* as the case may be.

Third, add algebraically the *x*-components together and the *y*-components together.

Fourth, determine the magnitude of the resultant by

$$|R| = \sqrt{\left(\begin{array}{c}\text{algebraic sum} \\ \text{of } x\text{-components}\end{array}\right)^2 + \left(\begin{array}{c}\text{algebraic sum} \\ \text{of } y\text{-components}\end{array}\right)^2}$$

If one component of a vector is known the other component can be easily determined, for if the magnitude

$$|A| = \sqrt{A_x^2 + A_y^2} \qquad \text{then} \qquad A_x = \sqrt{|A|^2 - A_y^2} \qquad \text{and}$$
$$A_y = \sqrt{|A|^2 - A_x^2}$$

The reader should go through this development. However, if the vector and its angle are given, the problem must be worked out graphically with a rule and protractor by means of the parallelogram law. Simple trigonometry is valuable to work this type of problem, for by means of it the x- and y-components are readily obtained. This type of problem will be treated in the next chapter.

Exercises

1. Right triangles.

    a. Altitude = 40.
        Base = 30.
    Find the hypotenuse.

    b. Altitude = 5.
        Base = 8.66.
    Find the hypotenuse.

    c. Altitude = 5.
        Hypotenuse = 7.07.
    Find the base.

    d. Altitude = 18.
        Hypotenuse = 30.
    Find the base.

    e. Base = 1.3.
        Hypotenuse = 1.7.
    Find the altitude.

    f. Base = 678.
        Hypotenuse = 843.
    Find the altitude.

2. In each of the following examples, find the resultant vector and state in which quadrant it lies. The directions of the vectors are along the x and y axes as shown in Fig. 20. The magnitude of the vectors, if drawn to scale such as 10 to 1, 20 to 1, 100 to 1, etc., on a large sheet of paper, will help you to understand the problem clearly and solve it correctly.

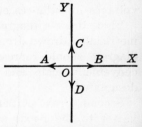

    a. $|A| = 6$, $|B| = 10$.
        $|C| = 14$, $|D| = 11$.

    b. $|A| = 49$, $|B| = 99$.
        $|C| = 391$, $|D| = 441$.

    c. $|A| = 7.0$, $|B| = 3.4$.
        $|C| = 9.9$, $|D| = 16.3$.

    d. $|A| = 900$, $|B| = 750$.
        $|C| = 1,325$, $|D| = 475$.

    e. $|A| = 0.2$, $|B| = 0.6$.
        $|C| = 0.1$, $|D| = 0.45$.

Fig. 20.—Direction of vectors in exercise problem 2.

3. In each of the following problems draw a vector diagram (not necessarily to scale) showing the various vectors, their component magnitudes along the x- and y-axis, and the resultant:

    a. $|A| = 100$, $A_x = 86.6$, $|B| = 100$, $B_x = 70.7$ (vectors A and B in the first quadrant).

    b. $|A| = 60$, $A_y = 30$, $|B| = 80$, $B_x = 60$ (vectors A and B in the second quadrant).

    c. $|A| = 1.2$, $A_x = 1.2$, $|B| = 3.2$, $B_y = 1.6$ (vector A in first quadrant, vector B in fourth).

    d. $|A| = 8$, $A_x = 6$, $|B| = 3$, $B_y = 2$ (vector A in second quadrant, vector B in fourth).

e. $|A| = 340$, $A_y = 100$, $|B| = 180$, $B_x = 80$ (vector A in third quadrant, vector B in first).

f. $|A| = 400$, $A_y = 150$, $|B| = 500$, $B_x = 250$, $|C| = 300$, $C_x = 200$ (vector A in first quadrant, vector B in second, and vector C in third).

Note: All the *x*- and *y*-components are expressed as positive numbers in the problems above. The actual sign is to be determined by the student from a knowledge of the quadrant in which the vector lies.

CHAPTER 5

TRIGONOMETRY

In the last chapter we learned how to resolve a vector or force into its horizontal component along the x-axis and its vertical component along the y-axis. After this operation had been performed to each vector to be added, the algebraic sum of the x-components gave a resultant x-component and the algebraic sum of the y-components gave a resultant y-component. The hypotenuse of the triangle formed by the resultant x-component and the resultant y-component is called the geometric or vector sum of all the vectors or forces added. But this gives us no information concerning the value of the angles in this triangle. We also mentioned in the last chapter a problem that had an angle given, but we could not solve it with the tools we then had.

Trigonometry is the tool that deals with the angles of a right triangle and their relationship to the sides of the triangle. If we have one angle and one side of a right triangle given, we can determine the other two sides and angle by using simple trigonometry. We can now appreciate the value of this new tool and how by its use we can solve practical vector problems involving forces, impedances, voltages, currents, etc.

Trigonometric Functions.—Trigonometry deals with what are known as "trigonometric functions" of the angle. Such a function is a ratio between two sides of the right triangle.

In Fig. 21, a line is drawn through the point O at an angle α (alpha) with the horizontal line the x-axis. At some point R_1 on this line drop a perpendicular to X_1 on the x-axis. This perpendicular of course, cuts the x-axis at right angles, and we have the right triangle with sides a, b, and c. In this right triangle it is possible to make three different ratios of the sides, that is, a/b, c/b, and c/a.

Now, let us take some other point R_2 on this line and drop another perpendicular to X_2 on the x-axis. In this case we have formed another right triangle with sides A, B, and C. It is also possible in this triangle to form the different ratios of the sides, that is, A/B, C/B, and C/A.

We could continue to drop more perpendiculars from this line to the x-axis, forming more triangles, but the results would not be different, so we will consider the two right triangles abc and ABC. If we compare these ratios it will be found that a/b is the same as A/B, that c/b is the same as C/B, and that c/a is the same as C/A. Referring to Fig. 21, we find that both sides A and B are straight lines. Therefore, a proportion exists such that if a point is moved a unit distance along the side B it moves to the right a proportional amount, which if extended by a perpendicular to the x-axis, cuts off the proportional distances on the x-axis. Similarly, the movement of this point a unit distance along the side B raises the point a proportional distance

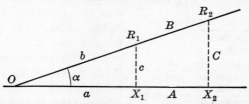

Fig. 21.—Relationship between similar triangles.

which in the above example was measured by c and C. The important thing to see, however, is that when these ratios are equal, regardless of the size of the right triangle, the corresponding angles of the two triangles are also equal. The triangles are said to be "similar" triangles.

If we are given a voltage V_1 and the ratio between it and another voltage V_2, it is easy to find the other voltage. For instance, if $V_1 = 10$ volts and we know that V_2 is five times as large as V_1, then $V_2 = 50$ volts. Mathematically, we say

$$\text{Ratio} = \frac{V_2}{V_1} = \frac{50}{10} = 5$$

Now if we have the ratio of a to b equal to one third and know that b is 27, then a must be 9. Since the ratios of the sides of a right triangle remain fixed for a given angle, we can find the other sides of this triangle if we know the various ratios and one side.

If we have any two straight lines intersecting to make some angle α, it is always possible to drop a perpendicular from a point on one line to the other and the result will then be a right triangle.

In this right triangle we have the *hypotenuse* (the longest side, which is always opposite the right angle); the *adjacent side* (the side next to the angle in question); and the *opposite side* (the side opposite the angle in question). In Fig. 21, the hypotenuse of triangle *abc* is *b*, the adjacent side is *a* and the opposite side is *c*. In triangle *ABC* the hypotenuse is *B*, the adjacent side is *A* and the opposite side is *C*.

Since the ratios hold the same for a given angle regardless of the length of the three sides, we can always form this angle by using a protractor to determine the correct angle between two intersecting straight lines. Now, drop a perpendicular from a point on one of the lines to the other line to complete the right triangle. The three sides of the triangle can then be measured and the ratios worked out from these measurements. This will result in the following ratios: *adjacent side to hypotenuse, opposite side to hypotenuse*, and *opposite side to adjacent side*. Knowing the angle and ratios, we can determine the length of the other sides if the length of one side is given. This can be applied to any other triangle having the same angle and, provided one side is known, the other sides can be determined. Figure 22 represents the relations discussed in this paragraph.

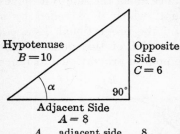

Ratio $\dfrac{A}{B} = \dfrac{\text{adjacent side}}{\text{hypotenuse}} = \dfrac{8}{10} = 0.8$

Ratio $\dfrac{C}{B} = \dfrac{\text{opposite side}}{\text{hypotenuse}} = \dfrac{6}{10} = 0.6$

Ratio $\dfrac{C}{A} = \dfrac{\text{opposite side}}{\text{adjacent side}} = \dfrac{6}{8} = 0.75$

Fig. 22.—Names of the sides of a right triangle with respect to the acute angle α.

Now, if we have another triangle with the same angle α and the adjacent side equal to 40, the other two sides can be determined from the above ratios.

This problem is shown in Fig. 23. From the above problem we know that the ratio $A/B = 0.8$ where $A = 40$. Solving, we get $B = 50$, the length of the hypotenuse. From the ratio $C/A = 0.75$ we can solve for C and get $C = 30$, the length of the opposite side. To prove this we can take the other ratio

$$C/B = 30/50 = 0.6$$

which checks with the ratio obtained above for this case.

This type of problem can always be worked graphically by using a rule and protractor as outlined above. For that matter, a table of these ratios could be made in this manner for all angles from 0 to 90 degrees, but there is no need of this, since

they have been computed very accurately and compiled in mathematical tables called "natural trigonometric functions of angles" or natural sines, cosines, and tangents.

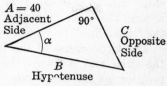

FIG. 23.—The names of the respective sides of a right triangle are not altered by its position.

When speaking about the trigonometric functions of an angle, we are talking in terms of right triangles as discussed above, but it is not always necessary to draw in the perpendicular to form the opposite side.

Definitions of Trigonometric Functions.—In order to simplify expressions we define the ratios by giving them names, as follows:

$$\text{Cosine} = \begin{pmatrix} \text{ratio of adjacent} \\ \text{side to hypotenuse} \end{pmatrix} = \frac{\text{adjacent side}}{\text{hypotenuse}} \quad (1)$$

$$\text{Sine} = \begin{pmatrix} \text{ratio of opposite} \\ \text{side to hypotenuse} \end{pmatrix} = \frac{\text{opposite side}}{\text{hypotenuse}} \quad (2)$$

$$\text{Tangent} = \begin{pmatrix} \text{ratio of opposite} \\ \text{side to adjacent side} \end{pmatrix} = \frac{\text{opposite side}}{\text{adjacent side}} \quad (3)$$

The reciprocal of these ratios gives three other functions, as follows:

$$\text{Secant} = \begin{pmatrix} \text{ratio of hypotenuse} \\ \text{to adjacent side} \end{pmatrix} = \frac{\text{hypotenuse}}{\text{adjacent side}} \quad (4)$$

$$\text{Cosecant} = \begin{pmatrix} \text{ratio of hypotenuse} \\ \text{to opposite side} \end{pmatrix} = \frac{\text{hypotenuse}}{\text{opposite side}} \quad (5)$$

$$\text{Cotangent} = \begin{pmatrix} \text{ratio of adjacent} \\ \text{side to opposite side} \end{pmatrix} = \frac{\text{adjacent side}}{\text{opposite side}} \quad (6)$$

These last three functions can always be replaced by the first three, and since they are used very seldom they will not be treated here. However, they can be found in tables and used just like the other functions in problems. Instead of writing out the whole word for these functions they are usually abbreviated as follows:

$$\text{Sine} = \sin \qquad \text{Cosecant} = \csc$$
$$\text{Cosine} = \cos \qquad \text{Secant} = \sec$$
$$\text{Tangent} = \tan \qquad \text{Cotangent} = \cot$$

Value of Function as the Angle Varies.—The above relationships can be associated with the radius of a circle as it moves around the circle making a varying angle with a fixed line called the "base line" or "positive x-axis," as shown in Fig. 24.

The hypotenuse of the triangle in any event is the radius of the circle and is always the same length. As it rotates from its position oa on the x-axis to the position oe on the y-axis, the angle it makes with the x-axis varies from 0 to 90 degrees.

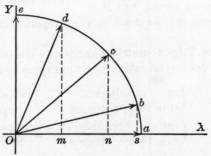

Fig. 24.—Value of trigonometric functions vary as the hypotenuse of a triangle traces the arc of a circle.

In the position oa, the hypotenuse coincides with the adjacent side and is equal to it, while the opposite side is zero. In this case the ratio of the adjacent side to the hypotenuse is 1 ($\cos 0° = 1$), and the ratio of the opposite side to the hypotenuse is zero ($\sin 0° = 0$), and the ratio of the opposite to the adjacent side is also zero ($\tan 0° = 0$). *Note:* Zero divided by any number is zero.

In the position oe, the hypotenuse coincides with the opposite side and is of the same length, the length of the adjacent side being zero. Then the ratio of the opposite side to the hypotenuse is 1 ($\sin 90° = 1$), the ratio of the adjacent side to the hypotenuse is zero ($\cos 90° = 0$), and the ratio of the opposite side to the adjacent side is infinity ($\tan 90° = \infty$). *Note:* Any number divided by zero gives infinity, which is larger than any number, much as zero is smaller than any number. Zero and infinity are really not numbers and hence must not be handled as numbers in mathematical operations.

If the hypotenuse (radius) is made of unit length, the ratio of the adjacent side to the hypotenuse is equal to the length of the adjacent side and the ratio of the opposite side to the hypotenuse is equal to the length of the opposite side.

Referring to Fig. 24, we can see that the adjacent side decreases from *oa*, which is 1, to *os* when the hypotenuse is in the position *ob*. As the hypotenuse takes on the positions *oc*, *od*, and lastly *oe* the adjacent side decreases from *no* to *mo* and then finally becomes of zero length. This means that the *cosine* of the angle varies from unity for 0 degrees to zero for 90 degrees, *decreasing* as the angle *increases*.

The opposite side is of zero length when the hypotenuse is in position *oa* and increases to *bs* when the hypotenuse takes on the position *ob*. As the hypotenuse takes on the positions *oc*, *od*, and finally *oe*, the opposite side increases in length from *cn* to *dm* and lastly is of unit length *oe*. This shows that the *sine* of the angle varies from zero at 0 degrees to unity at 90 degrees, *increasing* as the *angle increases*.

Consider the ratio of the opposite side to the adjacent side as the angle varies from 0 to 90 degrees. This ratio varies from 0 when the hypotenuse is in position *oa* to ∞ (infinity) when the hypotenuse is in position *oe*. When the hypotenuse makes an angle of 45 degrees with the *x*-axis this ratio is unity, so the tangent of the angle varies from zero to unity in the first 45 degrees and from unity to infinity in the next 45 degrees. The *tangent* of the angle *increases* as the *angle increases*.

It is of interest to note that the sine and cosine, opposite and adjacent sides in Fig. 24, never grow larger than the hypotenuse, which is 1, but the tangent, which is the ratio of the opposite side to the adjacent side, or sine to cosine, has both terms in the ratio varying. The opposite side grows larger while the adjacent side grow smaller. The result is that the tangent grows larger rather slowly up to 45 degrees but then grows larger rapidly as the angle increases to 90 degrees. In the case of the sine and cosine, only one term in the ratio varied.

The student should now inspect a table of trigonometric functions (a brief table is at the back of this book). These functions may be listed as natural sines and cosines in one table and natural tangents and cotangents in the other table. The investigation of these tables should verify the above discussion.

When the student is in doubt about trigonometric functions it will often help to draw a figure of a quadrant, as in Fig. 24. Other aids are given on page 304.

In trigonometric tables, angles up to 90 degrees only are given. That is one reason for dividing the circle into four 90-degree quadrants. In case an angle between 90 and 180 degrees is given, the trigonometric function of that angle is equal to 180 degrees. minus the angle in question. Then this angle will be between 0 and 90 degrees. The rule is to *measure the angle to the nearest base line—that is, to the x-axis.* For an angle lying in the third quadrant subtract 180 degrees and then look this angle up in the tables. In the fourth quadrant, subtract the angle from 360 degrees, which will again give angles between 0 and 90 degrees. This shows that tables from 0 to 90 degrees are sufficient to handle any angle one may meet in practice.

As shown before, the trigonometric functions are expressed in terms of ratios. Each function can be expressed in three different ways by changing the equation. Using the abbreviations

hyp = hypotenuse   sin = sine of angle
adj = adjacent side   cos = cosine of angle
opp = opposite side   tan = tangent of angle

we can now write

$$\sin = \frac{\text{opp}}{\text{hyp}} \tag{7}$$

$$\text{hyp} = \frac{\text{opp}}{\sin} \tag{8}$$

$$\text{opp} = \sin \text{hyp} \tag{9}$$

$$\cos = \frac{\text{adj}}{\text{hyp}} \tag{10}$$

$$\text{hyp} = \frac{\text{adj}}{\cos} \tag{11}$$

$$\text{adj} = \cos \text{hyp} \tag{12}$$

$$\tan = \frac{\text{opp}}{\text{adj}} \tag{13}$$

$$\text{adj} = \frac{\text{opp}}{\tan} \tag{14}$$

$$\text{opp} = \text{adj} \tan \tag{15}$$

The above equations are valuable when solving for unknown sides or angles in a right triangle. If any two sides of a right triangle are given the angles can be found by using one of the above equations and then looking in a table of trigonometric functions for the angle.

Example 1. In Fig. 25 we have given

adjacent side a = 8
hypotenuse c = 10

Find

opposite side b
angle α (alpha)
angle β (beta)

Solution. By Eq. (10),

$$\cos \alpha = \frac{\text{adj}}{\text{hyp}} = \frac{a}{c} = \frac{8}{10} = 0.8$$

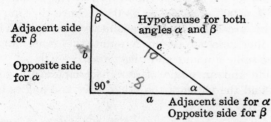

Adjacent side for β

Hypotenuse for both angles α and β

Opposite side for α

90°

Adjacent side for α
Opposite side for β

Fig. 25.—The names of the sides of a right triangle in terms of either acute angle.

Looking in a six-place trigonometric table, we find that the cosine of 36°52′ (36 degrees 52 minutes) gives 0.800034, which is close enough for practical purposes. Hence

$$\alpha = 36°52' \quad Ans.$$

The opposite side b can now be found by means of Eq. (9) or (15) given above. Using Eq. (9),

opposite side b = $\sin \alpha$ hyp
= (0.6)(10)
= 6 *Ans.*

By application of Eq. (15),

opposite side b = $\tan \alpha$ adj
= (0.75)(8.0)
= 6 *Ans.*

(tan α was found for 36°52′ in the tables)

Angle β can be found by using Eq. (7), (10), or (13), but it must be remembered that when using angle β the adjacent side is b and the opposite side is a. Using Eq. (7),

$$\sin \beta = \frac{\text{opp}}{\text{hyp}} = \frac{8}{10} = 0.8$$

Then, from the table,

$$\beta = 53°08' \text{ (nearly)} \quad Ans.$$

Note: This must be read up from the bottom of the page. The minutes are given on the right-hand side instead of the left-hand side when the angles at the top are used. (See Allen's "Six-place Tables.")

It will be noted that $\cos \alpha = 0.8$ and $\sin \beta = 0.8$. This is due to the fact that *the sum of the interior angles of a triangle is* 180 degrees. Since we are using right triangles, one of these angles equals 90° and hence the sum of the other two angles equals $180° - 90° = 90°$. This says that $\alpha + \beta = 90°$, so if $\alpha = 36°52'$, $\beta = 90° - \alpha = 90° - 36°52' = 53°08'$. Since the sum of α and β is 90° they are called "complementary angles." That is, if one angle increases a certain amount the other angle must decrease the same amount and vice versa.

If one side and an angle of a right triangle are given it is possible to find the value of the other sides and angles by means of trigonometry.

Example 2. In Fig. 25, let $b = 20$ and $\alpha = 30°$. Find a, c, and β.

Solution.

$$\text{Angle } \beta = 90° - \alpha = 90° - 30° = 60° \quad Ans.$$

By Eq. (11) and the use of the trigonometric tables,

$$c = \text{hyp} = \frac{\text{adj}}{\cos \beta} = \frac{b}{\cos \beta}$$
$$= \frac{20}{\cos 60°} = \frac{20}{0.5} = 40 \quad Ans.$$

By Eq. (15),

$$a = \text{opp} = \text{adj} \tan = 20 \tan \beta = (20)(1.732)$$
$$= (20)(1.732) = 34.64 \quad Ans.$$

The work can easily be checked by using other equations such as Eq. (12), as follows:

$$\text{adj} = \text{hyp} \cos \alpha$$

Substituting,
$$34.64 = (40)(\cos 30°)$$
$$= (40)(0.866)$$
$$= 34.64 \quad Check.$$

Applying this knowledge of trigonometry, we are able to work the problems mentioned in the preceding chapter. In other words, if we have a vector or force with magnitude and direction given, it is a simple matter to find its components along the x-axis and the y-axis. This type of problem will be handled in the next chapter on vector addition.

Inverse Trigonometric Functions.—In logarithms we used the antilogarithm, which is the number corresponding to a certain logarithm. In trigonometry it is advantageous to use similar expressions. The angle corresponding to a given ratio can be expressed in three ways, as follows:

$$\tan^{-1} 0.5 = 26°34'$$
$$\sin^{-1} 0.5 = 30°$$
$$\cos^{-1} 0.5 = 60°$$

These equations can be rewritten in the familiar form as follows:

$$\tan 26°34' = 0.5$$
$$\sin 30° = 0.5$$
$$\cos 60° = 0.5$$

The student should not confuse the above forms $\tan^{-1}$, $\sin^{-1}$, and $\cos^{-1}$ with negative exponents—they are merely abbreviations to simplify the mathematics.

Logarithms of Trigonometric Functions.—Also, the student should not confuse logarithmic sin, cos, tan, and cot with the natural functions. This table (such as found in Allen's "Six-place Tables") of logarithmic trigonometric functions is merely a table of logarithms of ratios for use in problems when dealing with logarithms and will not be referred to in this book unless so specified.

Exercises

In each of the following problems, construct the triangle, showing values of all the sides and angles. In solving them, use the equations on page 72 and the fact that the sum of the angles of a triangle equals 180°.

1. Hypotenuse = 60, angle = 40°.
2. Opposite side = 35, angle = 25°.
3. Adjacent side = 7.07, angle = 45°.
4. Adjacent side = 10, opposite side = 20.
5. Hypotenuse = 15, adjacent side = 5.
6. Opposite side = 50, hypotenuse = 90.

Each of the above problems should be checked by several other equations until the student is *positive* that he is familiar with each type of problem.

CHAPTER 6

VECTOR ADDITION

Already we have been using vectors in geometry but could not in all cases arrive at a solution until the principles of trigonometry were introduced. We are now ready to solve any such vector problems.

Reviewing, we remember that vectors in the same direction can be added arithmetically, vectors in the same direction or in exact opposition can be added algebraically, and vectors at right angles to each other can be added geometrically. Generalizing still another step, *vectors in any direction can be added vectorially*.

Perhaps the simplest geometric addition is when the two vectors are of equal magnitude and at right angles. In this case the resultant lies halfway between the two vectors (45 degrees from either one) and has a magnitude of

$$|R| = \sqrt{|a|^2 + |a|^2} = \sqrt{2a^2} = |a| \sqrt{2}$$

when a represents the magnitude of either vector. In words this

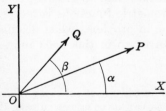

Fig. 26.

says that the resultant magnitude is equal to the square root of the sum of the squares of the magnitudes of the two vectors. See Fig. 11 for a similar illustration.

Vectorial Addition.—When the vectors are *not* at right angles, as illustrated in Fig. 26, it is customary to resolve the vectors into their components along the x-axis

Fig. 26.—Vector forces P and Q acting on the point O at angles of α and β respectively.

and the y-axis. The algebraic sum of the x-components gives a resultant x-component and the algebraic sum of the y-component gives a resultant y-component. These resultant x- and y-components are added geometrically to obtain the resultant vector.

Graphically, the vectors P and Q are resolved into their components P_x, P_y, Q_x and Q_y as shown in diagrams a and b of

Fig. 27. If these two diagrams are superimposed the result shown in Fig. 27c is obtained. Here the resultant magnitude of the x-component is obtained by algebraic addition of the x-components, thus

$$\text{Sum of } x\text{-components} = R_x = P_x + Q_x \qquad (1)$$

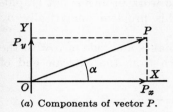

(a) Components of vector P.

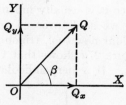

(b) Components of vector Q.

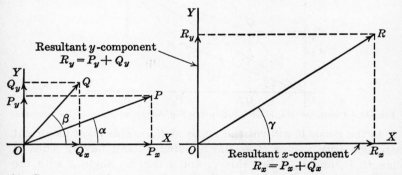

(c) Components of vectors P and Q.

(d) Algebraic sum of P and Q components to determine geometric resultant vector R.

FIG. 27.—Steps in resolving vectors into their components, which are added geometrically to determine the resultant vector sum.

Similarly, the resultant magnitude of the y-component is obtained by algebraic addition of the y-components, thus

$$\text{Sum of } y\text{-components} = R_y = P_y + Q_y \qquad (2)$$

The geometric sum of the resultant x- and y-components (R_x and R_y) gives the resultant vector R as shown in Fig. 27c. Since vectors R_x and R_y are at right angles to each other the resultant magnitude can be written

$$|R| = \sqrt{R_x^2 + R_y^2} \qquad (3)$$

Substituting for the magnitude of R_x and R_y in this equation we have the magnitude of the resultant

$$|R| = \sqrt{(P_x + Q_x)^2 + (P_y + Q_y)^2} \qquad (4)$$

The complete graphical solution to the problem is shown in Fig. 28.

Since it is usually inconvenient to work problems out graphically, we shall proceed to solve this problem analytically by using our new tool, trigonometry.

Figure 27a shows that vector P makes an angle of α with the x-axis. If a perpendicular is drawn from the extreme end of

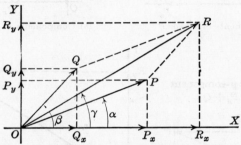

FIG. 28.—Complete graphical solution for the vector addition of two vectors.

P to the x-axis it will cut the x-axis at P_x. This gives us a right triangle with vector P as the hypotenuse and having sides of length P_x and P_y. But this vector makes an angle α with the x-axis, so by trigonometry we have

$$\cos \alpha = \frac{\text{adj}}{\text{hyp}} = \frac{P_x}{|P|}$$

or

$$P_x = |P| \cos \alpha \qquad (5)$$

Similarly,

$$\sin \alpha = \frac{\text{opp}}{\text{hyp}} = \frac{P_y}{|P|}$$

or

$$P_y = |P| \sin \alpha \qquad (6)$$

Similarly, in Fig. 27b we have a right triangle with hypotenuse $= Q$, opposite side $= Q_y$, and adjacent side $= Q_x$. This will give

$$\cos \beta = \frac{\text{adj}}{\text{hyp}} = \frac{Q_x}{|Q|}$$

or

$$Q_x = |Q| \cos \beta \qquad (7)$$

and
$$\sin \beta = \frac{\text{opp}}{\text{hyp}} = \frac{Q_y}{|Q|}$$

or
$$Q_y = |Q| \sin \beta \qquad (8)$$

Substituting Eqs. (5) and (7) in Eq. (1) gives

$$R_x = P_x + Q_x = |P| \cos \alpha + |Q| \cos \beta \qquad (9)$$

Substituting Eqs. (6) and (8) in Eq. (2) gives

$$R_y = P_y + Q_y = |P| \sin \alpha + |Q| \sin \beta \qquad (10)$$

Now, by substituting Eqs. (9) and (10) in (3), we get the resultant magnitude of the vector R in terms of the magnitude of vectors P, Q and trigonometric functions of the angles α and β, that is,

$$|R| = \sqrt{(|P| \cos \alpha + |Q| \cos \beta)^2 + (|P| \sin \alpha + |Q| \sin \beta)^2} \qquad (11)$$

This equation is perfectly general for finding the magnitude of the vector R, which is the sum of any two vectors, P and Q, making angles α and β respectively with the positive x-axis.

It is of interest to note that in Fig. 27 we have a right triangle with the magnitude of vector R the hypotenuse, the magnitude R_y the opposite side equal to $|P| \sin \alpha + |Q| \sin \beta$, and R_x the adjacent side equal to $|P| \cos \alpha + |Q| \cos \beta$. If we call the angle that vector R makes with the positive x-axis "γ" (gamma), we have

$$\tan \gamma = \frac{\text{opp}}{\text{adj}} = \frac{R_y}{R_x} = \frac{|P| \sin \alpha + |Q| \sin \beta}{|P| \cos \alpha + |Q| \cos \beta} \qquad (12)$$

Since we know the length of the opposite and adjacent side, the angle γ can be found by referring to any trigonometry table.

Equation (11) gives the *magnitude* of the resultant vector and Eq. (12) gives the *angle;* therefore, the resultant vector is completely determined.

Example 1.   Referring to Fig. 26 we have given

$$\begin{aligned} |P| &= 10 & \alpha &= 30° \\ |Q| &= 5 & \beta &= 60° \end{aligned}$$

Determine the resultant vector R.

Solution. Since P and Q are not at right angles with each other, we must use the above method to determine the resultant, that is, find the x- and y-components, which will be at right angles and hence can be added by geometric addition to obtain the final resultant.

The x-component of P by Eq. (5) is

$$P_x = |P| \cos \alpha = 10 \cos 30° = 10(0.866) = 8.66$$

The x-component of Q by Eq. (7) is

$$Q_x = |Q| \cos \beta = 5 \cos 60° = 5(0.5) = 2.5$$

The resultant x-component by Eq. (1) is

$$R_x = P_x + Q_x = 8.66 + 2.5 = 11.16$$

Now, the y-component of P by Eq. (6) is

$$P_y = |P| \sin \alpha = 10 \sin 30° = 10(0.5) = 5$$

and the y-component of Q by Eq. (8) is

$$Q_y = |Q| \sin \beta = 5 \sin 60° = 5(0.866) = 4.33$$

The resultant y-component by Eq. (2) is then

$$R_y = P_y + Q_y = 5 + 4.33 = 9.33$$

Equation (3) will now give us the magnitude of the resultant, thus

$$|R| = \sqrt{R_x^2 + R_y^2} = \sqrt{(11.16)^2 + (9.33)^2}$$
$$= \sqrt{124.6 + 87.04} = \sqrt{211.6}$$
$$= 14.54 \quad Ans.$$

Now that we have the magnitude we will solve for γ (gamma), the angle the resultant vector R makes with the positive x-axis.

From Eq. (12) we have

$$\tan \gamma = \frac{R_y}{R_x} = \frac{9.33}{11.16} = 0.836$$

From trigonometric tables, $\gamma = 39°54'$ *Ans.*

This gives the complete solution of the resultant vector R which is often written in engineering form as follows:[1]

$$R = |R|/\gamma$$
$$= 14.54/39°54' \quad Ans.$$

This answer is read, "magnitude R at an angle of gamma," or "14.55 at an angle of 39 degrees 54 minutes."

[1] This form of notation is adopted here because of its common use in engineering. Furthermore, it lends itself readily to handwriting. Sometimes vectors are noted by boldface type or by a dot or bar placed above the

Since a vector has both *magnitude* and *direction*, the above way of writing vectors is very convenient; it gives the magnitude (14.55) and the direction with respect to the positive x-axis (39°54′).

This problem was worked on the slide rule and hence the answer is not absolutely correct, but for ordinary engineering work it is entirely satisfactory.

It could have been solved by substituting directly in Eqs. (11) and (12) thus

$$|R| = \sqrt{(|P| \cos \alpha + |Q| \cos \beta)^2 + (|P| \sin \alpha + |Q| \sin \beta)^2}$$

Substituting the numerical values,

$$|R| = \sqrt{(10 \cos 30° + 5 \cos 60°)^2 + (10 \sin 30° + 5 \sin 60°)^2}$$

Looking up the trigonometric functions,

$$|R| = \sqrt{[10(0.866) + 5(0.5)]^2 + [10(0.5) + 5(0.866)]^2}$$

Performing the indicated multiplication,

$$|R| = \sqrt{(8.66 + 2.5)^2 + (5 + 4.33)^2}$$

Adding inside the parentheses and squaring,

$$|R| = \sqrt{(11.16)^2 + (9.33)^2} = \sqrt{124.6 + 87.04}$$

Adding under the radical and extracting the square root,

$$|R| = \sqrt{211.6} = 14.54 \quad Ans.$$

This answer is the same as was obtained above. Now, substituting in Eq. (12) we have

$$\tan \gamma = \frac{|P| \sin \alpha + |Q| \sin \beta}{|P| \cos \alpha + |Q| \cos \beta}$$

---

symbol. Then the equation can be written without vertical bars to denote magnitude, thus

$$\mathbf{R} = \dot{R} = \bar{R} = R\underline{/\gamma}$$

Using this notation requires boldface type, a dot, or a bar to denote every vector quantity. With such a system, the boldface type could be used in print and the dot or bar placed above the vector symbol when written longhand. From the standpoint of making the system consistent in both print and script, and in order to save time and effort, it is more convenient to use the vertical bars the few times that they are needed to denote the absolute value or magnitude only.

Substituting numerical values,

$$\tan \gamma = \frac{10 \sin 30° + 5 \sin 60°}{10 \cos 30° + 5 \cos 60°}$$

Looking up angles in trigonometric tables,

$$\tan \gamma = \frac{10(0.5) + 5(0.866)}{10(0.866) + 5(0.5)}$$

Performing the indicated multiplication, addition, and division,

$$\tan \gamma = \frac{5 + 4.33}{8.66 + 2.5} = \frac{9.33}{11.16} = 0.836$$

From tables $\gamma = 39°54'$.   *Ans.*

This answer also checks with the above results.

We will now work some examples to illustrate how vectors in quadrants other than the first are handled.

Example 2.   Find the vector sum of $A = 8/20°$ and $B = 20/120°$.

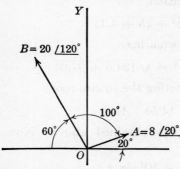

FIG. 29.—Vector diagram for Example 2.

Solution.   As in the preceding problem we find the magnitude of the x- and y-components; thus, by Eq. (5),

$$A_x = |A| \cos \alpha$$
$$= 8 \cos 20°$$
$$= 8(0.9397) = 7.5175$$

By Eq. (6),

$$A_y = |A| \sin \alpha$$
$$= 8 \sin 20°$$
$$= 8(0.545) = 2.737$$

It will be noted that vector B is in the second quadrant, so the x-component will be along the negative x-axis.   In this case we subtract the angle from 180° and get

$$180° - 120° = 60°$$

This is the angle that vector B makes with the negative x-axis. Proceeding as before, using Eq. (7), we get

$$B_x = |B| \cos \beta$$
$$= 20 \cos 120°$$
$$= 20(- \cos 60°)$$
$$= 20(-0.5) = -10$$

By inspection of the problem we can see that this must be negative. Now, by Eq. (8),

$$B_y = |B| \sin \beta$$
$$= 20 \sin 120°$$
$$= 20 \sin 60°$$
$$= 20(0.866) = 17.32$$

The sum of the x-components by Eq. (1) is

$$R_x = A_x + B_x$$
$$= 7.515 - 10 = -2.485$$

The sum of the y-components by Eq. (2) is

$$R_y = A_y + B_y$$
$$= 2.737 + 17.32 = 20.057$$

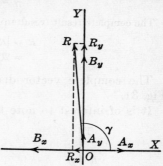

FIG. 30.—Vector diagram for Example 2.

These components are shown in Fig. 30.

The magnitude of the resultant vector R by Eq. (3) is

$$|R| = \sqrt{R_x^2 + R_y^2}$$
$$= \sqrt{(-2.485)^2 + (20.057)^2}$$

Note: The square of a negative number is a positive number.
Squaring and adding under the radical sign,

$$|R| = \sqrt{6.175 + 402.5}$$
$$= \sqrt{408.675}$$

Extracting the square root, the magnitude is

$$|R| = 20.22 \quad Ans.$$

The angle of the resultant vector R by Eq. (12) is

$$\tan \gamma = \frac{R_y}{R_x}$$
$$= \frac{20.057}{-2.485} = -8.062$$

Note: This is negative because it is in the second quadrant instead of the first. From trigonometric tables,

$$\gamma = 82°56'$$

This, however, is the angle vector R makes with the negative x-axis. If we subtract this from 180° we get the angle vector R makes with the positive

x-axis, thus

$$\gamma = 97°04' \quad Ans.$$

The complete result (resultant vector) can be written

$$R = |R|/\underline{\gamma}$$
$$= 20.22/\underline{97°04'} \quad Ans.$$

The complete vector diagram of this problem is shown in Fig. 31.

It is of interest to note that graphically the resultant vector

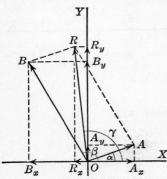

R can be found by completing the parallelogram having sides A and B, as shown in Fig. 31.

A thorough understanding of these two problems is sufficient to work most vector problems. One must be very careful to note the sense of the x- and y-components so that they can be added algebraically. Drawing a vector diagram will make this part of the problem clear.

FIG. 31.—Complete vector diagram for Example 2.

We can generalize and handle any number of vectors by this process. Each vector must be reduced to its x- and y-components and the resultant vector will be the geometric sum of the resultant x- and y-components.

Example 3.   We have given the following vectors:

$$A = |A|/\underline{\alpha} = 10/\underline{45°}$$
$$B = |B|/\underline{\beta} = 20/\underline{330°} \text{ or } 20/\overline{30°}*$$
$$C = |C|/\underline{\omega} = 5/\underline{200°}$$

Find the resultant sum $R = |R|/\underline{\gamma}$.

Solution.   Draw the vector diagram as shown in Fig. 32.   The magnitude of the resultant vector R for three vectors is given by

$$|R| = \sqrt{\begin{aligned}&(|A| \cos \alpha + |B| \cos \beta + |C| \cos \omega)^2 \\ &+ (|A| \sin \alpha + |B| \sin \beta + |C| \sin \omega)^2\end{aligned}} \qquad (13)$$

* It is common practice to use the symbol $\overline{}$ to denote that the angle is negative, while the symbol $/\underline{}$ is used to express positive angles.

It will be noted that this equation is like Eq. (11) with the exception that $|C| \cos \omega$ and $|C| \sin \omega$ are added. If more vectors were to be added they too would be included in each term under the radical, like $C/\underline{\omega}$.

Substituting in the values of this example, we get

$$|R| = \sqrt{\begin{array}{l}(10 \cos 45° + 20 \cos 330° + 5 \cos 200°)^2 \\ + (10 \sin 45° + 20 \sin 330° + 5 \sin 200°)^2\end{array}}$$

It will be recalled that if the vectors are not in the first quadrant we must find the angle they make with the x-axis and attach the correct sign. The

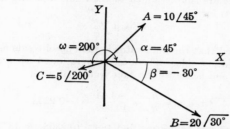

FIG. 32.—Vector diagram for Example 3.

sign to be attached depends on the sense, thus

$$\cos 330° = \cos (360° - 330°) = \cos 30°$$
$$\cos 200° = - \cos (200° - 180°) = - \cos 20°$$

Note: This is along the negative x-axis.

$$\sin 330° = - \sin (360° - 330°) = - \sin 30°$$

Note: This is along the negative y-axis.

$$\sin 200° = - \sin (200° - 180°) = - \sin 20°$$

Note: This is also along the negative y-axis.

Looking up these angles in a trigonometric table gives

$$|R| = \sqrt{\begin{array}{l}[10(0.707) + 20(0.866) - 5(0.9397)]^2 \\ + [10(0.707) - 20(0.5) - 5(0.342)]^2\end{array}}$$

Performing the indicated multiplication,

$$|R| = \sqrt{(7.07 + 17.32 - 4.698)^2 + (7.07 - 10 - 1.71)^2}$$

Adding terms within each parenthesis,

$$|R| = \sqrt{(19.692)^2 + (-4.64)^2}$$

Squaring the term in each parenthesis and adding,

$$|R| = \sqrt{387.7 + 21.53}$$
$$= \sqrt{409.23}$$

Extracting the square root,

$$|R| = 20.23 \quad Ans.$$

Now the angle γ for three vectors is determined by

$$\tan \gamma = \frac{|A| \sin \alpha + |B| \sin \beta + |C| \sin \omega}{|A| \cos \alpha + |B| \cos \beta + |C| \cos \omega} \tag{14}$$

This equation is similar to Eq. (12) with the exception that another vector's components are added. If more than three vectors are to be added, their components are simply added to the numerator and denominator as shown in Eq. (14) for

$$C = |C| \underline{/\omega}$$

It will be noted that the numerator is the opposite side and the denominator is the adjacent side. These terms were found when solving for the magnitude of R and hence we can take from that work

$$\tan \gamma = \frac{R_y}{R_x} = \frac{-4.64}{19.692} = -0.2358$$

From trigonometric tables we find $\tan^{-1} (0.2358)$ is $13°16'$. Since the quantity is negative, the resultant is located $-13°16'$ from the positive

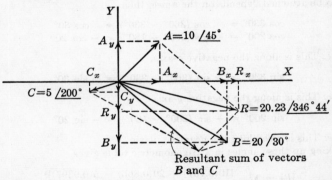

FIG. 33.—Vector diagram showing vectors A, B and C, their x- and y-components, the resultant vector sum of vectors B and C, and the resultant sum R for all three vectors in Example 3.

x-axis. Drawing the vector diagram is the best way to make this clear (See Fig. 33). Then,

$$\gamma = -13°16' \text{ or } 346°44' \quad Ans.$$

The vector sum can now be expressed

$$R = |R| \underline{/\gamma} = 20.23 \underline{/346°44'}$$
$$= 20.23 \underline{/\overline{13°16'}} \quad Ans.$$

Graphically, if there are three vectors, two (such as $|B|$ and $|C|$ in Fig. 33) can be added by the parallelogram law to get their resultant. Then this resultant can be added to the remain-

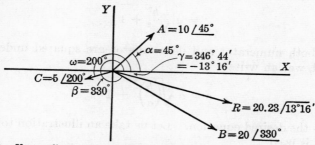

FIG. 34.—Vector diagram showing the magnitudes and angles of vectors A, B, C, and R for Example 3.

ing vector to get the total vector sum. The three vectors A, B, C and their sum R are shown in Fig. 34.

Solution of Right Triangles with the Slide Rule.—There is a short-cut method of obtaining the hypotenuse of a right triangle when the two sides are given. Since we shall be solving many right triangles, the development will be given here.

Referring to the right triangle in Fig. 35, we have

$$a^2 + b^2 = c^2$$

or
$$c = \sqrt{a^2 + b^2}$$

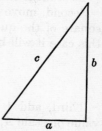

FIG. 35.—Right triangle for slide-rule solution by Eq. (15) when $b > a$.

Always select a as the shortest side. Then since multiplying both numerator and denominator of a fraction by the same thing (a^2 in this case) does not change the value of a fraction, the above equation can be written

$$c = \sqrt{\frac{a^2(a^2 + b^2)}{a^2}}$$

This may then be written

$$c = a\sqrt{\frac{a^2 + b^2}{a^2}}$$

Making two separate fractions under the radical gives

$$c = a \sqrt{\frac{a^2}{a^2} + \frac{b^2}{a^2}}$$
$$= a \sqrt{\frac{b^2}{a^2} + 1}$$

Since both numerator and denominator are squared under the radical, we can write

$$c = a \sqrt{\left(\frac{b}{a}\right)^2 + 1} \qquad (15)$$

This is the desired equation. Let us take an illustration to show how it is used.

Illustration.—Let $a = 6$, $b = 8$; to find c the hypotenuse.

Solution. First, set the hairline over b, (8), on scale D and move the slider so that a, (6), is also under the hairline. (Scale C on the slider.)

The quotient of b divided by a will be found opposite the initial index of Scale C on Scale D. In this case it will be 1.333. (The student should follow this on the slide rule.)

Second, move the hairline over the initial index and read the square of the quotient 1.333 on scale A under the hairline. In this case it will be 1.777 and is

$$\left(\frac{b}{a}\right)^2$$

Third, add 1 to this number and slide the hairline to that value on scale A, which in this case will be 2.777. We now have, on scale A, the quantity

$$\left(\frac{b}{a}\right)^2 + 1$$

Fourth, take the square root by looking under the hairline on scale D. In this case you will find 1.666, which is

$$\sqrt{\left(\frac{b}{a}\right)^2 + 1}$$

Fifth, move the initial index of scale C under the hairline and then move the hairline to a on scale C, which in this case will be

6. The answer will be found on scale D under the hairline and in this case will be 10. We then have the complete expression solved for c, that is,

$$c = a \sqrt{\left(\frac{b}{a}\right)^2 + 1} = 6 \sqrt{\left(\frac{8}{6}\right)^2 + 1} = 10 \quad Ans.$$

Note: In the development a was the shortest side, while in some of the above examples this is not true. Therefore, the a and b will have to be interchanged in these cases.

Exercises

In each of the following problems, draw a vector diagram approximately to scale and solve for the resultant vector sum (magnitude and angle):

1. Voltage vector $V_1 = 110\underline{/0°}$ (110 volts at an angle of 0° with positive x-axis).

Voltage vector $V_2 = 115\underline{/75°}$ (115 volts at an angle of 75° with positive x-axis).

2. Impedance vector $Z_1 = 100\underline{/40°}$.

Impedance vector $Z_2 = 50\underline{/15°}$ or $50\underline{/345°}$.

3. Current vector $I_1 = 3\underline{/215°}$.

Current vector $I_2 = 4\underline{/300°}$.

4. Voltage vector $V_1 = 150\underline{/60°}$.

Voltage vector $V_2 = 100\underline{/180°}$.

Voltage vector $V_3 = 50\underline{/300°}$.

5. Force vector $F_1 = 17\underline{/110°}$.

Force vector $F_2 = 15\underline{/320°}$.

Force vector $F_3 = 10\underline{/190°}$.

Work each of the following exercises by the slide-rule method and check for the resultant hypotenuse by the longer method:

6. $a = 3$, $b = 4$. Find c.

7. $a = 5$, $b = 5$. Find c.

8. $a = 14$, $b = 11$. Find c.

9. $a = 76$, $b = 21$. Find c.

10. $a = 1.28$, $b = 0.91$. Find c.

CHAPTER 7

COMPLEX QUANTITIES

The title of this chapter should not frighten the student, because we have been studying complex quantities in the last chapter. The vectors of the last lesson were complex quantities, because they had two components at right angles. In other words, *a complex quantity may be represented as a vector resolved into two components* 90 degrees apart, the x-component and the y-component.

In the last chapter the x-components were designated by using x as a subscript to the vector and the y-components were designated by using y as a subscript to the vector. The only way we could represent the complete vector was in engineering form as

$$c = |c|\underline{/\alpha} \tag{1}$$

It would often be an advantage to represent the vector in terms of the x and y-components. To do this with a minimum of labor the *x-components are written without subscripts and the y-components are prefixed with the letter j.* The above vector c can then be written

$$c = a + jb \tag{2}$$

Where a is the adjacent side and b is the opposite side of a right triangle, as shown in Fig. 36.

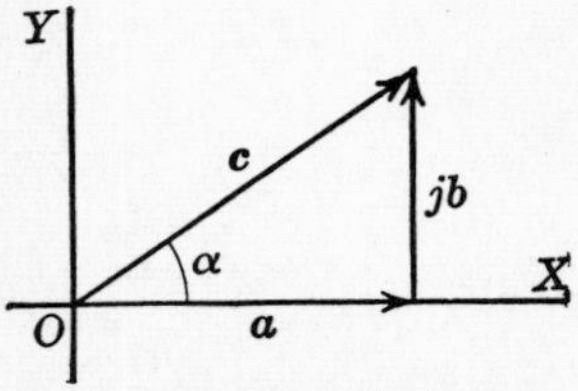

Fig. 36.—Graphical representation of a complex quantity.

In Eq. (2), the vector a always lies along the x-axis. When numerical values are substituted they are either positive or negative numbers which measure a magnitude along the x-axis. Since the magnitude and direction are specified by the numerical number, it in effect is a vector; however, it is not ordinarily written as a vector in bold face type or with a dot or dash over it. When using complex numbers it is understood to be a real number along the x-axis.

90

The letter j is known as an "operator" much like the operators of algebra already familiar to the student, for example, the plus $(+)$ sign, minus $(-)$ sign, division $(\div)$ sign, multiplication $(\times)$ sign, and radical $(\sqrt{\ })$ sign.

As the above signs tell us the operation to perform, so does the j operator tell us what to do. Thus the j operator, when multiplied by a number, has the effect of *turning the vector 90 degrees counterclockwise from its original position.*

In Eq. (2) and Fig. 36 the vector b is a real number which always lies along the x-axis. Multiplying this real number by the operator j makes it lie along the y-axis. When a numerical value is substituted for b it is not ordinarily written as a

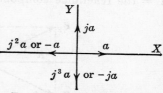

Fig. 37.—Graph showing effect of j operator when successively applied to the vector a.

vector, but understood to lie along the y-axis when multiplied by j.

Let us apply the operator j to the vector a along the positive x-axis as shown in Fig. 37. The vector ja must lie along the positive y-axis. Now if we apply another j we get j^2a which rotates vector ja 90 degrees and hence it will lie along the negative x-axis, but according to ordinary algebra this vector is negative and must be $-a$; therefore

$$j^2a = -a$$

Dividing by a, we get

$$j^2 = -1$$

or, taking the square root,

$$j = \sqrt{-1} \quad \text{(a definition of } j) \quad (3)$$

If we multiply j^2a by j the line is turned through another 90 degrees and will lie along the negative y-axis as shown in Fig. 36. If the j^2 is replaced by -1, we have

$$j^3a = j^2ja = -ja$$

Again, if $-ja$ is multiplied by j the vector along the negative y-axis will be rotated 90 degrees and will lie along the positive x-axis. That is

$$j^4a = (-ja)j = -j^2a = -(-1)a = a$$

and we have returned to the starting point again to get the same vector a. This shows that the system is consistent.

Expressing Vectors in Complex Notation.—We can now represent vectors not only in the first quadrant, as shown in Fig. 36, but in all four quadrants. Figure 38 shows impedance vectors in each quadrant. Z is the hypotenuse of a right triangle having sides R and jX, where $R =$ the resistance component and $X =$ the reactance component. (Large X, which is the react-

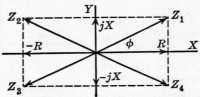

Fig. 38.—Impedance vector Z represented in all four quadrants.

ance, is not the same as small x, which is the x-axis.) The impedance vector Z_1 can be written

$$Z_1 = R + jX \quad \text{(first quadrant)} \quad (4)$$

the impedance vector Z_2 can be written

$$Z_2 = -R + jX \quad \text{(second quadrant)} \quad (5)$$

the impedance vector Z_3 can be written

$$Z_3 = -R - jX \quad \text{(third quadrant)} \quad (6)$$

and the impedance vector Z_4 can be written

$$Z_4 = R - jX \quad \text{(fourth quadrant)} \quad (7)$$

Just as in the last chapter the *magnitude* of the Z vector is the square root of the sum of the squares of the two sides of the right triangle, that is

$$|Z| = \sqrt{R^2 + X^2} \quad (8)$$

Also the angle ϕ (phi) is determined, as it was in the last chapter, by the equation

$$\tan \phi = \frac{\text{opp}}{\text{adj}} = \frac{X}{R} \quad (9)$$

The above equations for Z_1, Z_2, Z_3 and Z_4 are valuable for *adding vectors* because the x- and y-components are at right angles. The resultant x- and y-components can then be added geometrically to obtain the resultant.

Example 1. Add vector Z_1 to vector Z_2.
Solution.

$$\begin{aligned} Z_1 &= R + jX \\ Z_2 &= -R + jX \\ \hline Z_1 + Z_2 &= +2jX. \quad \textit{Ans.} \end{aligned}$$

Example 2. Subtract vector Z_3 from vector Z_4.
Solution.

$$\begin{aligned} Z_4 &= R - jX \\ Z_3 &= -R - jX \\ \hline Z_4 - Z_3 &= 2R. \quad \textit{Ans.} \end{aligned}$$

Multiplication of Vectors in Polar Form.—However, for multiplication the other form $A = |A|\underline{/\alpha}$ is advantageous. For illustration, multiply vector A by vector B where, $A = |A|\underline{/\alpha}$

$$B = |B|\underline{/\beta}$$

These vectors are expressed in polar coordinates; that is, they are expressed as a magnitude rotated through an angle from the base line.

To multiply two vectors expressed in polar coordinates, obtain the product of their magnitude and add the angles.

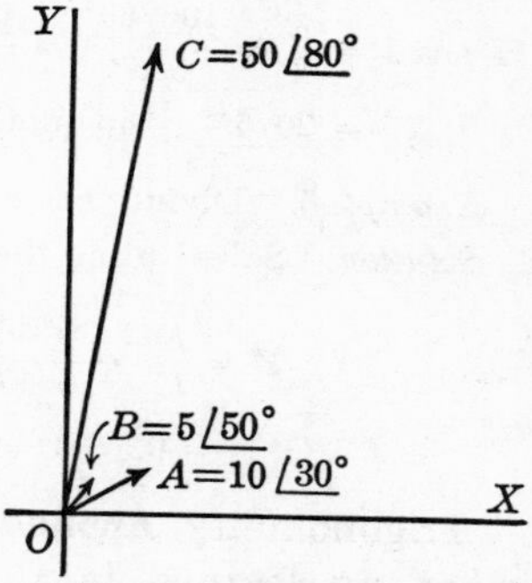

FIG. 39.—Multiplication of vectors A and B, which results in vector C.

Thus

$$C = AB = (|A|\underline{/\alpha})(|B|\underline{/\beta}) = |A||B|\underline{/\alpha + \beta} \tag{10}$$

Example 3. Multiply vector A by vector B where $A = 10\underline{/30°}$ and $B = 5\underline{/50°}$

Solution. Substituting these values in Eq. (10),

$$\begin{aligned} C &= (10)(5)\underline{/30° + 50°} \\ &= 50\underline{/80°} \quad \text{the product} \quad \textit{Ans.} \end{aligned}$$

Division of Vectors in Polar Form.—The division of vectors is just as easy as their multiplication. The rule is *to divide one vector by another in polar coordinates, obtain the quotient of the magnitudes and subtract the angle in the denominator from the angle in the numerator.* Applying this rule, let vector C be the quotient of vector A divided by vector B, thus

$$C = \frac{A}{B} = \frac{|A|/\alpha}{|B|/\beta} = \frac{|A|}{|B|} /\alpha - \beta \tag{11}$$

Example 4. Divide vector E by vector Z where $E = 100/60°$ and $Z = 5/5°$

Solution. Substituting these values in Eq. (11),

$$I = \frac{E}{Z} = \frac{100/60°}{5/5°}$$

Dividing the magnitudes $^{100}/_5 = 20$ and subtracting the denominator angle from the numerator angle gives

$$60° - 5° = 55°$$

Hence $I = \dfrac{E}{Z} = \dfrac{100/60°}{5/5°} = \dfrac{100}{5} /60° - 5°$

$= 20/55°$ the quotient. *Ans.*

Example 5. Divide vector E by vector I when $E = 8/10°$ and $I = 16/40°$

Solution. Substituting these values in Eq. (11),

$$Z = \frac{E}{I} = \frac{8/10°}{16/40°} = \frac{8}{16} /10° - 40°$$

$= 0.5/30°$ or $0.5/330°$ the quotient   *Ans.*

Trigonometry Applied to Complex Numbers.—According to what we learned in the last chapter, the magnitude of the x-component of c is $|c| \cos \alpha$ and the magnitude of the y-component of c is $|c| \sin \alpha$. In complex numbers we write

$$c = a + jb$$

but a is the x-component $|c| \cos \alpha$ and b is the y-component $|c|$ $\sin \alpha$; therefore, we can write

$$c = |c| \cos \alpha + j|c| \sin \alpha$$

Factoring out the $|c|$ on the right-hand side gives

$$c = |c| (\cos \alpha + j \sin \alpha) \tag{12}$$

In this equation $|c|$ is the magnitude of the vector and

$$(\cos \alpha + j \sin \alpha)$$

is the *trigonometric operator* which rotates the vector through the angle α in a counterclockwise direction from the positive x-axis.

The quantity $(\cos \alpha + j \sin \alpha)$ always has a magnitude of unity. It is a unit vector specifying the direction the magnitude must take. It can be thought of as the radius of a unit circle, as illustrated in Fig. 40.

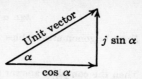

FIG. 40.—Unit vector as geometric sum of $\cos \alpha + j \sin \alpha$.

Relationship between Polar and Rectangular Forms.—The above relationship provides a method of changing from the rectangular form $(a + jb)$ to the polar form $|c|\underline{/\alpha}$ or vice versa. We can now write $\underline{/\alpha} = \cos \alpha + j \sin \alpha$, hence,

$$c = |c|\underline{/\alpha} = |c|(\cos \alpha + j \sin \alpha) = |c| \cos \alpha + |c|j \sin \alpha,$$

but $\qquad\qquad a = |c| \cos \alpha$
and $\qquad\qquad b = |c| \sin \alpha$

Therefore, $c = a + jb$

Example 6. Given $c = 20\underline{/30°}$ (polar form)
Change to rectangular form.
Solution. Replacing $\underline{/\alpha}$ by the operator, $(\cos \alpha + j \sin \alpha)$ and substituting the trigonometric values,

$$c = 20(\cos 30° + j \sin 30°) = 20(0.866 + j0.5)$$

Multiplying,

$$c = 17.32 + j10 \qquad \text{(rectangular form)} \quad Ans.$$

Example 7. Give $c = 30 + j50$ (rectangular form)

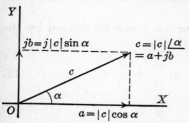

FIG. 41.—Polar and rectangular forms of representing a vector.

Change to polar form.

Solution. The magnitude of c is given by the relationship of Eq. (8). Thus

$$|c| = \sqrt{a^2 + b^2}$$

Substituting numerical values,

$$|c| = \sqrt{(30)^2 + (50)^2}$$

Squaring the terms under the radical and adding,

$$|c| = \sqrt{900 + 2500} = \sqrt{3400}$$

Extracting the square root,

$$|c| = 58.33 \qquad \text{(the magnitude)}$$

The angle is obtained by Eq. (9), thus

$$\tan \alpha = \frac{\text{opp}}{\text{adj}} = \frac{b}{a} = \frac{50}{30} = 1.666$$

From trigonometric tables,

$$\alpha = 59°02' \qquad \text{(approx.) (the angle)}$$

Then the complete answer in polar form is

$$c = |c|\underline{/\alpha} = 58.33\underline{/59°02'} \quad Ans.$$

It is important to note that the magnitude

$$\cos \alpha = \cos 59°02' = 0.514539$$
$$\sin \alpha = \sin 59°02' = 0.857467$$

Hence, $a = |c| \cos \alpha$

Substituting numerical values,

$$a = 58.33(0.514539)$$
$$= 30, \text{ which checks} \quad Check.$$

and, $b = |c| \sin \alpha$

Substituting numerical values,

$$b = 58.33 (0.857467)$$
$$= 50, \text{ which also checks} \quad Check.$$

This process of changing from polar to rectangular form and vice versa will be used to advantage later in the study of alternating current circuit theory.

True Mathematical Polar Form.—The polar form $c = |c|\underline{/\alpha}$ has been adopted because of its convenience in expressing a vector which has a *magnitude* $|c|$ and makes an *angle* α with the reference axes. From pure mathematics it is easy to develop the exact character of this quantity.

The magnitude of ϵ^x, $\sin x$, and $\cos x$ can be defined by the following series:

$$\epsilon^x = 1 + x + \frac{x^2}{\underline{|2}} + \frac{x^3}{\underline{|3}} + \frac{x^4}{\underline{|4}} + \frac{x^5}{\underline{|5}} + \cdots \qquad (13)$$

$$\sin \alpha = \alpha - \frac{\alpha^3}{\underline{|3}} + \frac{\alpha^5}{\underline{|5}} - \cdots \qquad (14)$$

$$\cos \alpha = 1 - \frac{\alpha^2}{\underline{|2}} + \frac{\alpha^4}{\underline{|4}} - \cdots \qquad (15)$$

In these equations the three dots at the end indicate that only a few terms of the series are written. Enough terms are usually written to indicate how the rest of the series can be written.

The expressions $\underline{|2}$, $\underline{|3}$, etc., in the denominator mean factorial, thus

$$\underline{|2} = 2 \cdot 1 = 2, \qquad \underline{|3} = 3 \cdot 2 \cdot 1 = 6, \qquad \underline{|4} = 4 \cdot 3 \cdot 2 \cdot 1 = 24, \text{ etc.}$$

Now if $j\alpha$ is substituted for x in Eq. (13), it can be written

$$\epsilon^{j\alpha} = 1 + j\alpha + \frac{(j\alpha)^2}{\underline{|2}} + \frac{(j\alpha)^3}{\underline{|3}} + \frac{(j\alpha)^4}{\underline{|4}} + \cdots \qquad (16)$$

but,

$$\begin{array}{ll} j = \sqrt{-1} & j^4 = 1 \\ j^2 = -1 & j^5 = \sqrt{-1} \\ j^3 = -\sqrt{-1} & j^6 = -1 \end{array}$$

Substituting these values in (16) gives

$$\epsilon^{j\alpha} = 1 + j\alpha - \frac{\alpha^2}{\underline{|2}} - j\frac{\alpha^3}{\underline{|3}} + \frac{\alpha^4}{\underline{|4}} + j\frac{\alpha^5}{\underline{|5}} - \cdots \qquad (17)$$

Separating the j terms, gives

$$\epsilon^{j\alpha} = \left(1 - \frac{\alpha^2}{\underline{|2}} + \frac{\alpha^4}{\underline{|4}} - \cdots\right) + j\left(\alpha - \frac{\alpha^3}{\underline{|3}} + \frac{\alpha^5}{\underline{|5}} - \cdots\right) \qquad (18)$$

But the two series of (18) are the same as those of (14) and (15), hence,

$$\epsilon^{j\alpha} = \cos \alpha + j \sin \alpha \qquad (19)$$

This shows that *the true mathematical polar form* of c is $|c|\epsilon^{j\alpha}$ where $\epsilon = 2.718 \cdots$ the base of natural logarithms. This establishes the exponential character of the angle, showing why the angles are added when vectors are multiplied. The vector c can be written in several forms, as follows:

$$c = |c|\underline{/\alpha} = |c|\epsilon^{j\alpha} = |c| (\cos \alpha + j \sin \alpha)$$
$$= |c| \cos \alpha + j|c| \sin \alpha \qquad (20)$$

Multiplication of Vectors in Rectangular Form.—The multiplication of vectors in rectangular form is more cumbersome than the multiplication of vectors in polar form. Usually it is easier to change from rectangular to polar form for multiplication than to perform the multiplication in rectangular form. However, in some cases, such as certain theoretical developments, multiplication in rectangular form is valuable, and it should therefore be understood by the student.

Illustration.   Multiply $(a + jb)(c + jd)$.

Solution.   Performing the algebraic multiplication, as outlined in Chap. 3, results in

$$(a + jb)(c + jd) = (ac - bd) + j\,(ad + bc) \qquad (21)$$

In checking this equation the student must remember that j^2 can be replaced by -1.

Example 8.   Given:

$$a + jb = 3 + j4 = 5\underline{/53°08'}$$
$$c + jd = 8 + j6 = 10\underline{/36°52'}$$

First multiply these vectors in rectangular form and then check by using polar form.

Solution.   By rectangular multiplication,

$$(3 + j4)(8 + j6) = (3)(8) - (4)(6) + j(3)(6) + j(4)(8)$$
$$= 0 + j50 = 50\underline{/90°}\quad Ans.$$

Checking by polar multiplication,
$$(5\underline{/53°08'})(10\underline{/36°52'}) = 50\underline{/90°} = 0 + j50 \quad Check.$$

Division of Vectors in Rectangular Form.—The division of vectors in rectangular form is even more cumbersome than their multiplication in that form.   In order to divide two vectors, it is necessary to rationalize the fraction, as follows:

Illustration.   Divide $(a + jb)$ by $(c + jd)$.

Solution.   First, set up the problem in fraction form.

Second, multiply both numerator and denominator by the denominator with the j term sign changed.

Third, multiply out both numerator and denominator.

The operations are illustrated as follows:

$$\frac{a + jb}{c + jd} = \frac{(a + jb)(c - jd)}{(c + jd)(c - jd)} = \frac{(ac + bd) + j\,(bc - ad)}{c^2 + d^2}$$

The term $c - jd$ is called the "conjugate" of $c + jd$ because it has the *same magnitude* but its angle is the *negative* of $c + jd$. The product of a number by its conjugate is a real number since the j term disappears.   This removes all j operators from the denominator and makes a rationalized complex number.

Fourth, the quotient can be written in rectangular form as follows:

$$\frac{a + jb}{c + jd} = \frac{ac + bd}{c^2 + d^2} + j\,\frac{bc - ad}{c^2 + d^2} \qquad (22)$$

Example 9.   Given: $a + jb = 3 + j4 = 5\underline{/53°08'}$

$$c + jd = 8 + j6 = 10\underline{/36°52'}$$

First divide these vectors in rectangular form and then check by using polar form.

Solution.

$$\frac{3 + j4}{8 + j6} = \frac{(3 + j4)(8 - j6)}{(8 + j6)(8 - j6)} = \frac{24 + 24 + j(32 - 18)}{(64) + (36)} = \frac{48 + j14}{100}$$

$$= 0.48 + j0.14 = 0.50\underline{/16°16'} \quad Ans.$$

Checking by polar division,

$$\frac{5\underline{/53°08'}}{10\underline{/36°52'}} = 0.5\underline{/16°16'} = 0.48 + j0.14 \quad Check.$$

Exercises

1. Write $c = |c|\underline{/\alpha} = 50\underline{/30°}$ in rectangular form, $(a + jb)$.
2. Write $c = |c|\underline{/\alpha} = 10\underline{/300°}$ in rectangular form.
3. Write $c = a + jb = -20 + j30$ in polar form.
4. Multiply $A = 25\underline{/15°}$ by $B = 60\underline{/80°}$.
5. Divide $A = 25\underline{/15°}$ by $B = 60\underline{/80°}$ and express in rectangular form.

CHAPTER 8

CURVES AND GRAPHS

Curves and graphs are widely used to show relationships clearly. They bring together the principles of both algebra and geometry in a pictorial way that greatly increases their utility.

A curve is a smooth line representing the relationship between two or more variables. Such curves are often used by engineers for visualizing design relationships. A common procedure to obtain a curve is to vary one quantity and note the simultaneous values of the other quantities. After sufficient data have been obtained, the points are plotted on appropriate graph paper and a smooth line is drawn through them to show the relationship. Algebraic equations can also be solved by plotting curves. These methods are not so readily adapted to high accuracy as pure algebraic methods, yet they often permit the solution of problems so difficult that pure algebraic methods become impractical. A curve is a special type of graph. A graph is a pictorial representation showing the relationship between two or more quantities. Graphs are used extensively by newspapers, magazines, technical journals, engineers, and business people concerned with relative values. In one of the most common types of graphs, the adjacent points are joined by straight lines. This should be done unless there is a good reason for drawing a smooth curve through them. Common graphs of this type are those that show temperature plotted against time, stock market values plotted daily, and volume of business plotted monthly. Business men often base important decisions upon information obtained from graphs.

Engineering curves are usually plotted on cross-section paper. Cross-section paper comes in a variety of forms to meet various needs. Some of the more common forms are rectangular coordinate paper, logarithmic paper, and polar coordinate paper.

System of Rectangular Coordinates.—We have already been using a system of coordinates. Such a system is shown in

Fig. 42. Here we have the x- and y-axes at right angles. Let each axis be considered as a number scale with the intersection of the axes as the zero point of each scale. The point P, any point on the plane, can be located by dropping perpendiculars to the two axes as shown in Fig. 42. Let x represent the distance to the y-axis and y represent the distance to the x-axis. The point P given in Fig. 42 can be represented by the symbol (3, −2) which means that starting at the origin the point P is located by going a distance +3 along the positive x-axis and then going down a distance of −2 parallel to the negative y-axis. The +3 and −2 are often referred to as the coordinates of the point P.

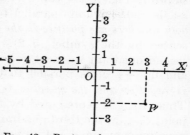

FIG. 42.—Rectangular coordinate system.

In order to make it easy to locate any such point P (the point P is said to be plotted), it is very convenient to use cross-section

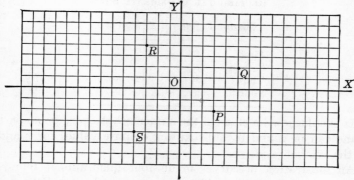

FIG. 43.—Rectangular coordinate system superimposed on cross-section paper.

paper, as shown in Fig. 43. Such paper is made by ruling off the plane into equal squares with sides parallel to the axes. The side of a square may be taken as unit length to represent a number.

If we do not know the coordinates of a point P we can refer to them as (x, y). In the above case x = +3 and y = −2 and hence the coordinates are (3, −2). *Note:* The first number in the parenthesis is always the x dimension and the second number is the y-dimension. The point is often subscribed with the symbol $(x,\ y)$, thus: $P_{(x,y)}$. To illustrate, the point $P_{(3,-2)}$ definitely locates the point P on the plane shown in Fig. 43.

Figure 43 illustrates the way to place the axes if all four quadrants are to be used in plotting a curve. The point $Q_{(x,y)}$ shown in Fig. 43 is located by going $+5$ units along the positive x-axis and $+2$ units parallel to the positive y-axis. Therefore *both numbers are positive in the first quadrant*. Thus, Q is represented by the symbol $(5, 2)$. To locate a point $R_{(x,y)}$ in the second quadrant we must go -3 units along the negative x-axis and up $+4$ units parallel to the positive y-axis. *The x value is negative and the y value is positive in the second quadrant.* Thus, $R_{(x,y)}$ is represented by the symbol $(-3, 4)$. To locate a point $S_{(x,y)}$ in the third quadrant we must go -4 units along the negative x-axis and -4 units along (or parallel) to the negative y-axis. Therefore, *both numbers are negative in the third quadrant.* Thus $S_{(x,y)}$ is represented by the symbol $(-4, -4)$. The point $P_{(x,y)}$ in the *fourth quadrant* is represented by *a positive x value* and *a negative y value*. As mentioned above the symbol in this case for $P_{(x,y)}$ is $(3, -2)$.

RECTANGULAR COORDINATE SIGNS

Quadrant	Sign of X	Sign of Y
First	+	+
Second	−	+
Third	−	−
Fourth	+	−

It should now be clear to the student that every point on the plane can be found by substituting definite values for x and y in the symbol (x,y).

An illustration of curves in all four quadrants is found in magnetic circuit theory. The curves are known as B-H curves where B represents the lines of induction and H represents the magnetic field strength. In Fig. 44 the magnetic force H is along the x-axis and the magnetization B is along the y-axis.

Usually it is not necessary to use all four quadrants to plot a curve. When only one quadrant is needed the usual practice is to use the first. In this case all numbers will be positive. When negative numbers are involved, other quadrants must be used. Usually some study of the problem will result in a judicious selection of quadrants.

Vacuum tube characteristic curves furnish a good illustration of using the first and second quadrants. When the plate voltage is held constant, the plate current can be plotted as a function of the grid voltage. This means that a current meter is placed in the plate lead and a volt meter connected from the grid to the cathode or filament. The grid voltage is changed in steps and for each grid voltage reading a corresponding plate current reading is recorded. These coordinate points are plotted on cross-section paper marked off in the first and second quadrants. Such curves can be found in vacuum-tube books.

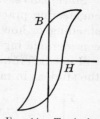

Fig. 44.—Typical *B-H* curve.

It will be noted that the curves found in vacuum-tube books are smooth lines. This means that the values change gradually between points. When taking data to obtain such a curve, any irregular points should be checked to be sure that they are not errors in taking the readings. It is always a good practice to

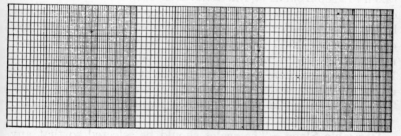

Fig. 45.—Three-cycle semilogarithmic graph paper.

plot the curve as the data is taken, so any irregularities can be checked before destroying the experimental setup.

When a wide range of values are to be plotted it is often desirable to use a logarithmic scale or scales. This type of paper has other distinct advantages, such as that of keeping the percentage accuracy the same for all values. An illustration of the use of this type of paper is to show the frequency characteristics of an audio amplifier. Semilogarithmic cross-section paper is generally used for these curves. It has a logarithmic scale along only one side, as shown in Fig. 45.

The *y*-axis values are usually marked voltage amplification, or *db* gain. The *x*-axis values are marked in cycles per second along a logarithmic scale. Typical examples are to be found in the other books of this series.

Since curves are so frequent in radio and communication engineering practice, the student should have a *thorough* understanding of how to make and use them. It will often require considerable ingenuity to select proper scales so that the curves will not be crowded. The following pointers are given to guide the student in making *any* graphical representations.

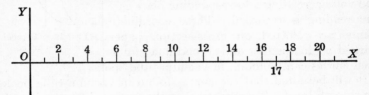

Fig. 46.—Selection of scales.

Scale Selection.—A scale should be selected so that the curve will cover the limits of the paper. However, care should be taken to keep from using fractional divisions, as this will make the curve difficult to plot. To illustrate, suppose we have a curve having a maximum x value of 17 and the cross-section paper has only 10 lines. If 17 is plotted on the tenth line, each line will represent 1.7 and it will be difficult to find points from 0 to 17. If each division were marked to represent 2, the 17 would not cover the whole scale but it would be easy to plot the points. This is illustrated in Fig. 46. Each major division is marked with even numbers.

Desirable Slope.—The scales should be selected so that any change in slope can be easily and accurately determined. Also, if the slope is too steep or not steep enough, the readings on one or the other scale will be crowded and thus the accuracy in reading will be lowered. Therefore, the scales should be selected so that the curve is as nearly 45 degrees with the x-axis as practicable. This is especially true if the curve is a straight line. *Note:* A curve is a general expression for a line of any shape, so a straight line is a curve. As an example, a straight-line capacity capacitor gives a straight-line curve when capacity is plotted against the dial setting.

Not only should the proper slope of a curve be obtained, but the student should be familiar with just how it can be determined. As a practical illustration, consider the curve in Fig. 47, which is the plate characteristic for a type 250 vacuum tube with zero grid voltage. It is desired to find the plate conductance of the tube when the plate current varies from 60 to 80 mils. As will be given later, the plate conductance is the slope of the $I_p - E_p$ characteristic curve as presented in Fig. 47. In other words, the slope of a curve is the angle it makes with the positive x-axis. It can also be thought of as the tangent of the angle the line makes with the positive x-axis. In this particular case the slope is tan θ given in Fig. 47, but tan θ = opposite side/adjacent side. Perhaps the best way to determine this is to form the triangle as shown in Fig. 47. The opposite side has a length of $80 - 60 = 20$ mils change in plate current. The adjacent side has a length of $190 - 160 = 30$ volts. The slope of this curve is then

$$\text{Slope} = \frac{I_2 - I_1}{E_2 - E_1} = \frac{0.08 - 0.06}{190 - 160}$$

$$= \frac{0.02}{30} = 0.000666 \text{ mho, } = 666 \ \mu \text{ mho}$$

which is a measure of the plate conductance of the vacuum tube.

The slope of a curve is of great importance in many engineering problems. *Calculus*, for example, is based upon this fundamental idea, so the student should learn all he can about it.

In the above illustration we had a change in plate current for a given change in plate voltage. A more familiar ratio is that of the miles covered in an hour, commonly called "miles per hour." Many engineering problems have to deal with ratios

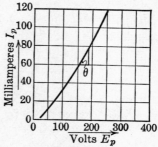

FIG. 47.—Slope determination.

and each of these ratios or rates can be represented graphically as the slope of a curve.

Many Points Are Desirable.—When taking data to plot a curve it is advantageous to plot many points. This is especially true when the values do not fall on a smooth curve. The general practice in such cases is to plot many points and then draw a smooth curve through the greatest number of points in order to minimize any errors in obtaining the data. The simplest curve to plot is a straight line, which requires a minimum of only two points.

Curve Labeling.—Every curve should be titled on the curve sheet with the name of the curve, the date it was taken, and by

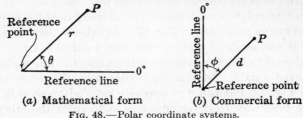

(a) Mathematical form   (b) Commercial form

Fig. 48.—Polar coordinate systems.

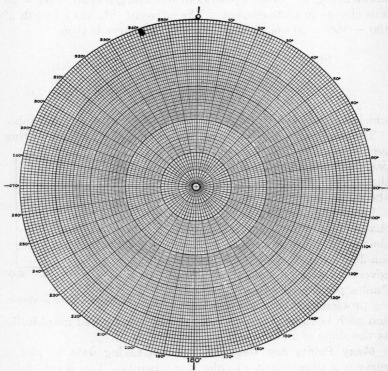

Fig. 49.—A commercial form of polar coordinate paper.

whom it was taken. Also it is very advantageous to show a wiring diagram if it pertains to any electrical circuit and the serial numbers of any pieces that are being calibrated, etc. It is a help to record the data from which the curve was plotted on the curve sheet. In other words, put on the sheet everything

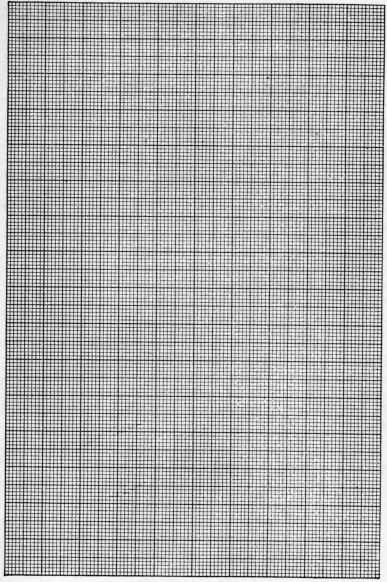

Fig. 50.—Millimeter cross-section paper.

that will help to convey a complete picture of the conditions and the results of the experiment.

System of Polar Coordinates.—Some data are best presented on polar coordinate paper. Common illustrations are field patterns of microphones, loud-speakers, and directional antennas.

To specify a point P by polar coordinates it is necessary to know the *distance* from the *reference point* to the point P and the *angle* this line makes with the *reference line*. In the mathematical form, as shown in Fig. 48a, the reference point corresponds to the origin used in rectangular coordinates and the reference line corresponds to the positive x-axis. To reach the point P the distance r is laid off along the x-axis and then the line is rotated counterclockwise through the positive angle θ. The same point could be reached by rotating the line clockwise through a negative angle which would be equal to $-(360° - \theta)$.

In commercial practice, such as navigation and directional antenna design, the reference line is north and the angles are measured clockwise. Figure 48b illustrates a commercial form of polar coordinate system. The true azimuth of the point is measured by ϕ and its distance from the reference point is d. A sample of polar coordinate paper for commercial applications is shown in Fig. 49.

The point P can be represented in polar coordinates by the symbol (r, θ) or (d, ϕ) as illustrated in Fig. 48. To make it easy to locate any such point the polar coordinate paper can be printed with many radial lines along which the distance can be measured and many circles around which the angle can be measured.

Exercises

1. Experimental data give the following information in regard to a sample of transformer steel:

B	H	B	H
0	1.0	0	−1.0
2,000	1.3	−2,000	−1.3
4,000	1.7	−4,000	−1.7
6,000	2.2	−6,000	−2.2
8,000	3.4	−8,000	−3.4
8,300	4.0	−8,300	−4.0
8,000	2.2	−8,000	−2.2
6,000	0.0	−6,000	0.0
4,000	−0.6	−4,000	0.6
2,000	−0.8	−2,000	0.8
0	−1.0	0	1.0

Plot the *B-H* curve on cross-section paper, as shown in Fig. 50.

2. Field intensity measurements on a radio broadcasting station are made by going due north of the transmitter. Plot the ground wave field intensity on log-log paper[1] from the following data:

Miles	Millivolts per Meter	Miles	Millivolts per Meter
1	94		
1.5	61	12	5.0
2	45	14	3.9
3	28.5	16.5	3.0
4	20.5	20	2.1
5	15.5	25	1.4
6	12.5	30	1.0
8	8.6	40	0.55
10	6.4	60	0.26
		80	0.12

What is the distance to the 25, 10, 5, 2.5, and 0.5 mv per m contours? Draw the inverse distance curve through the point 100 mv per m at 1 mile.

3. The computation of field intensity measurements at 1 mile for a 1-kw broadcast transmitter using a three-tower directional antenna system results in the following data:

Azimuth	Millivolts per Meter	Azimuth	Millivolts per Meter	Azimuth	Millivolts per Meter	Azimuth	Millivolts per Meter
0	369.5	90	33.3	180	129.6	270	29.2
10	337.5	100	58.6	190	182.6	280	61.5
20	288.3	110	87.3	200	220.0	290	99.5
30	228.5	120	108.1	210	229.3	300	150.2
40	175.0	130	113.6	220	222.2	310	208.4
50	126.6	140	100.2	230	194.3	320	268.5
60	88.1	150	64.5	240	157.4	330	320.6
70	65.9	160	27.0	250	116.0	340	361.4
80	33.7	170	67.5	260	76.6	350	378.1

Plot these data on polar coordinate paper. Draw the root-mean-square field intensity circle at 191 mv per m. The area of this circle is the same as the area within the irregular pattern. This value can be checked by squaring the thirty-six readings of millivolts per meter, dividing their sum by 36, and extracting the square root. A sample of suitable polar coordinate paper is shown in Fig. 49.

[1] To plot such data, the Federal Communications Commission normally uses Logarithmic, 7 × 2.2 cycles, No. 358-127, printed by Keuffel and Esser Co., N.Y.

CHAPTER 9

SIMULTANEOUS EQUATIONS

In radio and communication engineering, problems often arise in which two desired unknown quantities can be determined when two sets of conditions are known. This method of attack is very powerful and can be expanded to find an n number of desired unknowns if a set of n independent conditions are known.

Sets of Two Linear Equations.—The following illustration shows how a problem may lead to a set of two linear equations, sometimes called "simultaneous equations." Let us consider the formula

$$Rk - \alpha t = 1 \tag{1}$$

where R = resistance of a metal after being heated through t.

k = constant, the reciprocal of the resistance at the initial temperature.

α = constant, the temperature coefficient of the resistance.

t = temperature change in degrees centigrade.

It is found by trial that $R = 108$ when $t = 20$ and that $R = 128$ when $t = 70$. With these two sets of conditions, it is desired to find the constants k and α. Substituting the two sets of information in Eq. (1) results in

$$108k - 20\alpha = 1 \quad \text{(using first set of conditions)} \tag{2}$$
$$128k - 70\alpha = 1 \quad \text{(using second set of conditions)} \tag{3}$$

It is easy to find numbers for k and α that will satisfy Eq. (2) but not Eq. (3), and to find other numbers for k and α that will satisfy Eq. (3) but not Eq. (2). There is only one pair of numbers for k and α that will satisfy both equations at the same time and this pair is the solution of the set of two equations. There are three methods of finding these values of k and α and these methods will be given later. The solution to this problem is

$$k = 0.01 \quad Ans.$$
$$\alpha = 0.004 \quad Ans.$$

110

The student can check these answers by substituting them back in Eqs. (2) and (3) and finding that both sides of the equations are equal.

This is a practical illustration, showing that the resistance of copper changes 0.4 per cent per degree centigrade.

Equations (2) and (3) represent straight lines. The one point at which they cross in a plane gives the solution. In this case k is plotted along one axis and α is plotted along the other.

Methods of Solving Simultaneous Equations.—There are four ways of solving simultaneous equations, *the graphical method, the multiplication-addition method, the substitution method,* and *the determinant method.* The determinant method is the result of a systematic application of the multiplication-addition method.

Illustration of the graphical method.—The following set of two equations is to be solved by the graphical method:

$$x + 2y = 3 \qquad (4)$$
$$x - 2y = 2 \qquad (5)$$

First, make a table of values for each equation as shown in Fig. 51a. When making a table of values it is convenient to solve the equation for y.

Thus $\qquad x + 2y = 3$ is written $y = \dfrac{3 - x}{2} \qquad (6)$

and $\qquad x - 2y = 2$ is written $y = \dfrac{-2 + x}{2} \qquad (7)$

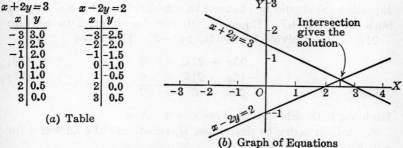

$x + 2y = 3$		$x - 2y = 2$	
x	y	x	y
−3	3.0	−3	−2.5
−2	2.5	−2	−2.0
−1	2.0	−1	−1.5
0	1.5	0	−1.0
1	1.0	1	−0.5
2	0.5	2	0.0
3	0.0	3	0.5

(a) Table

(b) Graph of Equations

Fig. 51.—Graphical method of solving two simultaneous equations.

Second, draw on one set of axes the two graphs as shown in Fig. 51b. The two lines cross at only one point, the point where

$$x = 2.5 \quad Ans.$$
$$y = 0.25 \quad Ans.$$

This pair of numbers is the solution to the set of simultaneous equations. They give the point of intersection of the two straight lines.

In plotting a linear (straight-line) equation it is only necessary to solve the equation for two points and draw a straight line through these two points. The line can be drawn more accurately if the two points are not too close together.

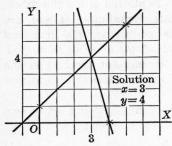

FIG. 52.—Graphical solution for Example 1.

Example 1. Solve the following simultaneous equations by the graphical method:

$$x - y + 1 = 0$$
$$4x + y - 16 = 0$$

Solution.

$$y = x + 1 \qquad y = 16 - 4x$$

x	y		x	y
0	1		4	0
5	6		3	4

$$x = 3 \quad Ans.$$
$$y = 4 \quad Ans.$$

Illustration of Multiplication-addition Method.—The following set of two equations is to be solved by the multiplication-addition method:

$$5x + 3R = 14 \qquad (8)$$
$$4x + 7R = 2 \qquad (9)$$

First, to eliminate R, inspection of the terms $+3R$ and $+7R$ reveals that 21 is the L.C.M. (least common multiple) of 3 and 7. Equation (8) should be changed to contain $+21R$ by multiplying both sides by $+7$. Equation (9) can be changed to contain $-21R$ by multiplying both sides by -3. This gives

$$35x + 21R = 98 \qquad (10)$$
$$-12x - 21R = -6 \qquad (11)$$

Adding $\qquad \overline{23x + 0 = 92}$

Dividing both sides by 23 gives $x = 4 \quad Ans.$

Second, in order to determine R, substitute the answer 4 for x in Eq. (8), giving

$$20 + 3R = 14$$

Adding -20 to both sides

gives $\qquad\qquad 3R = -6$

Dividing both sides by 3

gives $$R = -2 \quad Ans.$$

Check: Substitute 4 for x and -2 for R in both Eqs. (8) and (9), thus

$$5x + 3R = 14 \qquad 4x + 7R = 2$$
$$20 - 6 = 14 \qquad 16 - 14 = 2$$
$$14 = 14 \qquad 2 = 2$$

Hence, the solution $x = 4$ and $R = -2$ has just been proved correct.

Example 2. Solve the following simultaneous equations by the multiplication-addition method:

$$5x + 7y = 3$$
$$3x + 14y = 6$$

Multiplying the first equation by -2 and adding the second gives

$$-10x - 14y = -6$$
$$\underline{3x + 14y = 6}$$

gives $$-7x = 0$$
Hence, $$x = 0 \quad Ans.$$

Substituting $x = 0$ in the first equation, $y = \frac{3}{7}$ *Ans.*

Illustration of the Substitution Method.—The following set of two equations is to be solved by the substitution method:

$$4x + 3R = 5 \tag{12}$$
$$6x - 7R = 19 \tag{13}$$

First, solve Eq. (12) for R, obtaining

$$R = \frac{5 - 4x}{3} \tag{14}$$

Second, copy Eq. (13) but in the place of R write the fraction as given in Eq. (14). This is permissible because R is equal to this fraction. The result of this substitution is then

$$6x - \frac{7(5 - 4x)}{3} = 19 \tag{15}$$

This equation contains only one unknown number, x. The unknown number R has been eliminated by substitution. Multiply both sides of the equation by 3, giving

$$18x - 7(5 - 4x) = 57$$

Removing the parentheses

gives $\qquad 18x - 35 + 28x = 57$

Collecting terms, $\qquad 46x = 92$

Hence, $\qquad x = 2 \quad Ans.$

Third, substitute 2 for x in Eq. (14), giving

$$R = \frac{5 - 4x}{3} = \frac{5 - 8}{3} = -1 \quad Ans.$$

Check: Substitute $x = 2$ and $R = -1$ in Eqs. (12) and (13), thus

$$4x + 3R = 5 \qquad 6x - 7R = 19$$
$$8 - \quad 3 = 5 \qquad 12 + \quad 7 = 19$$
$$5 = 5 \qquad\qquad 19 = 19$$

Hence, $x = 2$ and $R = -1$ is the one and only solution to this set of simultaneous equations.

The substitution method, just shown, can be used in more difficult situations than the multiplication-addition method. This can be illustrated by noting the following pair of equations:

$$3x + 2R = 4 \tag{16}$$
$$x^2 + R^2 = 5 \tag{17}$$

Equation (16) is a linear equation (of the first degree, since x and R appear to the first power). Equation (17) is a quadratic equation (of the second degree, since x and R appear to the second power).

First, solve Eq. (16) for R, obtaining

$$R = \frac{4 - 3x}{2} \tag{18}$$

Second, substitute this value of R in Eq. (17) to obtain

$$x^2 + \left(\frac{4 - 3x}{2}\right)^2 = 5 \quad \text{or} \quad x^2 + \frac{16 - 24x + 9x^2}{4} = 5$$

Multiplying both sides by 4,

$$4x^2 + 16 - 24x + 9x^2 = 20$$

Collecting terms, $\qquad 13x^2 - 24x - 4 = 0 \tag{19}$

This is an equation in x only and can be solved for x very easily by the methods of the next chapter. The above set of simultaneous equations could not be solved by the multiplication-addition method.

Example 3. Solve by the substitution method the following problem:
The sum of the three angles of a triangle is 180°. If one acute angle of the right triangle is four times the size of the other, determine the size of the two acute angles.

Solution. From the first statement let α and β be the two acute angles to get

$$\alpha + \beta + 90° = 180°$$
or
$$\alpha + \beta = 90°$$

From the second statement,

$$\alpha = 4\beta$$

Substituting this value of α in the first equation gives

$$4\beta + \beta = 90$$
$$\beta = 18° \quad Ans.$$
and
$$\alpha = 4\beta = 4(18)° = 72° \quad Ans.$$

Classification of Linear Simultaneous Equations.—Some sets of equations have no solution. To illustrate, the equations

$$2x + 3R = 5$$
$$2x + 3R = 7$$

contradict each other, and are *inconsistent.* The graphical method shows that they are parallel lines and hence do not meet to give a solution.

Some sets of equations are *dependent,* because one equation can be made exactly like the other by multiplying by some number. To illustrate, the first equation of the set,

$$3x + 6R = 7.5$$
$$2x + 4R = 5$$

becomes the second when it is multiplied by $\frac{2}{3}$. The graphical method shows that both equations represent the same straight line, hence they have an infinite number of solutions. Such equations are sometimes called "indeterminate equations."

All sets of equations that are neither *inconsistent* nor *dependent* are called "*independent.*" Their graphs are distinct nonparallel lines and they always have a single solution. That is, they cross at only one point. If the equations are written in general form, we have

$$a_1x + b_1y = c_1 \tag{20}$$
$$a_2x + b_2y = c_2 \tag{21}$$

where a_1, b_1, c_1, a_2, b_2, and c_2 are any numbers. It can be shown that the equations are independent if

$$a_1b_2 - a_2b_1 \neq 0 \tag{22}$$

and either dependent or inconsistent if $\quad a_1b_2 - a_2b_1 = 0 \quad$ (23)

Illustration of Independent.—Consider the simultaneous equations

$$2x + 4y = 10 \tag{24}$$
$$5x - y = 8 \tag{25}$$

From the notation of Eqs. (20) and (21), the quantity

$$a_1b_2 - a_2b_1,$$

for example, can be written

$$(2)(-1) - (5)(4) \neq 0 \quad \text{or} \quad -2 - 20 \neq 0$$

Hence the equations are independent and have only one solution.

Illustration of Dependent.—Consider the simultaneous equations

$$2x + 4y = 10 \tag{26}$$
$$5x + 10y = 25 \tag{27}$$

From the above notation, $a_1b_2 - a_2b_1$ for this illustration is

$$(2)(10) - (5)(4) = 0 \quad \text{or} \quad 20 - 20 = 0$$

Hence the equations are either dependent or inconsistent. In this case we see that they are dependent because, if Eq. (26) is multiplied by 2.5, Eq. (27) results.

Illustration of Inconsistent.—Consider the simultaneous equations

$$2x + 18y = 9 \tag{28}$$
$$x + 9y = 10 \tag{29}$$

From the above notation, $a_1b_2 - a_2b_1$ for this illustration is

$$(2)(9) - (1)(18) = 0 \quad \text{or} \quad 18 - 18 = 0$$

showing that the equations are either dependent or inconsistent. In this case multiplying Eq. (29) by 2 gives $2x + 18y = 20$ which does not check with the right-hand side of Eq. (28); hence the equations are inconsistent.

Second-order Determinants.—From the multiplication-addition method, a handy tool known as a "determinant" can be developed.

Two simultaneous equations can be written in general form, as follows:

$$a_1x + b_1y = c_1 \qquad (20)$$
$$a_2x + b_2y = c_2 \qquad (21)$$

To develop this new tool multiply the general Eq. (20) by b_2 and Eq. (21) by $-b_1$ giving

$$a_1b_2x + b_1b_2y = c_1b_2 \qquad (30)$$

and

$$-a_2b_1x - b_1b_2y = -c_2b_1 \qquad (31)$$

Adding,

$$\overline{(a_1b_2 - a_2b_1)x = b_2c_1 - b_1c_2}$$

or

$$x = \frac{b_2c_1 - b_1c_2}{a_1b_2 - a_2b_1} \qquad (32)$$

Similarly, multiply Eq. (20) by $-a_2$ and Eq. (21) by a_1 giving

$$-a_1a_2x - a_2b_1y = -a_2c_1 \qquad (33)$$

and

$$a_1a_2x + a_1b_2y = a_1c_2 \qquad (34)$$

Adding,

$$\overline{(a_1b_2 - a_2b_1)y = a_1c_2 - a_2c_1}$$

or

$$y = \frac{a_1c_2 - a_2c_1}{a_1b_2 - a_2b_1} \qquad (35)$$

Equations (32) and (35) are the desired equations which will give the solution of the general Eqs. (20) and (21).

It is more convenient to write these solutions by the notation of determinants, as follows:

$$x = \frac{\begin{vmatrix} c_1 & b_1 \\ c_2 & b_2 \end{vmatrix}}{\begin{vmatrix} a_1 & b_1 \\ a_2 & b_2 \end{vmatrix}} \qquad (36)$$

$$y = \frac{\begin{vmatrix} a_1 & c_1 \\ a_2 & c_2 \end{vmatrix}}{\begin{vmatrix} a_1 & b_1 \\ a_2 & b_2 \end{vmatrix}} \qquad (37)$$

The term $\begin{vmatrix} c_1 & b_1 \\ c_2 & b_2 \end{vmatrix}$

is called a *determinant* and is equal to $c_1b_2 - b_1c_2$. In other words, from the product of the two *elements* c_1b_2 in the *principal diagonal* the product of the elements b_1c_2 in the other diagonal is subtracted. This is the numerator in the fraction of Eq. (32) expressed in plain algebra and also the numerator of Eq. (36) expressed in determinant notation.

Illustration of Determinants.—The following two equations are to be solved by the method of determinants:

$$2x + 3y = 6 \qquad (38)$$
$$3x - 8y = 24 \qquad (39)$$

Substituting in Eq. (36) for x gives

$$x = \frac{\begin{vmatrix} 6 & 3 \\ 24 & -8 \end{vmatrix}}{\begin{vmatrix} 2 & 3 \\ 3 & -8 \end{vmatrix}} = \frac{(6)(-8) - (3)(24)}{(2)(-8) - (3)(3)} = \frac{-48 - 72}{-16 - 9} = \frac{120}{25}$$

$$= 4.8 \quad Ans.$$

Substituting in Eq. (37) for y gives

$$y = \frac{\begin{vmatrix} 2 & 6 \\ 3 & 24 \end{vmatrix}}{\begin{vmatrix} 2 & 3 \\ 3 & -8 \end{vmatrix}} = \frac{(2)(24) - (6)(3)}{(2)(-8) - (3)(3)} = \frac{48 - 18}{-16 - 9} = \frac{30}{-25}$$

$$= -1.2 \quad Ans.$$

The student should substitute these values in the original equation to check that they are correct.

Example 4.   Solve by determinants

$$2x - y = 1$$
$$x + 3y = 11$$

Solution.

By Eq. (36) $x = \dfrac{\begin{vmatrix} 1 & -1 \\ 11 & 3 \end{vmatrix}}{\begin{vmatrix} 2 & -1 \\ 1 & 3 \end{vmatrix}} = \dfrac{3 + 11}{6 + 1} = \dfrac{14}{7} = 2 \quad Ans.$

By Eq. (37) $y = \dfrac{\begin{vmatrix} 2 & 1 \\ 1 & 11 \end{vmatrix}}{\begin{vmatrix} 2 & -1 \\ 1 & 3 \end{vmatrix}} = \dfrac{22 - 1}{6 + 1} = \dfrac{21}{7} = 3 \quad Ans.$

Sets of Three Linear Equations.—With three linear equations it is possible to solve for three unknowns, provided the equations are independent.

One linear equation constitutes a line (one dimension). Two linear equations define a surface (two dimensions). Three linear equations define a solid (three dimensions). The graphical method is not so useful with three linear equations since it is normally only two dimensional; hence it will not be treated here.

The multiplication-addition method and the substitution method will be treated by means of examples.

Illustration of Multiplication-addition Method.—The following set of three equations is to be solved for x, y, and z:

$$2x - 3y - z = -4 \qquad (40)$$
$$3x + y + 2z = 7 \qquad (41)$$
$$4x - 2y + 3z = -1 \qquad (42)$$

The plan is to eliminate x from the first two equations and then from the last two equations of the above set. This will result in a new set of two equations in two unknowns, namely y and z. This set can then be solved by any of the methods just explained.

Proceeding with the solution,

Multiply Eq. (40) by -3	$-6x + 9y + 3z = 12$	(43)
and multiply Eq. (41) by 2	$6x + 2y + 4z = 14$	(44)
Adding,	$11y + 7z = 26$	(45)
Now multiply Eq. (41) by 4	$12x + 4y + 8z = 28$	(46)
and multiply Eq. (42) by -3	$-12x + 6y - 9z = 3$	(47)
Adding,	$10y - z = 31$	(48)

The new set of Eqs. (45) and (48) when solved give

$$y = 3 \quad Ans.$$
$$z = -1 \quad Ans.$$

Substituting these values in Eq. (40) shows that

$$x = 2 \quad Ans.$$

The check consists of substituting these values in all three of the original Eqs. (40), (41), and (42) to see if they are true. This is left to the student.

There are many possible ways of using this method. In the above example, what multipliers should be used to eliminate y from Eqs. (40) and (41); and from Eqs. (41) and (42)? What multipliers should be used to eliminate z from Eqs. (40) and (41); and from Eqs. (41) and (42)?

Illustration of Substitution Method.—The following set of three equations is to be solved for x, y, and z:

$$3x + 2y - 4z = 3 \qquad (49)$$
$$2x + y + 3z = 8 \qquad (50)$$
$$5x + 3y + 2z = 14 \qquad (51)$$

The method is to solve for one of the numbers x, y, or z in one of the equations, substitute its value in the other two equations, and then solve the resulting set of two equations.

For illustration, solve Eq. (50) for y, since its coefficient is unity.

$$y = 8 - 2x - 3z \qquad (52)$$

Substituting this value of y in Eqs. (49) and (51) and simplifying gives

$$3x + 2(8 - 2x - 3z) - 4z = 3 \text{ or } x + 10z = 13 \qquad (53)$$
$$5x + 3(8 - 2x - 3z) + 2z = 14 \text{ or } x + 7z = 10 \qquad (54)$$

Solving Eqs. (53) and (54) yields

$$x = 3 \quad Ans.$$
$$z = 1 \quad Ans.$$

Substituting these values of x and z in Eq. (52) results in

$$y = 8 - 6 - 3 = -1 \quad Ans.$$

The student can now check these answers by substitution in the original Eqs. (49), (50), and (51) to verify the work.

Third-order Determinants.—In a manner similar to the development of second-order determinants, it is possible to set up determinants for the solution of three simultaneous equations.

The three simultaneous equations can be written in general form, as follows:

$$a_1x + b_1y + c_1z = d_1 \qquad (55)$$
$$a_2x + b_2y + c_2z = d_2 \qquad (56)$$
$$a_3x + b_3y + c_3z = d_3 \qquad (57)$$

The solution of these equations is given by the following determinants and the corresponding algebraic equations:

$$x = \frac{\begin{vmatrix} d_1 & b_1 & c_1 \\ d_2 & b_2 & c_2 \\ d_3 & b_3 & c_3 \end{vmatrix}}{\begin{vmatrix} a_1 & b_1 & c_1 \\ a_2 & b_2 & c_2 \\ a_3 & b_3 & c_3 \end{vmatrix}} = \frac{\begin{array}{l} d_1b_2c_3 + b_1c_2d_3 + c_1d_2b_3 \\ -d_1c_2b_3 - b_1d_2c_3 - c_1b_2d_3 \end{array}}{\begin{array}{l} a_1b_2c_3 + b_1c_2a_3 + c_1a_2b_3 \\ -a_1c_2b_3 - b_1a_2c_3 - c_1b_2a_3 \end{array}} \qquad (58)$$

$$y = \frac{\begin{vmatrix} a_1 & d_1 & c_1 \\ a_2 & d_2 & c_2 \\ a_3 & d_3 & c_3 \end{vmatrix}}{\begin{vmatrix} a_1 & b_1 & c_1 \\ a_2 & b_2 & c_2 \\ a_3 & b_3 & c_3 \end{vmatrix}} = \frac{\begin{array}{l} a_1d_2c_3 + d_1c_2a_3 + c_1a_2d_3 \\ -a_1c_2d_3 - d_1a_2c_3 - c_1d_2a_3 \end{array}}{\begin{array}{l} a_1b_2c_3 + b_1c_2a_3 + c_1a_2b_3 \\ -a_1c_2b_3 - b_1a_2c_3 - c_1b_2a_3 \end{array}} \qquad (59)$$

$$z = \frac{\begin{vmatrix} a_1 & b_1 & d_1 \\ a_2 & b_2 & d_2 \\ a_3 & b_3 & d_3 \end{vmatrix}}{\begin{vmatrix} a_1 & b_1 & c_1 \\ a_2 & b_2 & c_2 \\ a_3 & b_3 & c_3 \end{vmatrix}} = \frac{\begin{matrix} a_1b_2d_3 + b_1d_2a_3 + d_1a_2b_3 \\ -a_1d_2b_3 - b_1a_2d_3 - d_1b_2a_3 \end{matrix}}{\begin{matrix} a_1b_2c_3 + b_1c_2a_3 + c_1a_2b_3 \\ -a_1c_2b_3 - b_1a_2c_3 - c_1b_2a_3 \end{matrix}} \qquad (60)$$

The positive terms are obtained from the product of the three elements in the diagonals running down from left to right and the negative terms are obtained from the product of the three elements in the diagonals running down from right to left.

It will be noted that the denominators are the same in each case, being the coefficients of x, y, and z of the original Eqs. (55), (56), and (57). The numerators can be obtained from the denominators by replacing the coefficients of the unknowns in question by the known terms d_1, d_2, and d_3.

Illustrations of Determinants.—The following set of three equations is to be solved by the method of determinants:

$$x - y - z = -6 \qquad (61)$$
$$2x + y + z = 0 \qquad (62)$$
$$3x - 5y + 8 = 13 \qquad (63)$$

Substituting the coefficients in Eq. (58) gives x.

$$x = \frac{\begin{vmatrix} -6 & -1 & -1 \\ 0 & 1 & 1 \\ 13 & -5 & 8 \end{vmatrix}}{\begin{vmatrix} 1 & -1 & -1 \\ 2 & 1 & 1 \\ 3 & -5 & 8 \end{vmatrix}} = \frac{-78}{39} = -2 \quad Ans.$$

Substituting the coefficients in Eq. 59 gives y.

$$y = \frac{\begin{vmatrix} 1 & -6 & -1 \\ 2 & 0 & 1 \\ 3 & 13 & 8 \end{vmatrix}}{\begin{vmatrix} 1 & -1 & -1 \\ 2 & 1 & 1 \\ 3 & -5 & 8 \end{vmatrix}} = \frac{39}{39} = 1 \quad Ans.$$

Substituting the coefficients in Eq. 60 gives z.

$$z = \frac{\begin{vmatrix} 1 & -1 & -6 \\ 2 & 1 & 0 \\ 3 & -5 & 13 \end{vmatrix}}{\begin{vmatrix} 1 & -1 & -1 \\ 2 & 1 & 1 \\ 3 & -5 & 8 \end{vmatrix}} = \frac{117}{39} = 3 \quad Ans.$$

The student can verify these answers by substituting them back in the original Eqs. (61), (62), and (63).

After a little experience with using determinants, the tool becomes well polished and easy to operate in solving otherwise rather tedious problems.

Example 5. Solve by determinants,

$$\begin{aligned} 2x + 3y + z &= 4 \\ x + 2y + 2z &= 6 \\ 5x + y + 4z &= 21 \end{aligned}$$

Solution.

By Eq. (58), $x = \dfrac{\begin{vmatrix} 4 & 3 & 1 \\ 6 & 2 & 2 \\ 21 & 1 & 4 \end{vmatrix}}{\begin{vmatrix} 2 & 3 & 1 \\ 1 & 2 & 2 \\ 5 & 1 & 4 \end{vmatrix}} = \dfrac{32 + 126 + 6 - 42 - 8 - 72}{16 + 30 + 1 - 10 - 4 - 12}$

$$= \frac{42}{21} = 2 \quad Ans.$$

By Eq. (59), $y = \dfrac{\begin{vmatrix} 2 & 4 & 1 \\ 1 & 6 & 2 \\ 5 & 21 & 4 \end{vmatrix}}{\begin{vmatrix} 2 & 3 & 1 \\ 1 & 2 & 2 \\ 5 & 1 & 4 \end{vmatrix}} = \dfrac{48 + 40 + 21 - 30 - 84 - 16}{16 + 30 + 1 - 10 - 4 - 12}$

$$= -\frac{21}{21} = -1 \quad Ans.$$

By Eq. (60), $z = \dfrac{\begin{vmatrix} 2 & 3 & 4 \\ 1 & 2 & 6 \\ 5 & 1 & 21 \end{vmatrix}}{\begin{vmatrix} 2 & 3 & 1 \\ 1 & 2 & 2 \\ 5 & 1 & 4 \end{vmatrix}} = \dfrac{84 + 90 + 4 - 40 - 12 - 63}{16 + 30 + 1 - 10 - 4 - 12}$

$$= \frac{63}{21} = 3 \quad Ans.$$

Any Number of Linear Equations.—From the discussion of sets of two and three equations, it becomes apparent that the number of independent equations is the same as that of unknown numbers. The multiplication-addition and substitution methods, or a combination of the two, can be applied to any number of equations. One equation is necessarily used in eliminating each unknown number until there remains only one equation in one unknown, which can be solved for that unknown. If one equation of the set can be changed into the exact form of another equation of the set, then they are dependent. If two of the equations of the set contradict each other, then the set is inconsistent.

Determinants are especially convenient in solving simultaneous equations of the higher order. The procedure is to set down the general form of the set of equations, then form the denominator by setting up the array of coefficients of the unknowns. The numerators can be made from the denominators by replacing the coefficients of the unknown with the known terms. The diagonals running down from left to right are positive and those running down from right to left are negative. Furthermore, the theory of minors must be used to secure all the terms. For illustration a fourth order determinant will contain 24 terms. In the fourth order determinant,

$$\begin{vmatrix} a_1 & b_1 & c_1 & d_1 \\ a_2 & b_2 & c_2 & d_2 \\ a_3 & b_3 & c_3 & d_3 \\ a_4 & b_4 & c_4 & d_4 \end{vmatrix}$$

the term a_1 must be multiplied by its minor which is the determinant remaining when the row and column containing a_1 is removed. This gives 6 terms. Performing this operation for the terms b_1, c_1, and d_1 results in 18 more terms to make the total of 24 terms.

Summary.—First let us define some of the terms used in this chapter.

1. A *linear equation* is a statement of equality with the unknowns only of the first degree. In other words, it states that everything on the left side of the equal sign is exactly equal to everything on the right side of the equal sign, and if there are two unknowns (such as x and y), they are only of the first power, not squared (such as x^2 or y^2) or multiplied by each other (such as xy).

2. *Simultaneous equations* are statements of equality that are true at the same time and have a common solution.

3. *Independent equations* are statements of equality that are all different, but have a single common solution.

4. *Dependent equations* are statements of equality that are alike and therefore have an infinite number of solutions.

5. *Inconsistent equations* are statements of equality that cannot both be true at the same time, and therefore do not have a common solution.

Now, with these five definitions clearly in mind, you can see what the problems at the end of this chapter are like. For example, suppose you have two equations that are not alike and do not disagree. Then they fit definitions 1, 2, and 3 above and are called "independent linear simultaneous equations." If both of them have x and y and there are no other unknowns, then the two equations can be solved for x and y. You will be able to find one and only one value of x and one and only one value of y that will make both equations true at the same time.

If the equations are dependent you will find that any set of values for x and y that suit one equation will also suit the other equation. This means that you really have only one equation and not two.

But if the equations are inconsistent you cannot find one set of values for x and y that will suit both equations at the same time. Hence you do not have a problem that you can solve.

Many students have trouble trying to solve dependent and inconsistent sets of equations. The fact is that they are not to be solved. The student must understand this or he will be held back in his later work. The only kind of simultaneous equations that can be solved are independent ones. The exercises of this chapter are made to help you pick out the independent sets of equations from the dependent and inconsistent ones.

Students and teachers are often called upon to solve practical problems. In doing so they might be required to set up a set of simultaneous equations. As an illustration, the currents of a network can be found if the voltages and impedances are known. What is to be done if the equations made up turn out to be dependent or inconsistent? If they are dependent, it means that the student has not obtained enough independent equations. Hence he will have to set up more equations until he has as many independent equations as he has currents (or unknowns) to be determined. If the equations are inconsistent, it means that he has taken some wrong steps. Therefore, he must go back and correct the equations that he set up wrongly.

Now that it is clear that you must have independent simultaneous equations before you can solve them properly, you will see that this chapter tells you how to solve for them in four different ways. Sometimes one way is better than another. Therefore, you should become acquainted with all of the methods of solving simultaneous equations.

1. The *graphic method* is used only with two equations involving only two unknowns, but it is very useful in helping to understand the meaning of independence, dependence, and inconsistence. Try it on each kind of problem and see for yourself.

2. The *multiplication-addition method* is not very often used except for the more simple problems. Sometimes, however, you will find that it will save you time, and you should practice it until you know how it works.

3. The *substitution method* is more useful because it can be used in all problems of simultaneous equations. Therefore you must become thoroughly acquainted with it.

4. The *method of determinants* is quite fully explained in this chapter. There are no tricks intentionally not told to you, but the more you use this method the more you will see that it is a very practical method to use in solving sets of equations. It is very important that you get the equations in the standard form before you start to apply this method. Then the expansion of the determinants by diagonals must be thoroughly understood. The following illustration should make this clear for you.

Rewrite the first two columns on the right-hand side of the determinant and draw diagonals as indicated, the product of the terms in the right-hand diagonals being positive and those in the left-hand diagonals negative.

$$= + \ aei + bfg + cdh - ceg - afh - bdi$$

Instead of rewriting the columns the arrows can be curved around to get the same terms, as follows.

$$\begin{matrix} 1 & 6 & 2 & 5 & 3 & 4 \\ + & - & + & - & + & - \end{matrix}$$

$$= + \ aei + bfg + chd - ceg - bdi - ahf$$

The arrows show you how to write down the plus and minus signs as the chapter explains. The method of determinants avoids much of the algebraic work that is required in the other methods. Learn to use it.

Exercises

Inspect the following sets of equations for dependence or inconsistence and solve the independent sets:

1. $x + 3y = 7.$
  $4x + 12y = 28.$
2. $x + 2y = 13.$
  $2x - y = 1.$
3. $3x + y = 10.$
  $9x + 3y = 13.$
4. $3R_1 + R_2 - 2R_3 = 5.$
  $12R_1 + 4R_2 - 8R_3 = 20.$
5. $IR + 2E - IZ = 21.$
  $2Z - 2\dfrac{E}{I} - 8R = 16.$
  $3IR + IZ - E = 7.$

6. $2x + 3y + z = 17.$
  $x + y + 2z = 23.$
  $14x + 5y - 3z = 3.$
7. $\dfrac{7}{x} - \dfrac{5}{y} = -9.$
  $\dfrac{2}{x} + \dfrac{4}{y} = 11.$
8. $ax + by = 2ab.$
  $bx + ay = a^2 + b^2.$
9. $1.2x - 1.7y = 8.$
  $0.4x + 1.1y = 5.$
10. $10 = 0.5R_1 + 0.25R_2.$
  $20 = 10R_1 - 4R_2.$

The student should use all the methods outlined in order to become familiar with them.

CHAPTER 10

QUADRATIC EQUATIONS

Many problems arise in engineering which can be worked by an equation containing the unknown quantity squared. *The quadratic equation is an equation which contains the unknown quantity to the second power.* The values of the unknown quantity which will satisfy this equation are called "roots of the equation." There are in general two roots that will satisfy the equation.

The simplest type of quadratic equation is called a "pure quadratic." In the pure quadratic equation the unknown term is squared and there is no unknown term raised to the first power. The general form of a pure quadratic is

$$ax^2 + c = 0 \tag{1}$$

The solution of this equation is to solve for x by transposing c to the right hand side, dividing both sides by a, and extracting the square root of both members, thus

$$x = \sqrt{-\frac{c}{a}} \tag{2}$$

Example 1. Solve: $2x^2 - 8 = 0$.

Solution. Transposing, $\qquad 2x^2 = 8$
Dividing by 2, $\qquad\qquad\qquad x^2 = 4$
Extracting the square root of both sides, $x = +2$ *Ans.*
or $\qquad\qquad\qquad\qquad\qquad x = -2$ *Ans.*

Illustration of a Quadratic Equation.—The following illustration shows how a problem may lead to a quadratic equation. Referring to Fig. 53, it is desired to select the resistance R such that the resistance between terminals 1 and 2 is 4 ohms.

The conditions of the problem can be expressed by the equation

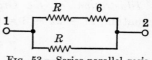

Fig. 53.—Series-parallel resistors.

$$4 = \frac{R(R + 6)}{R + (R + 6)} \tag{3}$$

Multiplying both sides of the equation by $2R + 6$, to clear the equation of fractions,

$$4(2R + 6) = R^2 + 6R \qquad (4)$$

Transposing all terms to the left-hand side,

$$R^2 - 2R - 24 = 0 \qquad (5)$$

This is a quadratic equation in R. If factored, it can be written

$$(R - 6)(R + 4) = 0 \qquad (6)$$

This equation is true if $R = 6$, hence $(6 - 6) = 0$ or if $R = -4$ so that $(-4 + 4) = 0$. The resistance R can then be either 6 ohms or -4 ohms. The value normally selected would be 6 ohms, because it is easier to obtain than a -4 ohm resistance device. The two answers are the two roots of the equation.

Example 2. Solve the following equation by factoring.

$$x^2 - 4x - 21 = 0$$

The product of the two factors must equal -21 and their sum must equal -4. It is soon discovered that $+3$ and -7 are factors that meet this condition, hence the equation can be factored and written

$$(x + 3)(x - 7) = 0$$

The solutions, then, are

$$x = -3 \quad Ans.$$
or
$$x = 7 \quad Ans.$$

Methods of Solution.—Quadratic equations can be solved by the methods of graphing, factoring, completing the square, or using the quadratic formula. The most useful method is the *quadratic formula*.

The *factoring method* is illustrated above. The other methods will be illustrated below.

Illustration of the Graphic Method.—Solve the quadratic equation, $x^2 - 2x - 3 = 0$ by graphing the curve

$$y = x^2 - 2x - 3.$$

Since the zero is replaced by y, the solutions of x will be the value of x when $y = 0$.

To draw the graph of $y = x^2 - 2x - 3$ the values of y are obtained when x is given values as shown in Fig. 54a. The solution will be the values of x when $y = 0$. In this case $x = -1$

and $x = 3$ are the desired roots.   Moreover, if 0 is substituted for y in the equation these same roots can be obtained by any of the other methods of solution.

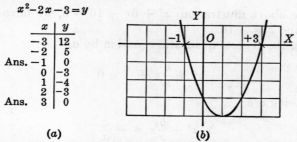

$x^2 - 2x - 3 = y$

x	y
-3	12
-2	5
Ans. -1	0
0	-3
1	-4
2	-3
Ans. 3	0

(a) (b)

FIG. 54.—Graphical method of solving a quadratic equation.

The solution can be checked by *substituting first one root and then the other* to see if the original equation is satisfied, thus:

For $x = -1$

$$(-1)^2 - 2(-1) - 3 = 0 \qquad \text{or} \qquad 1 + 2 - 3 = 0 \quad Check.$$

and $x = 3$

$$(3)^2 - 2(3) - 3 = 0 \qquad \text{or} \qquad 9 - 6 - 3 = 0 \quad Check.$$

Illustration of Completing the Square.—Solve

$$x^2 + 6x - 16 = 0$$

by completing the square.

Transposing, -16 $x^2 + 6x = 16$ (7)

Adding 9 to both members $x^2 + 6x + 9 = 25$ (8)

Taking the square root of both members,

$$x + 3 = \pm 5 \tag{9}$$

Hence, $x = 5 - 3 = 2 \quad Ans.$

or $x = -5 - 3 = -8 \quad Ans.$

Another *method of checking* by *multiplying the factors* is as follows: If $x = 2$, then $x - 2 = 0$; if $x = -8$, then

$$x + 8 = 0;$$

and the product

$$(x - 2)(x + 8) = x^2 + 6x - 16 = 0 \tag{10}$$

This checks the original equation.

Quadratic Formula.—The general form of the quadratic equation can be expressed

$$ax^2 + bx + c = 0 \tag{11}$$

In the above illustration, $x^2 + 6x - 16 = 0$, we have $a = 1$, $b = 6$, and $c = -16$.

Dividing the general quadratic equation by a,

$$x^2 + \frac{b}{a}x + \frac{c}{a} = 0 \tag{12}$$

Transposing c/a

$$x^2 + \frac{b}{a}x = -\frac{c}{a} \tag{13}$$

This corresponds to Eq. (7) in the above illustration. Adding to both members the square of $b/2a$,

$$x^2 + \frac{b}{a}x + \frac{b^2}{4a^2} = -\frac{c}{a} + \frac{b^2}{4a^2} \tag{14}$$

In the above illustration note that $\frac{1}{2}$ of 6 when squared gives 9. See Eq. (8).

Find the square root of both members of the equation, using both $+$ and $-$ roots of the right-hand member, thus

$$x + \frac{b}{2a} = \pm \sqrt{\frac{b^2}{4a^2} - \frac{c}{a}} \tag{15}$$

This corresponds to Eq. (9) of the illustration. Using first the positive value and then the negative one results in two new equations of x,

$$x = \frac{-b}{2a} + \sqrt{\frac{b^2}{4a^2} - \frac{c}{a}} \tag{16}$$

and

$$x = \frac{-b}{2a} - \sqrt{\frac{b^2}{4a^2} - \frac{c}{a}} \tag{17}$$

These equations correspond to $x = 5 - 3 = 2$ and

$$x = -5 - 3 = -8$$

in the above illustration.

If the $b/2a$ of Eq. (15) is transposed to the other side, the c/a term multiplied by $4a$ in both numerator and denominator, and the two terms under the radical reduced to a common denominator, then

$$x = \frac{-b}{2a} \pm \sqrt{\frac{b^2 - 4ac}{4a^2}} \tag{18}$$

Since the square root of $4a^2$ is $2a$, it can be written outside the radical as a common denominator, thus

$$x = \frac{-b \pm \sqrt{b^2 - 4ac}}{2a} \tag{19}$$

This is the *quadratic formula*, which should be *memorized*. In words it is usually stated "*x equals minus b plus or minus the square root of b squared minus four ac, all divided by two a.*"

Example 3. Solve the following equation by means of the quadratic formula:

$$3R^2 - 7R + 4 = 0$$

In applying the formula it is noted that a is $+3$, b is -7, and c is $+4$, the unknown number being R instead of x. Making these substitutions in Eq. (19), the formula gives

$$R = \frac{-(-7) \pm \sqrt{(-7)^2 - 4(3)(4)}}{2(3)}$$

Simplifying further,

$$R = \frac{7 \pm \sqrt{49 - 48}}{6}$$

Hence

$$R = \frac{7 + 1}{6} = \frac{4}{3} \quad Ans.$$

and

$$R = \frac{7 - 1}{6} = 1 \quad Ans.$$

Check by the sum and product of the roots method is done as follows: Adding the two roots as given in Eqs. (16) and (17),

$$\frac{-b}{2a} + \frac{-b}{2a} = \frac{-b}{a}$$

Adding the two roots in the answers,

$$\frac{4}{3} + 1 = \frac{7}{3}$$

or

$$\frac{-(-7)}{3} = \frac{-b}{a}$$

Multiplying the two roots as given in Eqs. (16) and (17) by the method as illustrated on page 41 for $(x + y)(x - y) = x^2 - y^2$,

$$\left(\frac{-b}{2a}\right)^2 - \left(\sqrt{\frac{b^2}{4a^2} - \frac{c}{a}}\right)^2 = \frac{c}{a} \tag{20}$$

In this example the product of the two roots is $(\frac{2}{3})(1) = \frac{2}{3}$ which should and does equal c/a.

The quadratic equation will now be explained in more detail. The general form of the quadratic equation is

$$ax^2 + bx + c = 0 \qquad (11)$$

The first term ax^2 is made up of a product of a known number a and the unknown number x raised to the second power, (x^2). The second term is also a product of a known number, b, and the unknown number, x. The third term is simply another known number, c. It might be asked why these terms, added together, make a quadratic quantity that is equal to zero. That will be seen to be true when a, b, c, and x are explained. First, a is a known number. It can be a positive number (greater than zero) or a negative number (less than zero). It can never be zero (see definition at end of the chapter). Second, b can also be a positive or negative number, but it can also be zero. Third, c can be a positive or negative number or zero. Now if a, b, and c are integer numbers it is easy to find a value of x that will make the quadratic quantity

$$ax^2 + bx + c$$

equal to zero. To illustrate, if $a = 2$, $b = -5$, and $c = 3$, then $ax^2 + bx + c$ will be the quadratic quantity $2x^2 - 5x + 3$. Hence it is plainly possible to find a value for x that will make this quadratic quantity in x equal to zero. In fact there are two values of x that will make $2x^2 - 5x + 3$ equal to zero.

But instead of going into the methods of finding these values of x it is more important at this point of the discussion to understand what the problem is. These coefficients a, b, and c, even though they are known numbers, might cause the student considerable trouble unless he realized what they meant. Instead of being numerals, each of them might be a quantity, so we should really consider them as expressions. Just as a stands for the whole thing by which x^2 is multiplied, b stands for the whole thing by which x is multiplied, and c stands for the whole thing by which unity (1) is multiplied. Since c is made up of the constant terms, it is often referred to as the constant of the equation. If the quadratic equation is not arranged so that the coefficient of x^2, which is a, can be seen and dealt with as a term or quantity, it must be rearranged. Likewise the coefficient of x, namely b, must be rearranged and collected into a quantity. When a, b, and c can be written down and the equation is arranged according to the descending powers of x with the right side of the equation zero, then the quadratic equation is in its standard form and is ready to solve. To illustrate, the quadratic equation

$$7 + kx + 9x^2 + k = 17x + 8\,kx^2 + 6$$

is rearranged as follows:

$$(9 - 8k)x^2 + (k - 17)x + (k + 1) = 0$$

This rearranged equation is the same as the other quadratic equation but is in its standard form with a equal to $(9 - 8k)$, b equal to $(k - 17)$ and c equal to $(k + 1)$. When the student is able to rearrange any kind of quadratic equation so that it will be in its standard form, which is the general form

$$ax^2 + bx + c = 0,$$

then he is ready to solve any quadratic equation he may encounter.

Use of the Discriminant $b^2 - 4ac$.—The quantity $b^2 - 4ac$ under the radical in the quadratic formula is called the *discriminant* because its value decides whether the roots are *equal or unequal, real or complex, rational or irrational*.

Case I. If $b^2 - 4ac$ is *zero* the roots are *equal* and *real*. For illustration, in the equation

$$4x^2 - 12x + 9 = 0$$

$a = 4$, $b = -12$, $c = 9$ and $b^2 - 4ac = 144 - 144 = 0$. The usual solution is written

$$x = \frac{12 + \sqrt{0}}{8} \qquad \text{and} \qquad x = \frac{12 - \sqrt{0}}{8}$$

both of which reduce to 1.5. Hence the roots are equal and real.

Case II. If $b^2 - 4ac$ is *positive* (greater than zero) the roots are *unequal* and *real*. For illustration, in the equation

$$3x^2 - 7x - 20$$

$a = 3$, $b = -7$, $c = -20$ and $b^2 - 4ac = 49 + 240 = 289$. The roots are

$$x = \frac{7 + \sqrt{289}}{6} = \frac{7 + 17}{6} = 4$$

and

$$x = \frac{7 - \sqrt{289}}{6} = \frac{7 - 17}{6} = -\frac{5}{3}$$

which are unequal and real.

Case III. If $b^2 - 4ac$ is *negative* (less than zero) the roots are *unequal* and *complex* numbers. For illustration, in the equation

$$3x^2 - 2x + 1 = 0$$

$a = 3$, $b = -2$, $c = 1$, and $b^2 - 4ac = 4 - 12 = -8$. The roots are

$$x = \frac{2 + \sqrt{-8}}{6} = \frac{1 + j\sqrt{2}}{3}$$

and

$$x = \frac{2 - \sqrt{-8}}{6} = \frac{1 - j\sqrt{2}}{3}$$

where $j^2 = -1$ or, taking the square root, $j = \sqrt{-1}$.

These roots are unequal and complex numbers.

Case IV. If $b^2 - 4ac$ is an *exact square* or *zero* the roots are *rational*, otherwise they are irrational. For illustration, in the equation

$$x^2 - 5x + 4 = 0$$

$a = 1$, $b = -5$, $c = 4$ and $b^2 - 4ac = 25 - 16 = 9$.

The roots are

$$x = \frac{5 + \sqrt{9}}{2} = 4$$

and

$$x = \frac{5 - \sqrt{9}}{2} = 1$$

These roots are rational numbers. But in the illustration of the equation

$$x^2 - 5x - 3 = 0$$

$a = 1$, $b = -5$, $c = -3$, and $b^2 - 4ac = 25 + 12 = 37$

The roots are

$$x = \frac{5 + \sqrt{37}}{2}$$

and

$$x = \frac{5 - \sqrt{37}}{2}$$

These roots are irrational numbers, because $\sqrt{37}$ cannot be expressed as a fraction.

It is very important to have a clear understanding of what the solution of a quadratic equation means. A further discussion of the discriminant should assist in giving a clear meaning of the solution.

A quadratic equation in one unknown number has two values of that unknown that will make it true. If x is the unknown number, there will always be two values of x that will satisfy the equation, but they don't have to be integers. They can be fractions, irrational numbers, or complex numbers. There is only one case in which the two values of x are equal and that is when the quadratic in x, namely, $ax^2 + bx + c$, is a perfect square. Probably the best way for the student to understand the meaning of all these different situations is by graphing the quadratic as illustrated in this chapter. Then the student will see for himself that the curve of the quadratic function y (y being the value of $ax^2 + bx + c$) crosses the x-axis twice in all cases but two. One is when the two values of x are equal and in this case the curve just touches the x-axis. The other case is when the curve does not touch or cross the x-axis. In this case both values of x that make y equal zero are complex numbers. One way of expressing the meaning of this solution is to say that the curve crosses the x-axis in two imaginary places, because the complex numbers involve the imaginary number $\sqrt{-1}$.

Example 4. Solve the following equations by the quadratic formula:

$$x^2 - 8x + 15 = 0 \qquad \text{(a)}$$
$$x^2 - 8x + 16 = 0 \qquad \text{(b)}$$
$$x^2 - 8x + 17 = 0 \qquad \text{(c)}$$

Determine from the value of the discriminant the case number. Plot a graph of the equations.

Solution. By the quadratic formula the solutions are

For Eq. (a), $\quad x = \dfrac{8 \pm \sqrt{64 - 60}}{2} = 4 \pm 1 = 3 \text{ or } 5 \quad Ans.$

For Eq. (b), $\quad x = \dfrac{8 \pm \sqrt{64 - 64}}{2} = 4 \quad Ans.$

For Eq. (c), $\quad x = \dfrac{8 \pm \sqrt{64 - 68}}{2} = 4 \pm j1 \quad Ans.$

The values of the discriminant are: For Eq. (a), $b^2 - 4ac = 4$, a positive number; hence the roots are unequal and real.—Case II. *Ans.*

For Eq. (b), $b^2 - 4ac = 0$; hence the roots are equal and real.—Case I. *Ans.*

For Eq. (c), $b^2 - 4ac = -4$, a negative number; hence the roots are unequal and complex numbers.—Case III. *Ans.*

By Case IV, the roots of Eq. (a), (b), and (c) are rational.

The graphical solutions are as follows:

Eq. (a)		Eq. (b)		Eq. (c)	
$y = x^2 - 8x + 15$		$y = x^2 - 8x + 16$		$y = x^2 - 8x + 17$	
y	x	y	x	y	x
8	1	9	1	10	1
3	2	4	2	5	2
0	3 *Ans.*	1	3	2	3
−1	4	0	4 *Ans.*	Imaginary	1	4 *Ans.*
0	5 *Ans.*	1	5	2	5
3	6	4	6	5	6
8	7	9	7	10	7

See Fig. 55 for the graphs of these equations. It will be noted that the imaginary solution locates the vertex of the parabola.

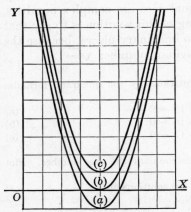

FIG. 55.—Graphic solutions of Eqs. (a), (b), and (c) in Example 4.

Higher Powered Equations. It is possible to solve equations to the third power in a manner similar to the above method of solving an equation to the second power, but, since this method will not be needed, it will not be treated here.

Some problems involving the fourth power can be worked by the quadratic formula and should be treated here, since the method will be useful for solving a few problems later in the course. These special equations can be reduced to

$$af^4 + bf^2 + c = 0 \qquad (21)$$

In this type of problem let $x = f^2$ and the general form of the quadratic formula results, that is,

$$ax^2 + bx + c = 0 \tag{11}$$

Example 5. In a certain series parallel circuit it is found that the frequency f can be expressed as

$$2 \times 10^{-12}f^4 - 6f^2 + 4 \times 10^{12} = 0$$

It is desired to solve this equation for f since this solution will give the frequency at which the circuit is resonant. At present we are interested only in the method; later in the course we shall be interested in the results of such a solution.

Solution. Applying the quadratic formula,

$$f^2 = \frac{6 \pm \sqrt{6^2 - 4(2 \times 10^{-12})(4 \times 10^{12})}}{2(2 \times 10^{-12})}$$

$$= \frac{6 \pm \sqrt{36 - 32}}{4 \times 10^{-12}} = \frac{6 \pm 2}{4 \times 10^{-12}}$$

$$f^2 = 2 \times 10^{12} \quad \text{or} \quad f^2 = 1 \times 10^{12}$$

Then, $\qquad f = 1.414 \times 10^6 \quad$ or $\quad f = 1 \times 10^6 \quad$ *Ans.*

Some Useful Definitions.

1. *A quadratic equation is an equation of the second order.* In other words, it is an equation in which the unknown number is raised to the second power (squared) and no higher power. The first power of the unknown can also be present in the equation but it doesn't have to be present. The second power *must* be present; if only the first power of the unknown is present, the equation is linear and not quadratic.

2. *A quantity is a product or sum of numbers.* These numbers may be known or unknown. Notice that a quantity is not an equation because it is not a statement of equality, and that it therefore does not have an equal sign in it.

3. *A term is a product of numbers.* These numbers may be known or unknown. Notice that a term can be a quantity, but that a quantity that is a sum is not a term.

4. *An expression is a term or quantity,* except that we think of an expression as a symbol that stands for something else or possibly for a class of things.

Exercises

1. $x^2 - 6x - 7 = 0$. Solve by the factoring method.
2. $x^2 + 12x = 28$. Solve by completing the square.

3. $x^2 - 6x - 4 = 0$. Solve by using the quadratic formula.

4. $5x^2 - 3x - 4 = 0$. Solve by any method.

5. $x + 1/x = 1\frac{3}{6}$. Solve by any method.

6. $2x^2 - (\sqrt{2r} + \sqrt{2s})x + \sqrt{rs} = 0$. Solve by any method.

7. $rsx^2 + rs = x(r^2 + s^2)$. Solve by any method.

8. Solve the following equation for x by using the quadratic formula: $kx^2 - 3kx + 9 = 0$. Then find the value of k that will make the roots equal. This is done by setting the discriminant equal to zero and solving for k.

9. $x^2 - (2 + k)x + 4 = 0$. Follow the procedure used in Exercise 8.

10. Solve the following equation for the resonant frequencies f.

$$2f^4 + 4608 = 200f^2.$$

CHAPTER 11

HYPERBOLIC TRIGONOMETRY

Since traveling waves on a transmission line are very conveniently expressed in terms of hyperbolic functions, this chapter will be devoted to the mathematics of these functions. To simplify the presentation, certain parallels will be made with circular trigonometry as studied in Chapter 5. Hyperbolic functions also have valuable applications in the design of attenuation networks and electric wave filters; hence they should be mastered before proceeding further in the course.

Real Circular and Hyperbolic Angles.—In Fig. 56a, a circle with a unit radius is drawn. The equation of this circle with its center at the origin is

$$x^2 + y^2 = 1 \quad \text{(equation of a circle)} \quad (1)$$

If values of y from -1 to $+1$ are substituted in this equation the values of x obtained from the equation will vary from -1 to $+1$ and the points (x, y) will be on the circumference of the circle, hence this equation locates all points on the circumference of the circle and is known as the equation of this circle.

If the sign of y^2 is changed from $+$ to $-$ the equation will no longer be the equation of a circle but that of a hyperbola as shown in Fig. 56b.

$$x^2 - y^2 = 1 \quad \text{(equation of a hyperbola)} \quad (2)$$

If values of y from $-\infty$ to $+\infty$ are substituted in Eq. (2) the corresponding values of x will vary from $-\infty$ to $+\infty$ and the points (x, y) will lie only on the curve as plotted in Fig. 56b and a similar branch on the other side of the y-axis not shown.

If a line is drawn from the origin O to some point P on the circumference of the circle it will make an angle β with the positive x-axis, as shown in Fig. 56a. If the radius of the circle is 1 inch and the shaded area AOP is 0.5 square inches, the angle β is 1 circular radian. Or, in equation form,

$$\beta = 2 \text{ (shaded area)} \quad \text{circular radians} \quad (3)$$

when radius $OA = $ unity.

When $\beta = 1$ radian the arc AP is 1 in; hence for the above case the angle β is equal to the length of the arc in inches. If β is to be expressed in degrees the conversion can be made by recalling that in half a circle there are π radians or 180 degrees; hence

$$1 \text{ circular radian} = 57.296° \qquad (4)$$

If a line is drawn from the origin O to some point P on the hyperbola in Fig. 56b an angle will be made with the positive

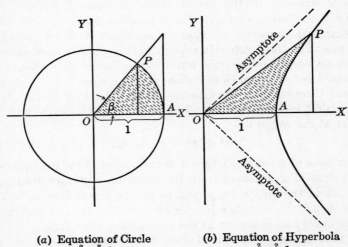

(a) Equation of Circle
$x^2 + y^2 = 1$
$\beta = 2$ (Shaded Area)

(b) Equation of Hyperbola
$x^2 - y^2 = 1$
$\alpha = 2$ (Shaded Area)

Fig. 56.—Comparison of circular and hyperbolic angle.

x-axis. If the distance from the origin O to the hyperbola along the x-axis is 1 in. and the shaded area AOP is 0.5 sq in., the measure is 1 hyperbolic radian. Or, in equation form,

$$\alpha = 2 \text{ (shaded area)} \qquad \text{hyperbolic radians} \qquad (5)$$

when distance $OA =$ unity.

Example 1. In Fig. 56 if $y = 0.5$ determine the value of x for the circle and for the hyperbola.

Solution. Substituting $y = 0.5$ in Eq. (1) for the circle,

$$x^2 + (0.5)^2 = 1$$
or $\qquad x = \sqrt{1 - (0.5)^2} = \sqrt{0.75} = \pm 0.866 \quad Ans.$

Substituting $y = 0.5$ in Eq. (2) for the hyperbola,

$$x^2 - (0.5)^2 = 1$$

or $$x = \sqrt{1 + (0.5)^2} = \sqrt{1.25} = \pm 1.118 \quad Ans.$$

Construction of Trigonometric Circular and Hyperbolic Angle.
Figure 57 illustrates a portion of Fig. 56, showing the construction of trigonometric functions for the circular angle β in Fig. 57a and hyperbolic angle α in Fig. 57b.

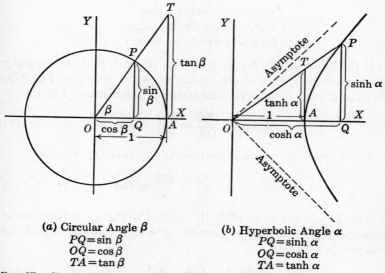

(a) Circular Angle β
$PQ = \sin \beta$
$OQ = \cos \beta$
$TA = \tan \beta$

(b) Hyperbolic Angle α
$PQ = \sinh \alpha$
$OQ = \cosh \alpha$
$TA = \tanh \alpha$

FIG. 57.—Construction of trigonometric function from circular and hyperbolic angle.

It will be recalled that the circular functions were explained in Chapter 5. A review will be given here. The circle of Fig. 57a is constructed with a radius of unity, then the hypotenuse of the triangle OP is unity and the sine of β is the distance PQ over OP (which is unity) hence

$$\sin \beta = \frac{PQ}{OP} = \frac{PQ}{1} = PQ \tag{6}$$

Similarly the cosine of β is OQ/OP, or simply

$$\cos \beta = \frac{OQ}{OP} = \frac{OQ}{1} = OQ \tag{7}$$

The tangent of β is the ratio PQ/OQ or if the similar triangle TAO is used the base $OA =$ unity and the tangent is simply

$$\tan \beta = \frac{\sin \beta}{\cos \beta} = \frac{PQ}{QQ} = \frac{TA}{OA} = \frac{TA}{1} = TA \qquad (8)$$

Referring now to Fig. 57b, similar relationships are drawn. In order to distinguish the trigonometric functions in a hyperbola the letter "h" (for hyperbola) is added and the functions are called

$$\sinh = \text{hyperbolic sine}$$
$$\cosh = \text{hyperbolic cosine}$$
$$\tanh = \text{hyperbolic tangent}$$

If the hyperbola is drawn from Eq. (2) such that $OA =$ unity the hyperbolic functions are readily drawn as shown in Fig. 57b. In this case the hyperbolic sine is simply the distance PQ, that is

$$\sinh \alpha = \frac{PQ}{OA} = \frac{PQ}{1} = PQ \qquad (9)$$

The hyperbolic cosine is simply the distance OQ, that is

$$\cosh \alpha = \frac{OQ}{OA} = \frac{OQ}{1} = OQ \qquad (10)$$

The hyperbolic tangent is the ratio PQ/OQ or, if the similar triangle TAO is used, the base $OA =$ unity and the hyperbolic tangent is simply

$$\tanh \alpha = \frac{\sinh \alpha}{\cosh \alpha} = \frac{PQ}{OQ} = \frac{TA}{OA} = \frac{TA}{1} = TA \qquad (11)$$

Example 2.   Using the positive value of x in Example 1, determine the value of the trigonometric and hyperbolic functions.

Solution.   The trigonometric functions are

By Eq. (6) $\sin \beta = PQ = y = 0.5$ *Ans.*
By Eq. (7) $\cos \beta = OQ = x = 0.866$ *Ans.*
By Eq. (8) $\tan \beta = \dfrac{PQ}{OQ} = \dfrac{y}{x} = 0.577$ *Ans.*

The hyperbolic functions are

By Eq. (9) $\sinh \alpha = PQ = y = 0.5$ *Ans.*
By Eq. (10) $\cosh \alpha = OQ = x = 1.118$ *Ans.*
By Eq. (11) $\tanh \quad = \dfrac{PQ}{OQ} = \dfrac{y}{x} = 0.447$ *Ans.*

It should be noted that the *circular angle β is measured in circular radians,* while the *hyperbolic angle α* is measured in *hyperbolic radians.* These definitions are given in equation form in Eqs. (3) and (5), respectively. However, for practical purposes of determining the circular angle β or the hyperbolic angle α, it is usually more convenient to use one of the trigonometric or hyperbolic functions given above.

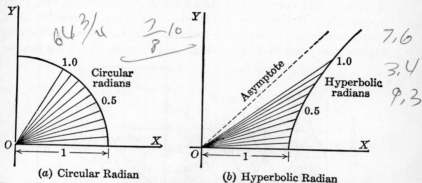

(a) Circular Radian   (b) Hyperbolic Radian

FIG. 58.—A circular and hyperbolic radian subdivided into 10 equal sectors of 0.1 radian each.

Figure 58a illustrates how a circular angle corresponding to 1 circular radian can be divided into 10 equal parts, each of 0.1 radian. If the radius is unity, each arc will be of a constant length of 0.1. Figure 58b illustrates how a hyperbolic angle corresponding to 1 hyperbolic radian can be divided into 10 equal hyperbolic angles, each of 0.1 radian. The arc corresponding to each subdivision increases as the hyperbolic angle increases. The length of the radii also increases (distance *OP*) with the angle. In this illustration the circular and hyperbolic radian are similarly defined on the basis of equal area of circular and hyperbolic sectors.

Example 3. Determine the circular angle β and the hyperbolic angle α when $y = 0.5$ and x is positive.

Solution. From Example 2,

$$\sin \beta = 0.5$$

Then, from the tables of trigonometric functions,

$$\beta = 30° = \frac{30}{57.296} = 0.5236 \text{ circular radians} \quad Ans.$$

Also, from Example 2,

$$\sinh \alpha = 0.5$$

Then, from the tables of hyperbolic functions and interpolating,

$$\alpha = 0.4810 \text{ hyperbolic radians.} \quad Ans.$$

Graphs of Circular and Hyperbolic Functions.—Already circular functions have been used to express the phase relations of voltage and current, but they cannot be used to express their magnitude. Hyperbolic functions, not being periodic, but continuously increasing or decreasing in nature, can be used to express the magnitude of voltage and current in a long line or

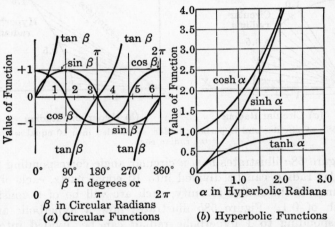

FIG. 59.—Graphical representation of circular and hyperbolic functions.

other networks requiring a change of magnitude of voltage and current.

Figure 59a illustrates trigonometric circular functions. The functions are periodic in nature. The sine function starts at 0, increases to +1, returns to 0, continues to −1 and returns to 0 ready to start another cycle of 360 degrees or 2π radians. The cosine function starts at +1, drops through 0 to −1, and returns through 0 to +1, ready to start another cycle of 360 degrees or 2π radians. The tangent function starts at 0, goes to $+\infty$, jumps to $-\infty$, and comes back to 0 ready to start another cycle of 180 degrees or π radians.

Figure 59b illustrates trigonometric hyperbolic functions. These functions are continuously increasing in nature. The hyperbolic sine function starts at 0 and increases to $+\infty$ as the hyperbolic angle in radians increases to $+\infty$. The hyperbolic cosine function starts at $+1$ and increases to $+\infty$ as the hyperbolic angle in radians increases to $+\infty$. For a given value of α, cosh α is always greater than sinh α, which in turn is always greater than tanh α.

The hyperbolic tangent function starts at 0 and increases to $+1$ as the hyperbolic angle in radians increases to $+\infty$.

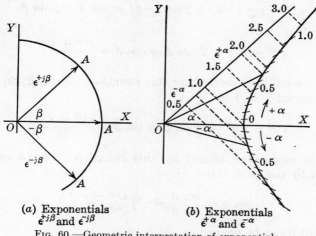

(a) Exponentials $\epsilon^{+j\beta}$ and $\epsilon^{-j\beta}$

(b) Exponentials $\epsilon^{+\alpha}$ and $\epsilon^{-\alpha}$

Fig. 60.—Geometric interpretation of exponentials.

Geometrical Interpretation of the Exponentials $\varepsilon^{+j\beta}$, $\varepsilon^{-j\beta}$, ε^{α}, and $\varepsilon^{-\alpha}$.—It will be recalled that $\epsilon^{+j\beta}$ multiplied by a vector will rotate the vector $+\beta$ radians in a counterclockwise direction. Similarly, $\epsilon^{-j\beta}$ multiplied by a vector will rotate the vector $-\beta$ radians in a clockwise direction. Figure 60a illustrates the effect of multiplying $\epsilon^{+j\beta}$ and $\epsilon^{-j\beta}$ by a unit vector (OA) originally lying along the positive x-axis.

If the points on the hyperbola of Fig. 60b corresponding to various hyperbolic angles are projected on the asymptote (the line bisecting the first quadrant—the hyperbola curve approaches this line and joins it at ∞) as shown in the figure, the distance from the origin to the respective projection will be a measure of ϵ^{α}. It will be noted that for positive values of α the value of $\epsilon^{+\alpha}$ is greater than unity and that negative values of α give $\epsilon^{-\alpha}$ which is less than 1 but never less than 0.

Exponentials Applied to Circular Functions.—For our use, trigonometric functions do not need to be given a geometrical interpretation. In fact, they are sometimes defined by an algebraic exponential form. For example, the identity for changing from polar to rectangular form, which is

$$\epsilon^{+j\beta} = \cos \beta + j \sin \beta \tag{12}$$

is added to the form when the sign of β is made negative, thus

$$\epsilon^{-j\beta} = \cos (-\beta) + j \sin (-\beta) = \cos \beta - j \sin \beta \tag{13}$$

the result is

$$\epsilon^{+j\beta} + \epsilon^{-j\beta} = 2 \cos \beta \text{ or } \cos \beta = \frac{\epsilon^{+j\beta} + \epsilon^{-j\beta}}{2} \tag{14}$$

$\cos \beta$ is sometimes defined by this equation. Now, if Eq. (13) is subtracted from Eq. (12),

$$\epsilon^{+j\beta} - \epsilon^{-j\beta} = 2j \sin \beta \text{ or } \sin \beta = \frac{\epsilon^{+j\beta} - \epsilon^{-j\beta}}{2j} \tag{15}$$

$\sin \beta$ is sometimes defined by this equation. Tan β can be defined by the ratio, thus

$$\tan \beta = \frac{\sin \beta}{\cos \beta} = -j \frac{\epsilon^{+j\beta} - \epsilon^{-j\beta}}{\epsilon^{+j\beta} + \epsilon^{-j\beta}} \tag{16}$$

Also, cot β can be defined as

$$\cot \beta = \frac{1}{\tan \beta} = \frac{\cos \beta}{\sin \beta} = j \frac{\epsilon^{j\beta} + \epsilon^{-j\beta}}{\epsilon^{j\beta} - \epsilon^{-j\beta}} \tag{17}$$

Exponentials Applied to Hyperbolic Functions.—From analogy with the circular trigonometric functions, the hyperbolic functions can be defined as follows:

$$\epsilon^{\alpha} = \cosh \alpha + \sinh \alpha \tag{18}$$
$$\epsilon^{-\alpha} = \cosh \alpha - \sinh \alpha \tag{19}$$

Subtracting Eq. (19) from Eq. (18) gives

$$\sinh \alpha = \frac{\epsilon^{\alpha} - \epsilon^{-\alpha}}{2} \tag{20}$$

$\sinh \alpha$ can be defined by this equation. Adding Eq. (18) and Eq. (19) gives

$$\cosh \alpha = \frac{\epsilon^{\alpha} + \epsilon^{-\alpha}}{2} \tag{21}$$

cosh α can be defined by this equation. Tanh α can be defined by the ratio

$$\tanh \alpha = \frac{\sinh \alpha}{\cosh \alpha} = \frac{\epsilon^\alpha - \epsilon^{-\alpha}}{\epsilon^\alpha + \epsilon^{-\alpha}} \qquad (22)$$

In some equations it is more convenient to use the reciprocal of tanh α which is known as "hyperbolic cotangent" and can be defined as follows:

$$\coth \alpha = \frac{1}{\tanh \alpha} = \frac{\cosh \alpha}{\sinh \alpha} = \frac{\epsilon^\alpha + \epsilon^{-\alpha}}{\epsilon^\alpha - \epsilon^{-\alpha}} \qquad (23)$$

Example 4. Determine the values of the exponentials for circular and hyperbolic functions when $y = 0.5$ and x is positive.

Solution. From Examples 2 and 3 and the use of Eq. (12),

$$\epsilon^{j\beta} = \cos \beta + j \sin \beta$$
$$\epsilon^{j0.5236} = 0.866 + j0.5 = 1\underline{/30°} \quad Ans.$$

From Examples 2 and 3 and the use of Eq. (18),

$$\epsilon^\alpha = \cosh \alpha + \sinh \alpha$$
$$\epsilon^{0.4812} = 1.118 + 0.5 = 1.618 \quad Ans.$$

Circular and Hyperbolic Identities.—These identities are tabulated on page 307, primarily for reference purposes. The proof of many of these identities can be made by substitution of the exponential forms given above. In these equations α is not necessarily a hyperbolic radian nor is β necessarily a circular radian. In general they can be considered as two different angles measured in radians.

Example 5. Develop the equation

$$\cosh^2 \beta - \sinh^2 \beta = 1$$

from the circular function identity

$$\sin^2 \beta + \cos^2 \beta = 1$$

Solution. In the circular function identity, replace β with $j\beta$ to get

$$\sin^2 j\beta + \cos^2 j\beta = 1$$
But, $$\sin j\beta = j \sinh \beta$$
and $$\cos j\beta = \cosh \beta$$
Hence, $$j^2 \sinh^2 \beta + \cosh^2 \beta = 1$$
or $$\cosh^2 \beta - \sinh^2 \beta = 1 \quad Ans.$$

Example 6. Determine the circular sine and hyperbolic sine of the complex quantity

$$\gamma = \alpha + j\beta = 0.4812 + j0.5236$$

Solution. Referring to the list of identities,

$$\sin \gamma = \sin (\alpha + j\beta) = \sin \alpha \cosh \beta + j \cos \alpha \sinh \beta$$
$$= \sin (0.4812) \cosh (0.5236) + j \cos (0.4812) \sinh (0.5236)$$

Converting from radians to degrees,

$$\sin \gamma = \sin (27.57°) \cosh (0.5236) + j \cos (27.57°) \sinh (0.5236)$$

Finding the values from the tables,

$$\sin \gamma = (0.4628)(1.14025) + j(0.8865)(0.54786)$$
$$= 0.5277 + j0.4857 = 0.7172\underline{/42°38'} \quad Ans.$$

From the list of identities,

$$\sinh \gamma = \sinh (\alpha + j\beta) = \sinh \alpha \cos \beta + j \cosh \alpha \sin \beta$$
$$= \sinh (0.4812) \cos (0.5236) + j \cosh (0.4812) \sin (0.5236)$$
$$= (0.5) (0.866) + j (1.118) (0.5)$$
$$= 0.433 + j0.559 = 0.7071\underline{/52°15'} \quad Ans.$$

Exercises

1. If a circle has a radius of 1 in. and the vector *OP* (Fig. 56) is rotated so that the shaded area is 2 sq. in., what is the value of β?

2. If a hyperbola measures 1 in. from *O* to *A* and the vector *OP* is turned clockwise so that the shaded area is 3 sq in., what is the value of α and ϵ^α (see Fig. 56)?

3. In Eq. (1) if $x = 0.707$ what are the possible values of y?

4. In Eq. (2) if $x = 2.0$ what are the possible values of y?

5. How does the value of $\cosh \alpha$ compare with $\sinh \alpha$ as α is varied? What are the corresponding values of $\tanh \alpha$?

6. Between what limits do $\sin \beta$ and $\cos \beta$ vary? What are the limits of $\tan \beta$?

7. What valuable property does $\epsilon^{j\beta}$ have when multiplied by a vector? How is this property different from ϵ^α multiplied by the same vector?

8. If $\tanh \alpha = 0.76159$, determine $\sinh \alpha$, $\cosh \alpha$, $\coth \alpha$, and α.

CHAPTER 12

DIFFERENTIAL CALCULUS
TREATING ALGEBRAIC FUNCTIONS

Arithmetic deals with the use of *numbers*, which are constant quantities, while *algebra* deals with the use of *symbols* representing either constant or variable quantities. *Calculus*, going one step farther, deals with the *nature* and variation of these quantities. Since calculus uses both arithmetic and algebra, it is studied last.

The basic ideas of calculus are simple and fascinating when one has a good working knowledge of such subjects as algebra and trigonometry. However, the large amount of detail and the abstract approach that is often made lead to disinterest and to a false notion that the subject is extremely difficult.

Calculus in its elementary forms can be divided into differential calculus and integral calculus, much as arithmetic processes can be divided into subtraction and addition. In both the calculus and the arithmetic the processes are inverse operations.

The purpose of studying calculus at this time is to become familiar with the nature of changing electrical quantities. Not that the student will be able to work out all calculus problems, because even the best mathematicians cannot do this, but that the student can work simple problems and be able to understand the meaning of calculus terms when they are found in the literature. This chapter will deal with differential calculus in elementary and graphical forms which treat algebraic functions, while the next chapter will deal with transcendental functions in a similar fashion. Then a treatment of elementary and graphical forms of integral calculus will be presented.

All algebraic functions of x are rational functions, while all other functions of x are transcendental or irrational functions of x. An algebraic function of x can in its most complicated form be expressed as a fraction with values of x in both the numerator and denominator.

Calculus Symbols.—The letter d is used in differential calculus to mean "a little bit of," hence "dx" means "a little bit of x." This little bit of x is a difference quantity, commonly called the "differential" or "element" of x. d can be remembered as the first letter of "difference" or "differential." "dx" is actually of indefinitely small size. Differential calculus can be simply explained as a mathematics of making and using indefinitely small difference calculations.

The symbol $\int$ as used in integral calculus is merely an elongated letter S which means "the sum of." This symbol which stands for the first letter of sum is usually called "the integral of," which means the whole or total. Integral calculus can be simply explained as the mathematics of making and using large sum calculations.

Integral and differential calculus symbols are often used in combination to express a quantity, thus $\int dx$ means "the sum of all the little bits of x." In other words, the whole quantity can be found by adding up all the indefinitely small little bits of x.

Limits.—In reality quantities must be finite or zero. In other words, we have something or we have nothing. This concept seems simple. The mathematician, however, has complicated the matter by devising two fictitious quantities, as it were, which are used to aid him in his reasoning processes. One is called "infinity," and is greater than any number or quantity. The other is called "an infinitesimal" and is smaller than any number or quantity.

How do we arrive at these fictitious quantities of infinity and an infinitesimal? The answer to this question is found in the use of limits. A variable quantity, if it increases indefinitely in size, is said to reach infinity in the limit. Likewise, if a variable quantity decreases indefinitely in size it becomes an infinitesimal and is said to reach zero in the limit. In the precise language of the mathematician, *a variable is said to approach a limit when its value becomes and remains arbitrarily close to the limit.* "Arbitrarily close" means that we can assign a number as close as we please to the limit and the variable will ultimately become and remain closer to the limit than this arbitrary or assigned number.

If the variable x approaches *infinity* as the limit, the fact is stated mathematically as

$$\lim_{x \to \infty} x = \infty$$

This states in words that the limit of the variable x equals infinity as x approaches infinity.

On the other hand if the variable x approaches zero as the limit it is called an "infinitesimal." This means that the variable becomes and remains as close as you please to zero. In mathematical language,

$$\lim_{x \to 0} x = 0$$

This says in words that the limit of x equals zero as x approaches zero.

The quantity dx is known as an infinitesimal, because in the calculus process of differentiation it approaches zero as the limit. By this limiting method the calculus process becomes an exact process. For illustration, the ratio dy/dx pronounced "dee-wy by dee-ex" is made up of two differential quantities each of which approaches zero in the limit to give $0/0$, which as such cannot be evaluated. Here is where the mathematician's reasoning process with infinitesimals comes to the rescue. The value of y is related to the value of x so long as values can be assigned to either one. For illustration, y may always be twice the value of x no matter how small x is made. In this case the ratio is 2 right up to the limit $0/0$, so it is reasonable to believe the value of $0/0$ for this case is 2. In other words, the indeterminate $0/0$ is evaluated by this limiting process.

The idea of limits is often useful, as illustrated by the following mathematical statement:

$$\lim_{x \to 2} x^2 = 4$$

This states in words that the limit of the variable x^2 equals 4 as x approaches 2. It is easy to see that $x^2 = 2^2 = 4$ in the limit.

The differential sign d is closely related to the incremental sign Δ (the Greek letter delta). The basic difference is that Δx stands for a finite increment of x while dx stands for an infinitesimal increment of x.

Relative Smallness.—Our calculations will deal with small quantities having various degrees of smallness. It is, therefore, important to know what degrees of smallness we can omit and still arrive at an answer with the required accuracy.

The size of a quantity depends upon the measuring stick. The earth is very small in comparison to our solar system, yet the earth is very large in comparison to a baseball. When dealing with the solar system, the earth should not be omitted, but the baseball could for most purposes be neglected. The earth, in this case, is said to have a first degree of smallness, while the baseball has a second degree of smallness. A flea on the baseball would then have a third degree of smallness.

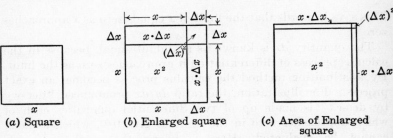

(a) Square   (b) Enlarged square   (c) Area of Enlarged square

Fig. 61.—A square enlarged to show degrees of smallness.

The degree of smallness can be illustrated by enlarging the square of Fig. 61a. The area of this square is $x \cdot x = x^2$. If the square is enlarged by adding a strip having a width of Δx on the two sides as shown in Fig. 61b, then the total area is

$$(x + \Delta x)^2 = x^2 + 2x \cdot \Delta x + (\Delta x)^2 \qquad (1)$$

To illustrate the geometry, let $x = 5$ and $\Delta x = 1$, then the area of the original square is $x \cdot x = 5 \cdot 5 = 25$ and the area of the enlarged square is $(x + \Delta x)^2 = (5 + 1)^2 = 36$. Adding the areas of the enlarged square of Fig. 61b gives $x^2 = 5^2 = 25$, $2(x \cdot \Delta x) = 2(5 \cdot 1) = 10$, and $(\Delta x)^2 = 1^2 = 1$, thus

$$x^2 + 2x \cdot \Delta x + (\Delta x)^2 = 25 + 10 + 1 = 36,$$

which checks the above value.

Now if Δx is made very small in comparison to x, as shown in Fig. 61c, it is readily seen that $(\Delta x)^2$ is of second order in smallness and can be omitted, thus

$$(x + \Delta x)^2 = x^2 + 2x \cdot \Delta x \qquad (2)$$

with an accuracy of the first order. To illustrate, let $x = 1,000$ and $\Delta x = 1$, then the area of the enlarged square by Eq. (1)

with accuracy to the second order is

$$(x + \Delta x)^2 = (1,001)^2 = 1,002,001$$

and by Eq. (2), the accuracy to the first order is

$$x^2 + 2x \Delta x = 1,000,000 + 2,000 = 1,002,000$$

By neglecting the second-order term $(\Delta x)^2$, the answer has changed approximately one part in a million. This makes it clear that if Δx is made small enough, by approaching the value of dx, the second, third, and higher order terms can be omitted.

Rates.—One of the most familiar illustrations of rate is the movement of an object which takes a certain amount of time. An automobile, for example, travels at a rate of 60 miles per hour. If the automobile has a uniform speed the whole distance, $x = 60$ miles, and the total time, $t = 1$ hr, can be used to express the rate mathematically, thus

$$\text{Rate} = \frac{x}{t} = \frac{\text{distance}}{\text{time}} \qquad (3)$$

Using the above values, Eq. (3) gives

$$\text{Rate} = \frac{60 \text{ miles}}{1 \text{ hr}} = 60 \text{ mph}$$

Since it is unusual to have a constant rate of speed for such a long period of time, it is logical to look for a way to express this rate at any particular instant. By writing dx as an incremental distance corresponding to an incremental interval of time, dt, the rate at any instant can be expressed by

$$\text{Rate} = \frac{dx}{dt} \qquad (4)$$

where dx = differential of x, pronounced "dee-ex."

dt = differential of t, pronounced "dee-tee."

This equation states that the mathematical rate of x at the particular instant is the ratio of the differentials dx divided by dt. The differential of any variable quantity is indicated by writing the letter d before the quantity, thus in this equation the symbol dx is not the product of d and x but represents an incremental difference quantity. This difference quantity dx known as a differential corresponds to the distance covered during the corresponding incremental difference quantity dt the time elapsed to cover that distance. Even though dx and dt are correspondingly very, very small quantities, the ratio will not be altered. This means that the automobile rate at any instant during the whole hour will be 60 miles per hour, since it has a uniform speed. However, if the automobile speed is not uniform, Eq. (3) cannot be used and resort must be made to Eq. (4), which is a simple differential calculus expression of rate. This

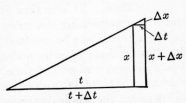

FIG. 62.—Triangle representation of a constant rate.

equation will hold true no matter how rapidly the rate or speed of the automobile is changing, because it considers such very, very small difference quantities. This is the heart of the calculus method, which makes it a most useful tool in expressing ideas and solving problems involving rates.

If the time t represents the base of a right triangle and the altitude is a measure of the distance x covered by the automobile from the beginning of the hour, as shown in Fig. 62, then the instantaneous rate at the end of an hour can be represented by the small similar triangle having a base of Δt and an altitude of Δx.

This triangle in Fig. 62 shows that as time t passes to become $t + \Delta t$, the distance grows from x to become $x + \Delta x$. In this

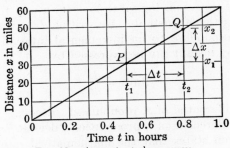

FIG. 63.—A constant-slope curve.

case, the distance x depends upon the time t and the small distance Δx depends upon the small time Δt. *An important thing to note is that the ratio still has a definite value even though both Δx and Δt become indefinitely small.*

Slopes.—Differentiation is the process of finding or calculating differentials of variables. This can be accomplished graphically by plotting the curve of the variable and then determining the slope of the curve. Consider the above illustration of an automobile traveling 60 miles per hour. This information if plotted will give the straight line curve shown in Fig. 63. By substituting in Eq. (3), the slope of this curve is found to be 60 miles per hour. Now, instead of considering all of the graph, use the portion of the curve between points P and Q. The slope of this portion of the curve is the change in distance $\Delta x = x_2 - x_1$ divided by the corresponding change in time $\Delta t = t_2 - t_1$, or, in equation form,

$$\text{Slope} = \frac{\Delta x}{\Delta t} = \frac{x_2 - x_1}{t_2 - t_1} \tag{5}$$

where Δx = the change in x, pronounced "delta ex."

Δt = the change in t, pronounced "delta tee."

If the values on the curve are substituted in Eq. (5), the result is

$$\text{Slope} = \frac{48 - 30}{0.8 - 0.5} = \frac{18}{0.3} = 60 \text{ mph}$$

This checks with the solution obtained by using Eq. (3) for the whole curve.

If the quantity Δx is made smaller and smaller, it can be made to approach the differential dx. Similarly Δt can be made to approach the differential dt. For illustration move the point Q closer and closer to the point P and the triangle will become smaller and smaller with the result that the slope or rate at the point P can be expressed in differential form by Eq. (4). This reveals that there are two types of rates, an average rate which is computed over a definite interval, such as from P to Q in the above illustration, and an instantaneous rate which is computed at one particular point such as P in the above illustration.

For a curve that is not a straight line the ratio of Δx to Δt as illustrated in Fig. 63 will not always give the slope at the point P. The slope of the curve, at the point P, is called the "tangent" to the curve. Hence, to find the derivative dx by dt at the point P, draw a tangent to the curve at that point and find the slope of this tangent.

$$\text{Slope} = \text{tangent} = \text{derivative}$$

The slope can also be expressed in terms of the limiting process as follows:

$$\text{Slope} = \lim_{\Delta t \to 0} \frac{\Delta x}{\Delta t} = \frac{dx}{dt} \qquad (6)$$

This says in words that the limit of the ratio of delta x to delta t as delta t approaches zero is the ratio of the differential of x to the differential of t.

Consider any curve such as the one shown in Fig. 64. Select any two points on the curve such as P and Q. The slope of the line joining these two points is the ratio $\Delta y/\Delta x$ as shown in the

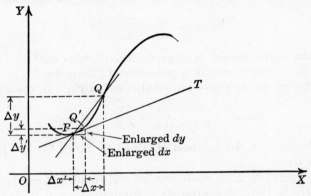

FIG. 64.—A variable-slope curve.

figure. It will be noted, however, that this line is not tangent to the curve at either point P or point Q. Now move the point Q down to Q', which is a step in the process of making $\Delta x \to 0$. The slope of the line joining P and Q' is now $\Delta y'/\Delta x'$, which is approaching the slope of the tangent to the curve marked PT. As the point Q is moved closer and closer to the point P, the slope of the line joining the two points will approach the tangent. In the limit it will equal the tangent to the curve at point P. The slope of the curve at point P is then dy/dx.

Example 1. A diode vacuum tube obeys the square law curve $i = e^2$ as shown in Fig. 65. Determine the slope of the curve at point P when the voltage is 5 volts and the current is 25 ma.

Solution. Draw the straight line ab tangent to the curve and through the point P. The slope of this straight line by Eq. (3) is

$$\text{Slope} = \frac{50 - 5}{7.5 - 3} = \frac{45}{4.5} = 10$$

measured in milliamperes per volt. *Ans.*

Functions.—When two variables are related in such a way that if the value of the first variable is furnished, it is possible to determine the value of the second variable, then the first variable

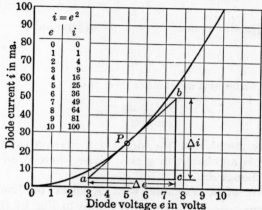

Fig. 65.—The square law curve of a diode vacuum tube.

is said to be a "function" of the second. In the diode vacuum tube of Example 1, it is possible to determine the voltage e if the current is known, hence i is a function of e. In this example, the voltage e can be applied at will; hence it is known as the "independent variable" while the current i depends upon the voltage e that is applied and is called the "dependent variable" or "function." To make this statement mathematically,

$$i = f(e) \qquad (7)$$

This equation states that i is a function of e. It does not mean that f is multiplied by (e), but that if e is known, it is possible to determine the dependent variable i. Substituting the value of $f(e) = e^2$ from Fig. 65 gives the exact

Fig. 66.—Here $y = c$, a constant.

expression from which i can be determined if e is given, that is,

$$i = e^2$$

Derivative of a Constant.—As shown in Fig. 66, when y is equal to a constant, which does not change in value, it has no rate or differential. The slope is zero because if the line ab is drawn through the point P tangent to the curve the slope is given by Eq. (5), thus

$$\text{Slope} = \frac{y_2 - y_1}{x_2 - x_1} = \frac{3 - 3}{5 - 1} = \frac{0}{4} = 0$$

Therefore, for the equation $y = c$, *the differential of a constant is zero*, thus

$$dy = dc = 0 \tag{8}$$

and *the derivative of a constant is zero*, thus

(I) $$\frac{dy}{dx} = \frac{dc}{dx} = 0 \tag{9}$$

This merely states that the slope of a horizontal line is zero. Since there is no change in y as x varies, there is no change in dy for the change dx.

Derivative of a Variable with Respect to Itself.—When $y = x$ as shown in Fig. 67 the slope at point P by Eq. (5) is

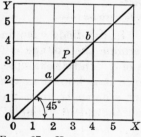

$$\text{Slope} = \frac{\Delta y}{\Delta x} = \frac{4 - 2}{4 - 2} = \frac{2}{2} = 1$$

For this curve $dy = dx$, hence the derivative

(II) $$\frac{dy}{dx} = \frac{dx}{dx} = 1 \tag{10}$$

Fig. 67.—Here $y = x$, a variable.

This equation states that when the x and y scales are alike the slope of a line making an angle of 45 degrees with the x-axis is unity.

Derivative of a Variable Multiplied by a Constant.—In the equation $y = cx$ let the value of y and x increase by an increment, thus

$$y + \Delta y = cx + c\,\Delta x$$

Subtracting

$$y \qquad\quad = cx$$

gives

$$\overline{\Delta y = \qquad\quad c\,\Delta x}$$

Dividing through by Δx, the slope is a constant.

$$\frac{\Delta y}{\Delta x} = c$$

Now, if the limit of this fraction is taken, the derivative form can be obtained, thus

(III)
$$\lim_{\Delta x \to 0} \frac{\Delta y}{\Delta x} = \frac{dy}{dx} = c$$
(11)

This equation states that the derivative of a variable multiplied by a constant is equal to the constant multiplied by the derivative of the variable. Referring to Fig. 68, the derivative or slope of the line $y = 0$ is $dy/dx = 0$, of the line $y = 0.5x$ is $dy/dx = 0.5$, of the line $y = x$ is $dy/dx = 1$, of the line $y = 2x$ is $dy/dx = 2$ and of the line $y = \infty\, x$, $dy/dx = \infty$. In other words, the derivative is the slope of the line which is the coefficient or constant multiplied by the variable.

The above method of adding an increment to each variable, subtracting the original function, and then taking the limit of the increment is the *basic method* for finding the derivative of a function. For practical purposes this procedure can be simplified by using differential quantities at the beginning instead of incremental quantities. Applying this idea, the above derivation is as follows:

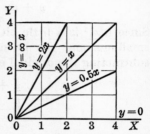

FIG. 68.—Here $y = cx$, curves of various constants multiplied by a variable.

Let the value of y and x increase by differential amounts, thus

$$y + dy = cx + c\,dx$$

Subtracting the original function $\quad y \quad\;\; = cx$

Then the differential $\quad\qquad\qquad dy = \quad\;\; c\,dx$

and the derivative
$$\frac{dy}{dx} = c$$

This checks the above solution.

Example 2.   State the derivative of the function

$$y = -2x$$

Solution. $\quad \dfrac{dy}{dx} = \dfrac{d(-2x)}{dx} = -2\dfrac{dx}{dx} = -2. \quad Ans.$

Derivative of a Variable with a Constant Exponent.—When $y = x^2$, a curve similar to the one in Fig. 65 results. The thing to remember is that as x increases, x^2 increases more rapidly, and hence y also increases more rapidly since it is equal to x^2. In Example 1, the slope of the curve at point P was found to be 10. At any other point it will not be this value, as was the case for a straight line, so it is desired to determine the value of dy/dx. This can be done very simply as follows: To the value of x, add a little bit to make it $x + dx$, and to y add a little bit to make it $y + dy$. Substituting these values in the above equation gives

$$y + dy = (x + dx)^2$$

Squaring the right-hand side gives

$$y + dy = x^2 + 2x\,dx + (dx)^2$$

Since $(dx)^2$ is a little bit of a little bit, it is of second order in smallness and can be neglected. Leaving this term out and subtracting the original equation $y = x^2$ results in

$$
\begin{aligned}
y + dy &= x^2 + 2x\,dx \\
y &= x^2 \\
\hline
dy &= 2x\,dx
\end{aligned}
$$

or dividing both sides by dx gives the desired derivative

$$\frac{dy}{dx} = \frac{d(x^2)}{dx} = 2x \tag{12}$$

This analytical method is a basic procedure for finding the derivative of a function.

Example 3. Determine the derivative of the curve at point P in Fig. 65.
Solution. Applying Eq. (12),

$$\frac{di}{de} = 2e = 2 \cdot 5 = 10 \quad Ans.$$

This checks the graphical solution of Example 1.

As another illustration let $y = x^3$. Then, as before, let both y and x increase a little bit to give

$$
\begin{aligned}
y + dy &= (x + dx)^3 \\
&= x^3 + 3x^2\,dx + 3x(dx)^2 + (dx)^3
\end{aligned}
$$

subtracting the original equation and neglecting the terms of second or higher order of smallness give

$$dy = 3x^2\,dx$$

Dividing both sides by dx gives the desired derivative

$$\frac{dy}{dx} = \frac{d(x^3)}{dx} = 3x^2 \qquad (13)$$

From Eqs. (10), (12), and (13), the following table can be made:

y	$\dfrac{dy}{dx}$
x^1	$1x^0$
x^2	$2x^1$
x^3	$3x^2$

This table shows a sequence which would lead us to guess that the derivative of x^4 is $4x^3$. To check this, differentiate the equation $y = x^4$ as shown above by adding a little bit of y and a little bit of x to get

$$y + dy = (x + dx)^4 = x^4 + 4x^3\,dx + 6x^2(dx)^2 + 4x(dx)^3 + (dx)^4$$

Neglecting second or higher order terms and subtracting the original equation gives

$$dy = 4x^3\,dx$$

or, in derivative form, $\dfrac{dy}{dx} = \dfrac{d(x^4)}{dx} = 4x^3 \qquad (14)$

Generalizing this procedure, let n be the exponent of x. Then the derivative must have n multiplied by x and the new exponent will be one less than n, thus

(IV) $\qquad\qquad \dfrac{dy}{dx} = \dfrac{d(x^n)}{dx} = nx^{n-1} \qquad (15)$

Example 4.   Find the derivative of $y = x^7$.

Solution.   Applying Eq. (15) $\dfrac{dy}{dx} = 7x^6$.   *Ans.*

This rule applies as well to negative and fractional powers, as shown in the following examples:

Example 5.   Find the derivative of $y = x^{-2}$.

Solution.   Applying Eq. (15) $\dfrac{dy}{dx} = -2x^{-3}$.   *Ans.*

Example 6.   Find the derivative of $y = \sqrt{x} = x^{1/2}$.

Solution.   Applying Eq. (15) $\dfrac{dy}{dx} = \dfrac{1}{2}\,x^{-1/2} = \dfrac{1}{2\sqrt{x}}$.   *Ans.*

Derivative of a Sum.—Let $y = u + v$ and, by the basic procedure, let these variables grow to give

$$y + dy = u + du + v + dv$$

Subtracting the original function,

$$y = u + v$$

Hence the differential of y is

$$dy = du + dv \quad (16)$$

Dividing both sides of the equation by dx gives the derivative

(V)
$$\frac{dy}{dx} = \frac{d(u + v)}{dx} = \frac{du}{dx} + \frac{dv}{dx} \quad (17)$$

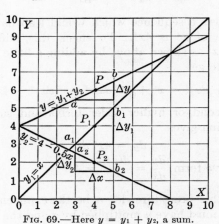

FIG. 69.—Here $y = y_1 + y_2$, a sum.

Example 7. Find the derivative of the sum of $y_1 = x$ and $y_2 = 4 - 0.5x$ both analytically and graphically.

Solution. $y = y_1 + y_2 = x + 4 - 0.5x$

By Eq. (17) $\dfrac{dy}{dx} = \dfrac{dx}{dx} + \dfrac{d(4)}{dx} - \dfrac{d(0.5x)}{dx} = 1 + 0 - 0.5 = 0.5$ *Ans.*

Referring to Fig. 69,

$$\frac{\Delta y_1}{\Delta x} = \frac{5 - 3}{5 - 3} = \frac{2}{2} = 1$$

$$\frac{\Delta y_2}{\Delta x} = \frac{1.5 - 2.5}{5 - 3} = \frac{-1}{2} = -0.5$$

Then
$$\frac{\Delta y}{\Delta x} = \frac{\Delta y_1}{\Delta x} + \frac{\Delta y_2}{\Delta x} = 1 - 0.5 = 0.5 \quad Ans.$$

Solving for the slope,

$$\frac{\Delta y}{\Delta x} = \frac{6.5 - 5.5}{5 - 3} = 0.5 \quad Check.$$

Equation (17) is more general than the example for straight lines because it holds for any curve. However, for any curve, it is possible to draw a tangent to the curve at the point of interest and then find the slope of the tangent to get the derivative for that point. If this is done, it will be found that the curve resulting from the sum of the other variables has the same slope as the sum of the slopes of the various variables. This is another way of stating Eq. (17).

Derivative of a Product.—Let $y = uv$ and as each variable grows

$$y + dy = (u + du)(v + dv)$$
$$= uv + u\,dv + v\,du + du\,dv$$

Subtracting the func-

tion, $y \qquad\qquad = uv$

The differential of y is $dy = \qquad u\,dv + v\,du$ (18)

The product $du\,dv$ was omitted because it is of the second order of smallness. Dividing both sides of the equation by dx results in the derivative of a product

(VI) $$\frac{dy}{dx} = \frac{d(uv)}{dx} = u\,\frac{dv}{dx} + v\,\frac{du}{dx}$$ (19)

This equation states that the derivative of a product is equal to the first variable multiplied by the derivative of the second variable plus the second variable multiplied by the derivative of the first variable.

Example 8. Find the derivative of the product $(x + 1)x^2$.
Solution. Let $u = x + 1$ and $v = x^2$

Then $$\frac{du}{dx} = \frac{d(x + 1)}{dx} = 1$$

and $$\frac{dv}{dx} = \frac{d(x^2)}{dx} = 2x$$

Substituting in Eq. (19),

$$\frac{d(x + 1)x^2}{dx} = (x + 1)2x + x^2 \cdot 1 = 3x^2 + 2x \quad Ans.$$

Derivative of a Quotient.—Let $y = \dfrac{u}{v}.$

As each variable grows, $y + dy = \dfrac{u + du}{v + dv}$

Performing the division indicated on the right-hand side to

obtain all terms of the first order of smallness and neglecting all
terms of the higher orders of smallness are done as follows:

$$v + dv \,\big|\, u + du \,\Big|\, \frac{u}{v} - \frac{u\,dv}{v^2} + \frac{du}{v}$$

$$u + \frac{u\,dv}{v}$$

$$-\frac{u\,dv}{v} + du$$

$$-\frac{u\,dv}{v} - \frac{u(dv)^2}{v^2}$$

$$+ du$$

$$+ du + \frac{du\,dv}{v}$$

The terms $\dfrac{u(dv)^2}{v^2}$ and $\dfrac{du\,dv}{v}$ were neglected in this division
because of their higher order of smallness.

Thus $$y + dy = \frac{u}{v} + \frac{v\,du}{v^2} - \frac{u\,dv}{v^2}$$

Subtracting, $$y \qquad\quad = \frac{u}{v}$$

$$\overline{\qquad\qquad dy = \qquad\qquad \frac{v\,du - u\,dv}{v^2}} \qquad (20)$$

and dividing both sides by dx gives the derivative

(VII) $$\frac{dy}{dx} = \frac{d}{dx}\left(\frac{u}{v}\right) = \frac{v\dfrac{du}{dx} - u\dfrac{dv}{dx}}{v^2} \qquad (21)$$

This equation states that the derivative of a fraction is equal to
the denominator multiplied by the derivative of the numerator
minus the numerator multiplied by the derivative of the denominator all divided by the denominator squared.

Example 9. What is the derivative of $\dfrac{x^2 + 2}{\sqrt{x}}$?

Solution. Let $u = x^2 + 2$ and $v = \sqrt{x} = x^{1/2}$

Then $$\frac{du}{dx} = 2x \qquad \text{and} \qquad \frac{dv}{dx} = \frac{1}{2}\,x^{-1/2}$$

Substituting in Eq. (21),

$$\frac{d}{dx}\left(\frac{x^2 + 2}{\sqrt{x}}\right) = \frac{\sqrt{x} \cdot 2x - (x^2 + 2) \, \frac{1}{2}\, x^{-\frac{1}{2}}}{x} = \frac{3\,\sqrt{x}}{2} - \frac{1}{x\,\sqrt{x}} \quad Ans.$$

Thus far we have developed the important derivatives for algebraic functions. In most cases graphs have been furnished to illustrate more clearly what happens. Now, to make use of this knowledge, some practical applications will be treated along with some more ideas about differential calculus. In other words, we have the tools; let's learn how to make good use of them.

Successive Derivatives.—The idea that a derivative may represent a rate of change has already been given. It is the ratio of the little bit of space covered in the corresponding little bit of time. Let us apply this idea to a freely falling object. From physics, the equation for a freely falling body is

$$s = 16t^2 \tag{22}$$

where s = space covered by the freely falling body, in feet.

t = time after the body begins to fall, in seconds.

This curve is plotted in Fig. 70 for a time period of 8 seconds. As time increases the space is covered more rapidly. This means that the velocity must be increasing. The velocity, if scientifically expressed, is the derivative of space with respect to time. If applied to Eq. (22), it gives

$$v = \frac{ds}{dt} = 32t \tag{23}$$

where v = velocity in feet per second.

When this curve is plotted, as shown in Fig. 70, it is noted that the velocity is steadily increasing. Now the rate at which the velocity is increasing is called the "acceleration." Taking the derivative of Eq. (23), which is the second successive derivative, results in

$$a = \frac{dv}{dt} = \frac{d^2s}{dt^2} = 32 \tag{24}$$

where a = acceleration in feet per second per second, and d^2s/dt^2 = the second derivative of s with respect to t. It can also be read "dee squared ess over dee-tee squared." This equation shows that the *acceleration*, due to the force of gravity, is a constant equal to 32 feet per second per second. This is represented in Fig. 70 by a horizontal straight line.

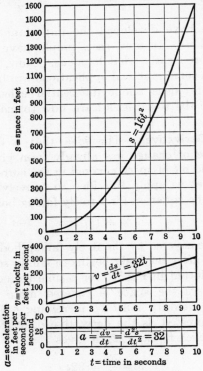

$s = 16t^2$

$v = \dfrac{ds}{dt} = 32t$

$a = \dfrac{dv}{dt} = \dfrac{d^2s}{dt^2} = 32$

$t =$ time in seconds

Fig. 70.—Derived curves.

Example 10. Determine the fifth derivative of the quantity

$$y = x^5 + 4x^2 + x.$$

Solution. Applying Eq. (15) successively,

The first derivative is $\dfrac{dy}{dx} = 5x^4 + 8x + 1$

The second derivative is $\dfrac{d^2y}{dx^2} = 20x^3 + 8$

The third derivative is $\dfrac{d^3y}{dx^3} = 60x^2$

The fourth derivative is $\dfrac{d^4y}{dx^4} = 120x$

The fifth derivative is $\dfrac{d^5y}{dx^5} = 120$ *Ans.*

There are three other quite common ways of expressing successive derivatives which are simpler to write as shown in the following table:

TABLE OF SUCCESSIVE DERIVATIVES

y	y	$f(x)$	x	x	$f(t)$
$\dfrac{dy}{dx}$	y'	$f'(x)$	$\dfrac{dx}{dt}$	$\dot{x}$	$f'(t)$
$\dfrac{d^2y}{dx^2}$	y''	$f''(x)$	$\dfrac{d^2x}{dt^2}$	$\ddot{x}$	$f''(t)$
$\dfrac{d^3y}{dx^3}$	y'''	$f'''(x)$	$\dfrac{d^3x}{dt^3}$	$\dddot{x}$	$f'''(t)$

Maxima and Minima.—One of the principal uses of differential calculus is to find maximum or minimum values. A *maximum point* has a *greater value* than the immediately preceding or following points while a *minimum point* has a *smaller value* than the immediately preceding or following points.

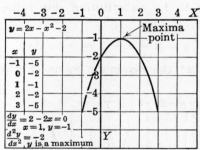

FIG. 71.—Curve with a maxima point.

In many practical engineering problems we are concerned with finding the conditions that will give the greatest (maximum) value or the least (minimum) value. To illustrate, it may be desired to find the conditions for the maximum efficiency of a machine or it may be desired to determine the conditions that will make the cost a minimum.

As a concrete case, consider the equation $y = 2x - x^2 - 2$ as plotted in Fig. 71. It appears from the curve that y reaches a maximum value when $x = 1$. This can be checked by solving for points very close to $x = 1$ and finding that they all have smaller values. Instead of doing all this guessing, differential calculus can be used to determine the maximum directly. It will be recalled that the derivative of a constant is zero. Such a curve is horizontal, that is, its slope is zero. Now, at the maximum height of the curve in Fig. 71, the slope is zero, that is, the curve is horizontal. Therefore, if we set the derivative $dy/dx = 0$ and solve for x, it is possible to determine the maximum[1] value of y by substituting this value of x in the original equation.

Performing these operations on the equation,

$$y = 2x - x^2 - 2$$

The derivative is

$$\frac{dy}{dx} = 2 - 2x$$

Setting this quantity equal to zero,

$$2 - 2x = 0$$

Solving for x,

$$x = 1 \quad Ans.$$

This means that the maximum will occur when the value of x is exactly equal to 1. Substituting this value of x into the original equation,

$$y = 2 - 1 - 2 = -1 \quad Ans.$$

This means that the maximum value of y is exactly equal to -1.

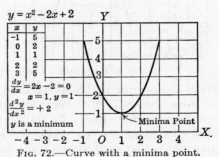

$y = x^2 - 2x + 2$

x	y
-1	5
0	2
1	1
2	2
3	5

$\frac{dy}{dx} = 2x - 2 = 0$

$x = 1, \; y = 1$

$\frac{d^2y}{dx^2} = +2$

y is a minimum

Fig. 72.—Curve with a minima point.

Example 11. Find the maximum load power P_L and value of load resistance R_L when the generator resistance is R_g and the equation of power transfer is

$$P_L = \frac{R_L}{(R_g + R_L)^2}$$

[1] In some cases, as will be shown later, this procedure may give a minimum or inflection point.

Solution. Since this equation is a fraction, let $u = R_L$ and $v = (R_g + R_L)^2$ in Eq. (21). The derivatives are then

$$\frac{du}{dR_L} = \frac{dR_L}{dR_L} = 1 \quad \text{and} \quad \frac{dv}{dR_L} = \frac{d(R_g + R_L)^2}{dR_L} = 2(R_g + R_L)$$

Now, substituting these values into Eq. (21) results in

$$\frac{dP_L}{dR_L} = \frac{(R_g + R_L)^2 - R_L 2(R_g + R_L)}{(R_g + R_L)^4} = \frac{R_g + R_L - 2R_L}{(R_g + R_L)^3} = 0$$

This equation is true when the numerator is zero, hence

$$R_g + R_L - 2R_L = 0 \quad \text{or} \quad R_L = R_g \quad Ans.$$

As another case, consider the equation $y = x^2 - 2x + 2$ which is plotted in Fig. 72. The curve appears to reach a minimum value of $y = 1$ when $x = 1$. To check this, take the first derivative and equate it to zero, thus

$$\frac{dy}{dx} = 2x - 2 = 0$$

Hence,

$$x = 1 \quad Ans.$$

Substituting this value in the original equation.

$$y = 1 - 2 + 2 = 1 \quad Ans.$$

Example 12. The cost C of handling vacuum tubes in a factory varies with the output N per day according to the relation

$$C = a + \frac{b}{N} + cN$$

where a, b, and c are constants. For what output will the cost be least?

Solution. Taking the first derivative and equating to zero, ·

$$\frac{dC}{dN} = \frac{-b}{N^2} + c = 0$$

Solving this equation,

$$N = \sqrt{\frac{b}{c}} \quad Ans.$$

It should be observed that if a tangent were drawn to either the maximum point of the curve in Fig. 71 or the minimum point of the curve in Fig. 72, the slope or first derivative is zero. In order to determine which of these values are maximum or minimum points, a portion of the curve can be sketched near these points. Another way to determine if the point is a maximum or a minimum is to take the second derivative. If the second derivative is negative, the point is a maximum, and, vice versa, if the second derivative is positive the point is a minimum. The rules to remember are as follows:

If $\frac{dy}{dx} = 0$ and $\frac{d^2y}{dx^2} = -$, y is a maximum.

If $\dfrac{dy}{dx} = 0$ and $\dfrac{d^2y}{dx} = +$, y is a minimum.

Applying these rules, the curve in Fig. 71 results in a negative second derivative, thus

$$y = 2x - x^2 - 2$$

First derivative $\dfrac{dy}{dx} = 2 - 2x$

Second derivative $\dfrac{d^2y}{dx^2} = -2$

Hence y is a maximum.

Similarly, applying these rules to the curve of Fig. 72 results in a positive derivative, thus

$$y = x^2 - 2x + 2$$

First derivative $\dfrac{dy}{dx} = 2x - 2$

Second derivative $\dfrac{d^2y}{dx^2} = +2$

Hence y is a minimum.

Inflection Point.—The above test for a maximum or minimum fails when the second derivative is zero. Resort should then be

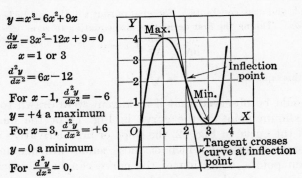

$y = x^3 - 6x^2 + 9x$

$\dfrac{dy}{dx} = 3x^2 - 12x + 9 = 0$

$x = 1$ or 3

$\dfrac{d^2y}{dx^2} = 6x - 12$

For $x - 1$, $\dfrac{d^2y}{dx^2} = -6$

$y = +4$ a maximum

For $x = 3$, $\dfrac{d^2y}{dx^2} = +6$

$y = 0$ a minimum

For $\dfrac{d^2y}{dx^2} = 0$,

$\left.\begin{array}{l} x = 2 \\ y = 2 \end{array}\right\}$ an inflection point

Fig. 73.—Curve with maxima, minima, and inflection point.

made to sketching the curve near the point in question. If the curve bends in opposite directions on either side of a given point that point is called an "inflection point." In other words, an inflection point separates an upward concave portion of a curve ($\smile$) from a downward concave portion of the curve ($\frown$). At an inflection point a tangent to the curve will cross the curve. The rule can be stated as follows:

If $\dfrac{dy}{dx} = 0$ and $\dfrac{d^2y}{dx^2} = 0$, y is an inflection point, a maximum, or a minimum. In this case, the curve should be plotted to determine its exact nature.

Example 13. Find the maximum, minimum, and inflection-point values and plot the curve

$$y = x^3 - 6x^2 + 9x$$

Solution. The first derivative is $\dfrac{dy}{dx} = 3x^2 - 12x + 9 = 0$

By the quadratic formula, $x = 1$ or 3

The second derivative is $\dfrac{d^2y}{dx^2} = 6x - 12$

If $x = 1$, $\dfrac{d^2y}{dx^2} = -6$, hence a maximum at

$$y = 1 - 6 + 9 = +4 \quad Ans.$$

If $x = 3$, $\dfrac{d^2y}{dx^2} = +6$, hence a minimum at

$$y = 27 - 54 + 27 = 0 \quad Ans.$$

Let $\qquad\qquad \dfrac{d^2y}{dx^2} = 6x - 12 = 0$

Then $\qquad\qquad x = 2$
and $\qquad\qquad y = 8 - 24 + 18 = +2 \quad Ans.$

From the plotted curve as shown in Fig. 73, we see that the last point is an inflection point.

$$y = x^3 - 6x^2 + 9x$$
$$\frac{dy}{dx} = 3x^2 - 12x + 9 = 0$$
$$x = 1 \text{ or } 3$$
$$\frac{d^2y}{dx^2} = 6x - 12$$

For $\qquad x = 1, \dfrac{d^2y}{dx^2} = -y = +4$ a maximum

For $\qquad x = 3, \dfrac{d^2y}{dx^2} = +y = 0$ a minimum

For $\qquad\qquad\qquad \dfrac{d^2y}{dx^2} = 0$

$\left.\begin{matrix} x = 2 \\ y = 2 \end{matrix}\right\}$ an inflection point

Summary.

1. Algebraic differentiation formulas:

(I) $\dfrac{dc}{dx} = 0$

(II) $\dfrac{dx}{dx} = 1$

(III) $\dfrac{d}{dx}(cx) = c$

(IV) $\dfrac{d}{dx}(x^n) = nx^{n-1}$

(V) $\dfrac{d}{dx}(u + v) = \dfrac{du}{dx} + \dfrac{dv}{dx}$

(VI) $\dfrac{d}{dx}(uv) = u\dfrac{dv}{dx} + v\dfrac{du}{dx}$

(VII) $\dfrac{d}{dx}\left(\dfrac{u}{v}\right) = \dfrac{v\dfrac{du}{dx} - u\dfrac{dv}{dx}}{v^2}$

2. Successive differentiation is the process of repeating the operation of differentiating a function. These successive operations result in the "first derivative," "second derivative," and so on to the "nth derivative."

3. If $\dfrac{dy}{dx} = 0$ and $\dfrac{d^2y}{dx^2} = -$, y is a maximum.

4. If $\dfrac{dy}{dx} = 0$ and $\dfrac{d^2y}{dx^2} = +$, y is a minimum.

5. If $\dfrac{dy}{dx} = 0$ and $\dfrac{d^2y}{dx^2} = 0$, y is an inflection point, a maximum, or a minimum. In this case, the curve should be plotted to determine its nature.

Exercises

Differentiate the following five equations:

1. $y = ax^2 + bx + c$
2. $y = \sqrt{2x^3}$
3. $y = (a + x)^2$
4. $y = x\sqrt{a + bx}$
5. $y = \dfrac{a - x}{a + x}$

6. What is the second derivative of $y = \sqrt{x}$?

7. The current I depends upon the temperature t of an incandescent lamp by the equation

$$I = a + bt + ct^2$$

What is the expression for the variation of the current corresponding to a variation of the temperature?

8. If the space covered is given by the equation

$$s = 4t^2 - 6$$

find the velocity and acceleration when $t = 2$.

9. Find the value of x and the value of y for the maximum and minimum values of the curve $y = x^3 - 3x + 4$

10. If the current $i = 16 \sqrt{t} + 8$ is expressed in amperes and the time t in seconds, what is the time when the current changes at the rate of 2 amp per sec?

CHAPTER 13

DIFFERENTIAL CALCULUS
TREATING TRANSCENDENTAL FUNCTIONS

As pointed out in the last chapter, a transcendental function is any function that is not a simple algebraic function. Transcendental functions are irrational functions such as ϵ^x, sin x, and log x.

The Law of Natural Growth.—The law of natural growth results when the increase in size of a quantity is always proportional to the size of the quantity. This is illustrated by nature when an organism's growth is proportional to the size of the organism. This could also be called a "logarithmic rate" of growing because the percentage increase is always proportional to the magnitude at that instant.

Studying two cases will help to clarify this law. Consider the difference between constant and natural growth as illustrated in simple and compound interest. With simple interest, the capital grows arithmetically at unit rate while with compound interest the capital grows logarithmically at unit rate.

Simple Interest.—Start with a capital of $1 and let the interest rate be $\frac{1}{10}$ or 10 per cent per year. The owner will then make 10 cents on this dollar each year. By saving this interest each year he will have a total capital of $2 at the end of 10 years, to double his property.

Stating this problem in general terms, let x be the original capital and $1/n$ be the yearly interest rate, then it will take n years to double his property, that is

$$x + n\left(\frac{x}{n}\right) = 2x \tag{1}$$

For the first year the owner has $1. At the end of the year he receives 10 cents in interest. He saves this 10 cents during the following year and collects another 10 cents at the end of the second year. This process is shown graphically in Fig. 74 for the whole 10 years. The total capital of the owner at any time is represented by the stair step curve.

Compound Interest.—As before, start with a capital of $1 and let the interest rate be $\frac{1}{10}$ or 10 per cent per year. If the interest is compounded every 10 years, then the owner will receive all the interest at the end of 10 years. This will amount to $1, making, with the original investment, a total capital of $2. In equation form, this can be stated,

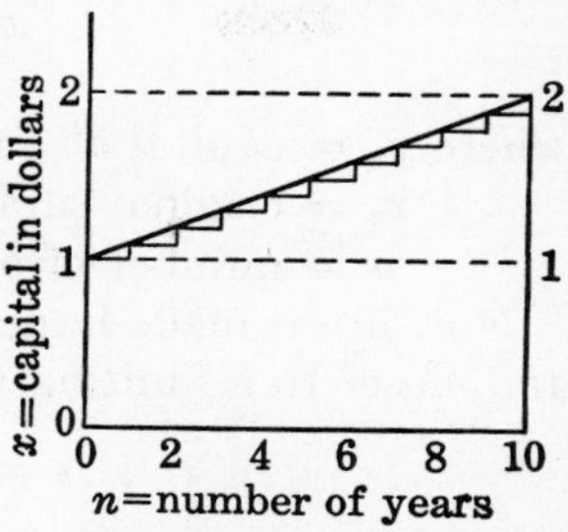

$$x_1 = x_0 + \frac{x_0}{1} = x_0\left(1 + \frac{1}{1}\right) = x_0 (2) \tag{2}$$

Fig. 74.—Curve of simple interest at the rate of 10 per cent for 10 years.

where x_1 = capital at end of 1 operation.

x_0 = original capital.

Now consider compounding the interest every 5 years for two operations. The initial capital is x_0, the interest for the first 5 years is one half the above amount or $\frac{x_0}{2}$ and for the next

5 years, the interest is $\dfrac{x_0 + \dfrac{x_0}{2}}{2}$; hence, in equation form,

$$x_2 = x_0 + \frac{x_0}{2} + \frac{x_0 + \dfrac{x_0}{2}}{2} = x_0\left(1 + 2\cdot\frac{1}{2} + \frac{1}{4}\right)$$
$$= x_0\left(1 + \frac{1}{2}\right)^2 = x_0(2.25) \tag{3}$$

If the interest is compounded three times in 10 years, this reasoning leads to the following equation:

$$x_3 = x_0 + \frac{x_0}{3} + \frac{x_0 + \dfrac{x_0}{3}}{3} + \frac{x_0 + \dfrac{x_0}{3} + \dfrac{x_0 + x_0/3}{3}}{3}$$
$$= x_0\left(1 + \frac{1}{3}\right)^3 = 2.37 \tag{4}$$

If the interest is compounded yearly, the equation is

$$x_{10} = x_0\left(1 + \frac{1}{10}\right)^{10} = 2.594 \tag{5}$$

A similarity will be noted among Eqs. (2), (3), (4), and (5). Generalizing for n operations,

$$x_n = x_0 \left(1 + \frac{1}{n}\right)^n \qquad (6)$$

where x_n = capital at end of n operations.

x_0 = original capital.

n = number of operations.

Now if n is made larger and larger, the value of x_n comes closer and closer to a limiting value which is the *natural number*

$$\epsilon = 2.7182818 \cdots \qquad (7)$$

This number is even more important than π, which equals 3.141592 $\cdots$ Let us summarize what ϵ (epsilon) means. As shown above, if \$1 grows at simple interest, it will become \$2, but if the interest is truly compounded for this same period of time, it will become \$2.718 . . . or ϵ times the original capital. If this truly compounded curve is drawn graphically, the curve of Fig. 75 results.

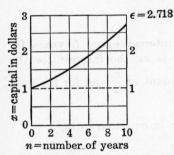

FIG. 75.—Curve of true compound interest at the rate of 10 per cent for 10 years.

Exponential Series.—There is another way of determining the value of the natural number ϵ. From the Eq. (6), we see that the quantity $(1 + 1/n)^n$ will become equal to ϵ if the number n is made indefinitely large. But by the binomial theorem, this quantity can be written

$$\left(1 + \frac{1}{n}\right)^n = 1 + 1 + \frac{1}{\underline{2}} \frac{n-1}{n} + \frac{1}{\underline{3}} \frac{(n-1)(n-2)}{n^2} + \cdots \qquad (8)$$

But, to express ϵ, n becomes very great, hence $(n-1)$ and $(n-2)$ are for all practical purposes equal to n, hence, we can write the series

$$\epsilon = 1 + 1 + \frac{1}{\underline{2}} + \frac{1}{\underline{3}} + \cdots \qquad (9)$$

which will give the value of ϵ to any desired accuracy by taking the required number of terms.

Carrying this reasoning one step farther, ϵ can be raised to the x power by expanding the expression

$$\left(1 + \frac{1}{n}\right)^{nx} = 1^{nx} + nx\,\frac{1^{nx-1}\,(1/n)}{\underline{1}} + nx\,(nx - 1)\,\frac{1^{nx-2}\,(1/n)^2}{\underline{2}} + \cdots$$

By making n indefinitely large, we reduce this equation to the *exponential series*

$$\epsilon^x = 1 + x + \frac{x^2}{\underline{2}} + \frac{x^3}{\underline{3}} + \cdots \qquad (10)$$

This series represents a natural growth curve as shown in Fig. 76 where $y = \epsilon^x$. At $x = 1$, the value of y is the natural number ϵ.

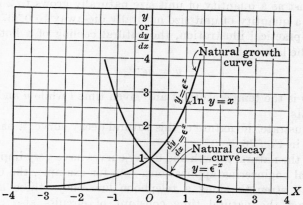

FIG. 76.—Curves of natural growth and of natural decay.

Example 1.   Compute the value of ϵ to five decimal places by using the exponential series.

Solution.

$$1 + 1 = 2.00000$$
$$1/\underline{2} = 0.50000$$
$$1/\underline{3} = 0.16667$$
$$1/\underline{4} = 0.04167$$
$$1/\underline{5} = 0.00833$$
$$1/\underline{6} = 0.00139$$
$$1/\underline{7} = 0.00020$$
$$1/\underline{8} = 0.00002$$

Then
$$\epsilon = 2.71828. \quad Ans.$$

The Law of Natural Decay.—Since the reverse process of growth is decay, consideration will now be given to natural decay or die-away curves. Just as ϵ is the measure of natural growth, so $1/\epsilon$ or ϵ^{-1} is the measure of natural decay. Applying this reasoning to the exponential series by changing the sign of x results in

$$\epsilon^{-x} = 1 - x + \frac{x^2}{\underline{2}} - \frac{x^3}{\underline{3}} + \cdots \tag{11}$$

Then, making $x = 1$, the value of ϵ^{-1} becomes

$$\frac{1}{\epsilon} = \epsilon^{-1} = 1 - 1 + \frac{1}{\underline{2}} - \frac{1}{\underline{3}} + \cdots = 0.36788 \cdots \tag{12}$$

Now, just as a quantity of unit size naturally grows to 2.71828, so does a quantity of unit size naturally die-away to 0.36788.

As a practical illustration, the natural cooling of a hot body obeys the law

$$y = a\epsilon^{-bt} \tag{13}$$

where y is the temperature at any given time t while a and b are constants.

To illustrate the nature of this natural decay curve, it has been plotted in Fig. 76.

Both the natural growth and decay curves have very important electrical engineering applications. As for example, the change in signal strength along a telephone line obeys these natural laws, and the natural time constant of circuits also can be explained by them.

Derivative of the Exponential Function ϵ^x.—When $y = \epsilon^x$, the curve of Fig. 76 results. It will be noted that this is simply an extension of the curve of Fig. 75. A further study will reveal that this curve has very special properties. Using the exponential series as given in Eq. (10), it is found that *the derivative is the same as the original value.*

Thus $\dfrac{d}{dx}(\epsilon^x) = 0 + 1 + \dfrac{2x}{\underline{2}} + \dfrac{3x^2}{\underline{3}} + \dfrac{4x^3}{\underline{4}} + \cdots$

$$= 1 + x + \frac{x^2}{\underline{2}} + \frac{x^3}{\underline{3}} + \cdots \tag{14}$$

This series is the same as that given in Eq. (10); hence

(VIII)
$$\frac{d}{dx}(\epsilon^x) = \epsilon^x \tag{15}$$

The derivative of the exponential function ϵ^x remains unchanged. In other words, the slope of the curve $y = \epsilon^x$ is always $dy/dx = \epsilon^x$.

Example 2. What is the derivative of ϵ^{-x}?

Solution. Taking the derivative of the series in Eq. (11),

$$\frac{d}{dx}\epsilon^{-x} = -1 + \frac{2x}{\lfloor 2} - \frac{3x^2}{\lfloor 3} + \frac{4x^3}{\lfloor 4} - \cdots$$

$$= -\left(1 - x + \frac{x^2}{\lfloor 2} - \frac{x^3}{\lfloor 3} + \cdots\right) = -\epsilon^{-x} \quad Ans.$$

Derivative of the Exponential Function ϵ^{ax}.—When a constant is multiplied by the variable exponent of an exponential function,

$$y = \epsilon^{ax} = 1 + ax + \frac{(ax)^2}{\lfloor 2} + \frac{(ax)^3}{\lfloor 3} + \cdots \tag{16}$$

The derivative of the series is then

$$\frac{dy}{dx} = \frac{d}{dx}(\epsilon^{ax}) = 0 + a + \frac{2a^2x}{\lfloor 2} + \frac{3a^3x^2}{\lfloor 2} + \cdots$$

$$= a\left(1 + ax + \frac{(ax)^2}{\lfloor 2} + \frac{(ax)^3}{\lfloor 3} + \cdots\right)$$

By Eq. (16), the series in the parenthesis is ϵ^{ax}; hence

(IX)
$$\frac{d}{dx}(\epsilon^{ax}) = a\epsilon^{ax} \tag{17}$$

The derivative of an exponential function ϵ^{ax} where a is a constant is equal to the constant a multiplied by the exponential ϵ^{ax}.

Example 3. Find the derivative of $y = \epsilon^{2x}$ and plot the curve of both functions.

Solution. By Eq. (15), $\dfrac{dy}{dx} = \dfrac{d}{dx}(\epsilon^{2x}) = 2\epsilon^{2x}$. *Ans.*

For the curves see Fig. 77. It will be noted that for each value of x, the slope of the derived curve is twice that of the original curve.

Natural and Common Logarithms.—The natural number ϵ is also important because of its mathematical use as the base of natural logarithms. The equation $y = \epsilon^x$ can be written

$$\ln y = x \tag{18}$$

because the natural logarithm of y is equal to the power x to which the base ϵ must be raised to produce the number.

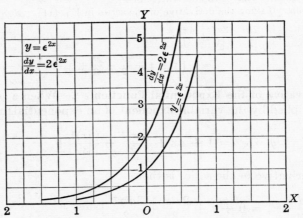

Fig. 77.—Exponential curves of ϵ^{2x} and $2\epsilon^{2x}$.

The relationship between natural and common logarithms is often of interest. A natural logarithm can be changed to a common logarithm by multiplying it by the common logarithm of ϵ, that is

$$\log x = \log \epsilon \ln x = 0.4343 \ln x \tag{19}$$

Conversely the common logarithm of x can be converted to the natural logarithm of x by multiplying it by the natural logarithm of 10, that is,

$$\ln x = \ln 10 \log x = 2.303 \log x \tag{20}$$

Example 4. Find the natural logarithm of $x = 6$ and then convert to find the common logarithm.

Solution. From tables, ln = 1.7918

By Eq. (19) $\log 6 = (0.4343)(1.7918) = 0.7782$.   *Ans.*
From tables $\log 6 = 0.7782$.   *Check.*

Example 5. Find the common logarithm of $x = 25$ and then convert to find the natural logarithm.

Solution.   From tables, log 25 = 1.3979

By Eq. (20)   ln 25 = (2.303)(1.3979) = 3.2193.   *Ans.*

From tables, ln 25 = ln 2.5 ln 10

$$= 0.9163 + 2.303 = 3.2193.   \text{Check.}$$

Derivative of a Natural Logarithm.—The problem is to find the derivative of the natural logarithm of x.   The equation is

$$y = \ln x$$

From the definition of logarithms,

$$x = \epsilon^y$$

Taking the derivative,

$$\frac{dx}{dy} = \frac{d}{dy}(\epsilon^y) = \epsilon^y = x$$

Inverting the terms in this equation,

$$\frac{dy}{dx} = \frac{1}{\dfrac{dx}{dy}} = \frac{1}{\epsilon^y} = \frac{1}{x} = x^{-1}$$

Therefore, substituting $y = \ln x$, we have

(X) $$\frac{d}{dx}(\ln x) = \frac{1}{x} \qquad (21)$$

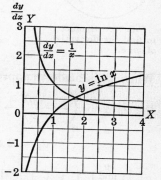

Fig. 78.—Curves of the natural logarithmic function of x and its derivative.

The curve of $y = \ln x$ and its derivative are shown in Fig. 78. It will be noted that the slope of the original curve keeps decreasing as the value of x increases.   The magnitude of this slope is expressed by the derived curve.

Example 6.   Find the derivative of $y = \ln (ax + b)$.

Solution.   Now, $$\epsilon^y = ax + b$$

Solving for x, $$x = \frac{1}{a}\epsilon^y - \frac{b}{a}$$

Then $$\frac{dx}{dy} = \frac{1}{a}\frac{d(\epsilon^y)}{dy} + 0 = \frac{1}{a}(ax + b)$$

Inverting, $$\frac{dy}{dx} = \frac{a}{ax + b}   \quad Ans.$$

Derivative of Sin θ.—The problem is to find the derivative of the equation $y = \sin \theta$.   Resorting to the basic idea of increasing each variable a little bit and subtracting the original function as shown in Fig. 79, we have

$$y + dy = \sin(\theta + d\theta)$$

Subtracting $\qquad y \qquad = \qquad \sin\theta$

$$dy = \sin(\theta + d\theta) - \sin\theta$$

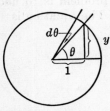

FIG. 79.—Geometry to find the derivative of sin θ.

But there is a trigonometric identity that can be written

$$\sin a - \sin b = 2\cos\frac{a+b}{2} \cdot \sin\frac{a-b}{2}$$

Now, making $a = \theta + d\theta$ and $b = \theta$, we get

$$dy = 2\cos\frac{\theta + d\theta + \theta}{2} \cdot \sin\frac{\theta + d\theta - \theta}{2}$$

$$= 2\cos\left(\theta + \frac{d\theta}{2}\right) \cdot \sin\frac{d\theta}{2}$$

When $d\theta$ is made to approach zero, $\sin\dfrac{d\theta}{2} \to \dfrac{d\theta}{2}$. Also, as $d\theta \to 0$ the term $\cos\left(\theta + \dfrac{d\theta}{2}\right) \to \cos\theta$; hence, the differential is

$$dy = 2\cos\theta \cdot \frac{d\theta}{2} = \cos\theta \cdot d\theta \qquad (22)$$

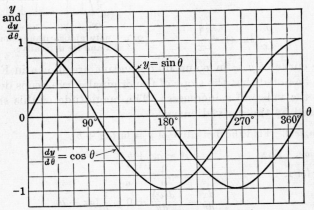

FIG. 80.—A sine curve and its derivative, a cosine curve.

The derivative of sin θ is therefore

(XI) $\qquad\qquad \dfrac{d}{d\theta}(\sin\theta) = \cos\theta \qquad\qquad (23)$

The curve of sin θ with its derived curve cos θ is shown in Fig. 80.

Example 7.   A sinusoidal voltage in a circuit can be expressed by the equation $E = \sin \omega t$ where the constant ω is the angular velocity of a vector and t is the time.

Determine the expression for the rate at which the voltage E changes with respect to time.

Solution.   Applying the above procedure,

$$E + dE = \sin (\omega t + \omega \, dt)$$

Subtracting

$$E = \sin \omega t$$

$$dE = \sin (\omega t + \omega \, dt) - \sin \omega t$$

Letting

$$a = \omega t + \omega \, dt \text{ and } b = \omega t$$

and using trigonometric identities, we get

$$dE = 2 \cos \frac{\omega t + \omega dt + \omega t}{2} \cdot \sin \frac{\omega t + \omega dt - \omega t}{2}$$

In this expression the cosine term approaches cos ωt as $dt \to 0$ and the sine term approaches $\frac{\omega \, dt}{2}$ as $dt \to 0$.

$$dE = 2 \cos \omega t \cdot \frac{\omega dt}{2} = \omega \cos \omega t \, dt$$

Hence,

$$\frac{d}{d\theta} (\sin \omega t) = \omega \cos \omega t \quad Ans.$$

Derivative of cos θ.—Following a procedure similar to that used for finding the derivative of sin θ, we have

$$y + dy = \cos (\theta + d\theta)$$

Subtracting

$$y = \cos \theta$$

$$dy = \cos (\theta + d\theta) - \cos \theta$$

From the trigonometric identity,

$$\cos a - \cos b = -2 \sin \frac{a + b}{2} \cdot \sin \frac{a - b}{2}$$

let $a = \theta + d\theta$ and $b = 0$; then

$$dy = -2 \sin \frac{\theta + d\theta + \theta}{2} \cdot \sin \frac{\theta + d\theta - \theta}{2}$$

$$= -2 \sin \left(\theta + \frac{d\theta}{2}\right) \cdot \sin \frac{d\theta}{2}$$

Neglecting $\frac{d\theta}{2}$ in comparison to θ and making $\sin \frac{d\theta}{2} \doteq \frac{d\theta}{2}$ result in the differential

$$dy = -2 \sin \theta \frac{d\theta}{2} = -\sin \theta \, d\theta \qquad (24)$$

The derivative of $\cos \theta$ is therefore

(XII) $$\frac{d}{d\theta} (\cos \theta) = -\sin \theta \qquad (25)$$

Successive Derivatives of sin θ and cos θ.—By using Eqs. (23) and (25), it is possible to take successive derivatives of these functions, thus

Original function $y = \sin \theta$

First derivative $\dfrac{dy}{d\theta} = \cos \theta$

Second derivative $\dfrac{d^2y}{d\theta^2} = -\sin \theta$

Third derivative $\dfrac{d^3y}{d\theta^3} = -\cos \theta$

Fourth derivative $\dfrac{d^4v}{d\theta^4} = \sin \theta$, the original function

The second derivative of $\sin \theta$ or $\cos \theta$ is equal to the original function but of opposite sign.

Example 8. Find the values of $y = \sin \theta$ when $\sin \theta$ is a maximum and a minimum.

Solution. Setting the first derivative equal to zero gives the required values of θ. Thus

$$\frac{dy}{d\theta} = \frac{d}{d\theta} (\sin \theta) = \cos \theta = 0$$

$\cos \theta$ is zero when $\theta = 90°$ and $270°$. For these values of θ the second derivative will indicate maximum or minimum values.

$$\frac{d^2y}{d\theta^2} = \frac{d}{d\theta} (\cos \theta) = -\sin \theta$$

When $\theta = 90°$, $\dfrac{d^2y}{d\theta^2} = -1$; hence, a maximum.

When $\theta = 270°$, $\dfrac{d^2y}{d\theta^2} = +1$; hence, a minimum.

The maximum value of $y = \sin 90° = +1$. *Ans.*
and the minimum value of $y = \sin 270° = -1$. *Ans.*

Derivative of tan θ.—Let $y = \tan \theta = \dfrac{\sin \theta}{\cos \theta}$

Using the formula for finding the derivative of a fraction,

$$\frac{dy}{d\theta} = \frac{\cos\theta \frac{d}{d\theta}(\sin\theta) - \sin\theta \frac{d}{d\theta}(\cos\theta)}{\cos^2\theta}$$

$$= \frac{\cos^2\theta + \sin^2\theta}{\cos^2\theta} = \frac{1}{\cos^2\theta} = \sec^2\theta$$

Therefore,

(XIII) $$\frac{d}{d\theta}(\tan\theta) = \sec^2\theta$$ (26)

Derivative of sinh θ.—Let $y = \sinh\theta$. Resorting to the basic idea of increasing each variable a little bit gives

$$y + dy = \sinh(\theta + d\theta)$$

Subtracting $$\underline{y \quad\quad = \quad\quad\quad\quad\quad\quad \sinh\theta}$$

$$dy = \sinh(\theta + d\theta) - \sinh\theta$$

Now let $a = \theta + d\theta$ and $b = \theta$

From the hyperbolic function identity,

$$\sinh a - \sinh b = 2\cosh\frac{a+b}{2} \cdot \sinh\frac{a-b}{2}$$

$$dy = 2\cosh\frac{\theta + d\theta + \theta}{2} \cdot \sinh\frac{\theta + d\theta - \theta}{2}$$

But for small values of $d\theta$, $\sinh\frac{d\theta}{2} \doteq \frac{d\theta}{2}$ and $\frac{d\theta}{2}$ can be neglected in comparison to θ, to give the differential

$$dy = 2\cosh\theta \frac{d\theta}{2} = \cosh\theta\, d\theta$$ (27)

Hence, the derivative is

(XIV) $$\frac{d}{d\theta}(\sinh\theta) = \cosh\theta$$ (28)

Example 9.   By the use of exponentials find the derivative of $\sinh\theta$.

Solution. $y = \sinh\theta = \dfrac{\epsilon^\theta - \epsilon^{-\theta}}{2}$

By Eq. (15) and Example 2 or using Eq. (17),

$$\frac{dy}{d\theta} = \frac{\epsilon^\theta + \epsilon^{-\theta}}{2} = \cosh\theta \quad Ans.$$

This method is much easier than using the basic idea as it was given in the development.

Derivative of cosh θ.—Let

$$y = \cosh \theta$$

Then
$$y + dy = \cosh (\theta + d\theta)$$

and subtracting the original function gives

$$dy = \cosh (\theta + d\theta) - \cosh \theta$$

Let $a = \theta + d\theta$ and $b = \theta$ in the hyperbolic identity

$$\cosh a - \cosh b = 2 \sinh \frac{a + b}{2} \cdot \sinh \frac{a - b}{2}$$

Hence,
$$dy = 2 \sinh \frac{\theta + d\theta + \theta}{2} \cdot \sinh \frac{\theta + d\theta - \theta}{2}$$

Neglecting $\frac{d\theta}{2}$ in the first sinh and letting $\sinh \frac{d\theta}{2} \doteq \frac{d\theta}{2}$ in the second sinh results in the differential

$$dy = 2 \sinh \theta \cdot \frac{d\theta}{2} = \sinh \theta \, d\theta \qquad (29)$$

and the derivative is

(XV)
$$\frac{d}{d\theta} (\cosh \theta) = \sinh \theta \qquad (30)$$

Successive Derivatives of sinh θ and cosh θ.—By using Eqs. (28) and (30), the successive derivatives of these functions are

$$\text{Original equation } y = \sinh \theta$$

$$\text{First derivative } \frac{dy}{d\theta} = \cosh \theta$$

$$\text{Second derivative } \frac{d^2y}{d\theta^2} = \sinh \theta, \quad \text{the original function}$$

$$\text{Third derivative } \frac{d^3y}{d\theta^3} = \cosh \theta, \quad \text{the first derivative}$$

This shows that the second and third derivatives of sinh θ and cosh θ repeat the original function and first derivatives.

Derivative of tanh θ.—Taking the derivative of the fraction

$$y = \tanh \theta = \frac{\sinh \theta}{\cosh \theta}$$

$$\frac{dy}{dx} = \frac{\cosh \theta \frac{d}{d\theta} (\sinh \theta) - \sinh \theta \frac{d}{d\theta} (\cosh \theta)}{\cosh^2 \theta}$$

$$= \frac{\cosh^2 \theta - \sinh^2 \theta}{\cosh^2 \theta} = \frac{1}{\cosh^2 \theta} = \operatorname{sech}^2 \theta$$

Hence,

(XVI) $$\frac{d}{d\theta} (\tanh \theta) = \operatorname{sech}^2 \theta \qquad (31)$$

Partial Derivatives.—In many engineering problems the value of the dependent variable depends upon more than one independent variable. In such cases, the common practice is to treat all but one of the variables as constants. As a concrete illustration, the area A of a rectangle is the product of the length of the two sides x and y, thus

$$A = xy \qquad (32)$$

The area depends upon the length of the two sides. As suggested above, if one side, say x, is held constant, the rate of area change can be written in differential form, thus

$$dA_x = x \, dy \qquad (33)$$

where the x subscript to A means that x is held constant during this operation.

Similarly, if y is held constant the differential change in area is

$$dA_y = y \, dx \qquad (34)$$

Another common way to make this statement is by using partial derivative signs (∂), thus

$$\frac{\partial A}{\partial y} = x \qquad (35)$$

This says that partial of A by partial of y is equal to x for this illustration. When partial derivative signs are used, only those terms to which the partial is applied are permitted to vary.

Similarly, $$\frac{\partial A}{\partial x} = y \qquad (36)$$

means that all terms by A and x are held constant during this operation.

The total differential of the area A is the sum of the differential when x is held constant plus the differential when y is held constant, thus

$$dA = dA_x + dA_y \qquad (37)$$

Substituting for dA_x and dA_y from the above equations gives the *total differential* of A

$$dA = x\,dy + y\,dx \qquad (38)$$

Now if the area changes size at a given rate of time, we can divide both sides of this equation by dt to get

$$\frac{dA}{dt} = x\frac{dy}{dt} = y\frac{dx}{dt} \qquad (39)$$

But, as given above, x and y can be replaced by the respective partial derivatives to get

$$\frac{dA}{dt} = \frac{\partial A}{\partial y}\frac{dy}{dt} + \frac{\partial A}{\partial x}\frac{dx}{dt} \qquad (40)$$

This is the *total derivative* of A.

Example 10. The volume of a cylinder is given by the expression

$$V = \pi r^2 h$$

where V = volume in cubic inches.

r = radius in inches.

h = height in inches.

At a particular instant $r = 10$ in. and is increasing 2 in. per sec, while at this same instant $h = 20$ in. and is increasing 0.5 in. per sec. Determine the rate at which the volume is changing.

Solution. $\dfrac{\partial V}{\partial r} = 2\pi r h$

$\dfrac{\partial V}{\partial h} = \pi r^2$

Substituting these values in Eq. (40) gives

$$\frac{dV}{dt} = 2\pi r h\frac{dr}{dt} + \pi r^2\frac{dh}{dt}$$

Substituting the values given in the problem,

$$\frac{dV}{dt} = 2(3.1416)(10)(20)(2) + (3.1416)(100)(0.5)$$

$$= 2513.28 + 157.08 = 2670.36 \text{ cu in. per sec.} \quad Ans.$$

Summary.

1. The natural growth curve is given by the exponential series,

$$y = \epsilon^x = 1 + x + \frac{x^2}{\underline{|2}} + \frac{x^3}{\underline{|3}} + \cdots$$

When $x = 1$, $y = \epsilon = 2.71828 \cdots$ the natural growth number ϵ.

2. The natural decay curve is given by the exponential series,

$$y = \epsilon^{-x} = 1 - x + \frac{x^2}{\underline{|2}} - \frac{x^3}{\underline{|3}} + \cdots$$

When $x = 1$, $y = \epsilon^{-1} = 1/\epsilon = 0.36788 \cdots$ the natural decay number $1/\epsilon$.

3. Conversion equations for natural and common logarithms:

$$\log x = \log \epsilon \ln x = 0.4343 \ln x$$
$$\ln x = \ln 10 \log x = 2.303 \log x$$

4. Transcendental differential formulas:

(VIII) $\quad \dfrac{d}{dx}(\epsilon^x) = \epsilon^x$

(IX) $\quad \dfrac{d}{dx}(\epsilon^{ax}) = a\epsilon^{ax}$

(X) $\quad \dfrac{d}{dx}(\ln x) = \dfrac{1}{x}$

(XI) $\quad \dfrac{d}{d\theta}(\sin \theta) = \cos \theta$

(XII) $\quad \dfrac{d}{d\theta}(\cos \theta) = -\sin \theta$

(XIII) $\quad \dfrac{d}{d\theta}(\tan \theta) = \sec^2 \theta$

(XIV) $\quad \dfrac{d}{d\theta}(\sinh \theta) = \cosh \theta$

(XV) $\quad \dfrac{d}{d\theta}(\cosh \theta) = \sinh \theta$

(XVI) $\quad \dfrac{d}{d\theta}(\tanh \theta) = \operatorname{sech}^2 \theta$

5. The second derivatives of sin and cos functions produce the original function but with the opposite sign.

6. The second derivatives of sinh and cosh functions produce the original function with the same sign.

7. Partial derivatives are useful in treating engineering problems having more than one independent variable.

Exercises

1. Determine the value of ϵ^x to five decimal places when $x = 2$.

2. Find the derivative of $y = \epsilon^{\alpha x + \beta x}$.

3. Find the derivative of $y = \ln x^2$.

4. Find the derivative of $y = \sin x = \dfrac{\epsilon^{ix} - \epsilon^{-ix}}{2j}$ by using exponentials.

5. Find the natural logarithm of 8 and then convert to find the common logarithm.

6. In an electrical circuit, the voltage

$$E = L \frac{di}{dt}$$

Where $i = I \sin \omega t$, determine the value of the voltage E.

7. Find the derivative of $y = \cos^2 \theta$.

8. Find the derivative of $y = \cot \theta = \dfrac{\cos \theta}{\sin \theta}$.

9. What is the second derivative of $y = \cosh \alpha x$?

10. Find the maximum or minimum of the function $F = x + 2xy + y$.

CHAPTER 14

INTEGRAL CALCULUS

The word "integral" means the whole or sum of all the little bits. Therefore, *integral calculus* is the mathematics of calculating the sum of all the little bits. The integral sign $\int$, as already explained, is an elongated letter S, meaning "the sum of." Mathematicians usually prefer to read this sign "the integral of." Thus, $\int dx$ means the sum of all the little bits of x but is usually read "the integral of dx." It may be written in the form of an integral equation, thus

$$y = \int dx \tag{1}$$

This equation states that y is equal to the sum of a vast number of very small quantities dx. In fact, these dx quantities are so indefinitely small that it requires the sum of an indefinitely large number of them to make up the total or integral quantity y.

The integral sign is quite closely related to the summation sign Σ (the Greek letter sigma). The basic difference is that Σ stands for the sum of a few or finite number of terms, while $\int$ stands for the sum of an indefinitely large number or infinite number of terms. It may be written in the form of a *summation equation*, thus

$$y = \Sigma y_k \tag{2}$$

where y is the sum of all the y_k terms that are to be added together.

Integration as used in integral calculus can be thought of as the inverse operation of differentiation as used in differential calculus. This can be compared to division as the inverse operation of multiplication. Integration is more difficult than differentiation, much as division is more difficult than multiplication. In general, integration of a variable cannot be performed unless the variable has already been found by the process of differentiation. For differentiation, the symbol of operation is $\dfrac{d}{dx}(\quad)$ where the quantity to be operated on is placed between the parentheses. The symbol of operation for integration is $\int (\;) \, dx$ where the quantity to be operated on is placed between the parentheses.

In this chapter we shall deal with several practical ways of making approximate sums. Then some of the integral formulas obtained directly from differentiation will be treated so that, in simple cases, it will be possible to find the exact sums.

Trapezoidal Rule.—The area enclosed by a curve can be approximated by dividing the area with a number of evenly spaced parallel lines and then adding together the area of each of

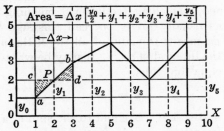

Fig. 81.—Area measured by the trapezoidal rule.

these individual strips. For illustration, it is desired to measure the area under the curve, that is, between the curve and the x-axis from ordinate y_0 to ordinate y_5 as shown in Fig. 81. First, consider the area of the trapezoid $a, P, b, 3,1$, which is a strip of width Δx and of average height y_1. Since the area in the shaded triangle acP above the curve is equal to the shaded triangle Pbd below the curve, the area of the trapezoid $a \, P$, b, $3,1$ is the same as the area of the rectangle c, d, $3,1$ which is equal to $(\Delta x)y_1$. The area under the curve from $x = 3$ to $x = 9$ can be measured in this fashion and is equal to $(\Delta x)(y_2 + y_3 + y_4)$. The area of the end strips, which are one half the width of the other strips, is equal to $\left(\dfrac{\Delta x}{2}\right) y_0$ and $\left(\dfrac{\Delta x}{2}\right) y_5$. The total area in this case therefore, is,

$$A = \Delta x \left(\frac{y_0}{2} + y_1 + y_2 + y_3 + y_4 + \frac{y_5}{2} \right)$$

In general, this equation can be written

$$A = \Delta x \left(\frac{1}{2} (y_0 + y_n) + y_1 + y_2 + \cdots + y_{n-1} \right) \qquad (3)$$

where A = approximate total area.

Δx = width of strips.

y = height of strips.

n = number of strips.

By using the summation sign this same equation can be expressed as follows:

$$A = \Delta x \left[\frac{1}{2}(y_o + y_n) + \sum_{k=1}^{k=n-1} y_k \right] \qquad (4)$$

where the summation sign $\sum\limits_{k=1}^{k=n-1}$ is read "the summation of all the y_k terms from $k = 1$ to $k = n - 1$." In words Eqs. (3) and (4) can be written

$$\begin{pmatrix} \text{Approximate} \\ \text{total area} \end{pmatrix} = \begin{pmatrix} \text{width} \\ \text{of} \\ \text{strip} \end{pmatrix} \begin{pmatrix} \dfrac{\text{sum of} \\ \text{extreme} \\ \text{ordinates}}{2} + \begin{matrix} \text{sum of} \\ \text{remaining} \\ \text{ordinates} \end{matrix} \end{pmatrix} \qquad (5)$$

The trapezoidal rule as expressed by these three equations assumes that the curve is a straight line across the top of each strip. If this is not so, the answer will approximate the total area. The accuracy of this approximation will increase if the number of strips for a given area are increased. The answer can, therefore, be made as accurate as you desire providing you are willing to do the extra work of adding the increased number of strips.

Example 1. If the scales in Fig. 81 are measured in inches, what is the area under the curve?

Solution. Substituting values in Eq. (4)

$$A = 2[\tfrac{1}{2}(1 + 4) + 2 + 3.5 + 3 + 3] = 28 \text{ sq in.} \quad Ans.$$

This can be checked by counting the squares.

Simpson's Rule.—Simpson's rule assumes that the curve between any three consecutive points is a parabola. This in general gives a better approximation than assuming that adjacent points are connected by a straight line as was done in the trapezoidal rule. This is due to the fact that if the points are chosen reasonably close together, the portion of the parabola between these points will practically coincide with any reasonable curve drawn through the points.

The area under any portion of a parabola is exactly $\frac{2}{3}$ of the enclosing rectangle as illustrated in Fig. 82. The area under any three points on a parabola is given by

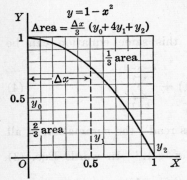

$$\text{Area} = \frac{1}{3} \Delta x (y_o + 4y_1 + y_2)$$

If these are the first three points giving the area in the first two strips, then the area in the second two strips is

$$\text{Area} = \frac{1}{3} \Delta x (y_2 + 4y_3 + y_4)$$

FIG. 82.—Area under a parabola measured by Simpson's rule.

In general, these areas can be added together to give the total area under the curve, thus

$$A = \frac{1}{3} \Delta x (y_o + 4y_1 + 2y_2 + 4y_3 + 2y_4 + \cdots + y_n) \quad (6)$$

where A = approximate total area.

Δx = width of strips.

y = height of strips.

n = number of strips (n being even).

Equation (6) may be expressed by using the summation sign, as follows:

$$A = \frac{\Delta x}{3} \left[(y_o + y_n) + 4 \sum_{k=1}^{k=\frac{n}{2}} y_{(2k-1)} + 2 \sum_{k=1}^{k=\frac{n}{2}-1} y_{2k} \right] \quad (7)$$

In words, this equation can be expressed

$$A = \frac{1}{3} \begin{bmatrix} \text{width} \\ \text{of} \\ \text{strip} \end{bmatrix} \left[\begin{pmatrix} \text{sum of extreme} \\ \text{ordinates} \end{pmatrix} + 4 \begin{pmatrix} \text{sum of remaining} \\ \text{odd-numbered} \\ \text{ordinates} \end{pmatrix} + 2 \begin{pmatrix} \text{sum of remaining} \\ \text{even-numbered} \\ \text{ordinates} \end{pmatrix} \right] \quad (8)$$

Example 2. Determine the area under the parabola of Fig. 82 if the scales are in inches.

Solution. Substituting in Eq. (6),

$$A = \frac{1}{3}(0.5)[1 + 4(0.75) + 0] = \frac{1}{6}(1 + 3) = \frac{2}{3} \text{ sq in. } Ans.$$

Example 3. If $n = 8$, write out the summation quantities in Eq. (7) and then express the whole equation.

$$\sum_{k=1}^{k=\frac{8}{2}=4} y_{(2k-1)} = y_{(2\cdot1-1)} + y_{(2\cdot2-1)} + y_{(2\cdot3-1)} + y_{(2\cdot4-1)}$$

$$= y_1 \qquad + y_3 \qquad + y_5 \qquad + y_7 \quad Ans.$$

$$\sum_{k=1}^{k=\frac{8}{2}-1=3} y_{2k} = y_{2\cdot1} + y_{2\cdot2} + y_{2\cdot3}$$

$$= y_2 \quad + y_4 \quad + y_6 \quad Ans.$$

$$A = \frac{\Delta x}{3}((y_0 + y_8) + 4(y_1 + y_3 + y_5 + y_7) + 2(y_2 + y_4 + y_6)) \quad Ans.$$

Area Integration.—The trapezoidal rule gives a roughly approximate area, while Simpson's rule gives a more accurate approximation. The next step is to find the exact area by using integral calculus. This can be done by using the integral equation

$$A = \int_a^b y \cdot dx \tag{9}$$

where, $A = $ the exact area.

$y = $ the ordinate or height of infinitesimal strip.

$dx = $ width of infinitesimal strip.

This equation says that the area under the curve from $x = a$ to $x = b$ is the sum of all the infinitesimal areas which are $y\,dx$. Referring to Fig. 78, the infinitesimal area $y \cdot dx$ has a height of y and a width of dx. Substituting the limits $a = 2$ and $b = 6$, and the value of $y = 4$, Eq. (9) becomes

$$A = \int_{x=2}^{x=6} 4\,dx$$

The constant 4 can be moved outside the integral sign without altering the value of the equation, thus

$$A = 4\int_{x=2}^{x=6} dx \tag{10}$$

Now, the integral of dx must be a function of x such that when $x = 2$ is substituted the area from $x = 0$ to $x = 2$ is given by the equation. Let us make a guess and assume that the integral of dx is x. Now when $x = 2$, the area $A = 4 \cdot 2 = 8$ which checks the area under the curve up to this point. Next substitute the value of $x = 6$ to get $A = 4 \cdot 6 = 24$ which checks the area under the curve up to this final point. This shows that our guess was correct, so integrating Eq. (10) results in

$$A = 4x \Big|_a^b = 4x \Big|_{x=2}^{x=6} \tag{11}$$

which says that the lower value $x = 2$ is substituted in the equation to give the area under the curve up to the point of interest. The upper value $x = 6$ will give the above area plus the area of interest so we subtract the above area from the total area to get the area of interest, thus

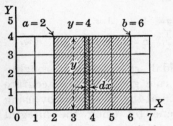

$$A = 4 \cdot 6 - 4 \cdot 2 = 24 - 8 = 16$$
$$Ans.$$

This answer gives the area under the curve from $x = 2$ to $x = 6$ as shown in Fig. 83.

Fig. 83.—Integration of the constant $y = 4$ between the limits $a = 2$ and $b = 6$.

Integral calculus enables us to get the exact area under any curve that we can integrate. Without it we would have to satisfy ourselves with approximate results or perform an infinite number of operations. Now that we see the usefulness of this new tool let us learn how to integrate.

Example 4. Find the area under the curve $y = 2$ from $a = 1$ to $b = 4$.
Solution. By Eq. (9),

$$A = \int_1^4 2\,dx = 2 \int_1^4 dx = 2x \Big|_1^4 = 2 \cdot 4 - 2 \cdot 1 = 6 \quad Ans.$$

Infinitesimals.—In order to get an exact answer, integration is used to add the infinite number of infinitesimal quantities making up the variable. Thus, dx is an infinitesimal part of the variable x. Or in other words, x is the integral sum of all the infinitesimal dx quantities in the variable x.

This can be visualized by considering a simple case. A bug walking down a string goes 1 inch the first minute, the second minute he goes ½ inch, the third minute, he goes ¼ inch, and thus each succeeding minute he travels just one half as far as he did the previous minute. How far will he travel if the time is increased without limit? The answer is 2 inches as shown in Fig. 84, because each minute the bug goes halfway to the final value of 2 inches.

Furthermore, the bug always has as far to travel as he went during the first minute. During the first minute he went 1 inch, which is halfway to the 2-inch mark. The second minute he went $\frac{1}{2}$ inch farther, leaving $\frac{1}{2}$ inch yet to go. During the

Fig. 84.—Graphical representation of the geometric series
$$S_n = 1 + \tfrac{1}{2} + \tfrac{1}{4} + \tfrac{1}{8} + \cdots$$

third minute, he went $\frac{1}{4}$ inch farther, leaving $\frac{1}{4}$ inch yet to go. The bug can spend as much time as you can think of and he will not be to the limiting value of 2 inches. However, if he could perform this operation an infinite number of times, the value of 2 inches would actually be reached. The last space covered in doing this an infinite number of times would be infinitesimally small. So it is no wonder that an integral will give an exact answer, since it evaluates an infinite number of infinitesimally small quantities.

Example 5. Find the ultimate sum of

$$S_n = \frac{2}{3} + \frac{1}{3} + \frac{1}{6} + \frac{1}{12} + \frac{1}{24} + \cdots$$

Solution. From this series we see that the first space covered is $\frac{2}{3}$; the next space covered is $\frac{1}{2}$ of this value or $\frac{1}{3}$. Since each succeeding step covers $\frac{1}{2}$ the previous distance, then the remaining distance must be equal to the distance covered in the last step. Hence, the ultimate sum of

$$S_n = \frac{2}{3} + \frac{2}{3} = 1\frac{1}{3} \quad Ans.$$

Constant of Integration.—Differentiation can be visualized as the process of finding the slope of a curve. Then, integration, the reverse process, can be visualized as the process of finding a curve when the slope is given. But knowing the slope is not enough information to locate a single curve. In fact, many reverse processes do not give a definite result as does the first process. For illustration, $2^2 = 4$ which is definite but $\sqrt{4}$ is either $+2$ or -2. Consider the equation of a horizontal line

$$y = C$$

The derivative or slope of this line is

$$\frac{dy}{dx} = 0$$

Referring to the family of curves in Fig. 85, we see that they all have a zero slope. Hence with the information of a zero slope,

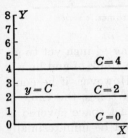

we know only that the line is horizontal; to locate it, we must know its distance from the x-axis. This distance can be represented by C, the distance to the curve along the y-axis. This means that *to every quantity that is integrated a constant must be added to locate the curve.* This constant may be zero or some other value.

FIG. 85.—A family of lines with the same zero slope.

Algebraic Integrals.—In the treatment that is to follow each algebraic integral equation will be given along with a brief proof, some graphical representation, and typical examples.

(I) $$\int 0 \cdot dx = C \qquad (12)$$

This equation merely says that the integral of any quantity, even of zero, must have a constant added to locate the curve. In other words, at any value of x the value of $y = C$ as shown in Fig. 85.

(II) $$\int 1 \cdot dx = x + C \qquad (13)$$

Consider the equation $y = x + C$ as shown in Fig. 86 for three values of C. Taking the differential of both sides of this equation gives

$$dy = dx$$

It will be noted that the constant C was lost in this operation, so in reversing the operation, the constant must be added. Now taking the integral of both sides gives

$$y = \int dy = \int dx = x + C$$

which proves Eq. (13) and says that *the integral of dx is equal to* $x + C$. The slope is determined by the coefficient of x, which in this case is one, and the constant C determines where the line crosses the y-axis.

Example 6.   When the slope of a line is -1, give the integral equation.
Solution.   This statement can be written

$$\frac{dy}{dx} = -1$$

or, in differential equation form, $dy = -1\,dx$.
Taking the integral of both sides,

$$y = \int dy = \int -1\,dx = -x + C \quad \textit{Ans.}$$

(III) $\int a\,dx = ax + C$ (14)

Consider the equation $y = ax + C$ as shown in Fig. 87 for two different values of the slope a and two different values of

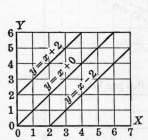

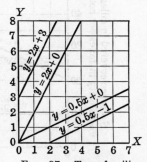

Fig. 86.—A family of lines with the same unity slope.

Fig. 87.—Two families of curves having different slopes.

the constant C, which gives the point at which the curve intersects the y-axis.   The differential equation is

$$dy = a\,dx$$

and the integral of this equation is

$$y = \int dy = \int a\,dx = ax + C$$

Thus the integral of the product $a\,dx$ is $ax + C$.

Example 7.   What is the integral of $\dfrac{1}{a}\,dx$?

Solution. By Eq. (14),

$$\int \frac{1}{a}\, dx = \frac{x}{a} + C \quad Ans.$$

Example 8. An automobile has a velocity of $v = 10$ mph. If the mileage indicator already reads 20 miles, integrate to find what the reading will be after 3 hr and show the results graphically.

Solution. The differential equation is $ds = v\, dt$

Taking the integral of both sides, the space covered is given by

$$S = \int ds = \int v\, dt = vt + C$$

Now the velocity $v = 10$ mph, the time $t = 3$ hr and the constant $C = 20$ miles already traveled, hence the speedometer reading will be

$$S = 10 \cdot 3 + 20 = 50 \text{ miles} \quad Ans.$$

See Fig. 88 for graphical representation.

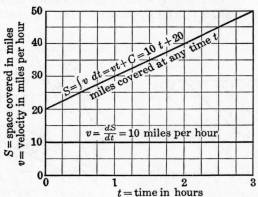

FIG. 88.—A graph which illustrates both integral and differential equations.

A study of Example 8 and the curves in Fig. 88 should help to clarify what is happening. The slope of the curve $S = vt + C$ is

$$\frac{dS}{dt} = v$$

a constant velocity represented by the horizontal line. Changing this equation from an expression of a slope to differential form and then integrating give the area under this curve for any time t. At time $t = 1$ hr, for illustration, the area is $10 \cdot 1 = 10$ miles traveled in this hour. This is represented by the S curve going from 20 miles at time $t = 0$ to 30 miles at time $t = 1$ hr.

This S curve starts at 20 because the mileage indicator originally had that reading.

$$\text{(IV)} \qquad\qquad \int x \, dx = \frac{1}{2} x^2 + C \qquad\qquad\qquad (15)$$

Integral equations can be solved only if some function is known which yields the desired differential equation. The process is then to determine the differential equations for all known functions. Reversing the process and adding a constant will then give the desired integral equation. This we have done, giving the answer first, and then checking it by differentiation. Thus, let

$$y = \frac{1}{2} x^2 + C$$

$$dy = 2\left(\frac{1}{2}\right) x \, dx = x \, dx \quad Check.$$

Hence, $\qquad y = \int dy = \int x \, dx = \frac{1}{2} x^2 + C$

Example 9. Solve ∫ *ax dx*.

Solution. Moving the constant a outside the integral sign and using Eq. (15),

$$\int ax \, dx = a \int x \, dx = \frac{1}{2} ax^2 + C \quad Ans.$$

$$\text{(V)} \qquad\qquad \int x^n \, dx = \frac{1}{n+1} x^{n+1} + C \qquad\qquad (16)$$

Let, $\qquad\qquad\qquad y = \frac{1}{n+1} x^{n+1} + C$

Then, $\qquad\qquad\qquad dy = x^n \, dx$

This checks the integral.

Hence, $\qquad y = \int dy = \int x^n \, dx = \frac{1}{n+1} x^{n+1} + C$

Example 10. Solve ∫ *x² dx*.

Solution. By Eq. (16) $\int x^2 \, dx = \frac{1}{3} x^3 + C.$ *Ans.*

$$\text{(VI)} \qquad\qquad \int x^{-1} \, dx = \int \frac{dx}{x} = \ln x + C \qquad\qquad (17)$$

This is an exceptional case to Rule V, because here we deal with infinite values for which Rule V does not apply. A search of derivatives will give a function, $y = \ln x + C$ the differential of which is

$$dy = \frac{1}{x}\, dx$$

so the problem is solved, and

$$y = \int dy = \int x^{-1}\, dx = \ln x + C$$

This solution is a striking example of a problem that cannot be solved until the corresponding differentiation is found. This can be further illustrated by the differential equation

$$dy = a^{-x^2}\, dx$$

which even today has not been integrated because no one has found a^{-x^2} when differentiating some other function.

(VII) $$\int (u + v)\, dx = \int u\, dx + \int v\, dx \qquad (18)$$

This merely states that the integral of an algebraic sum $(u + v)$ is the same as the sum of the integrals of u and v. This is a useful equation to reduce equations to standard forms which can be recognized and integrated.

Example 11.   Find the integral of $\int (x + 1)(x + 2)\, dx$.
Solution.   Multiplying, $(x + 1)(x + 2) = x^2 + 3x + 2$
Then, by Eq. (18),

$$\int (x^2 + 3x + 2)\, dx = \int x^2\, dx + \int 3x\, dx + \int 2\, dx$$
$$= \frac{1}{3} x^3 + \frac{3}{2} x^2 + 2x + C \quad Ans.$$

(VIII) $$\int u\, dx = ux - \int x\, du + C \qquad (19)$$

This is one of the most useful algebraic integrals and is known as "integration by parts." It says that if $x\, du$ can be found then $u\, dx$ can also be found. The equation can be derived as follows:
The differential of a product is

$$d(uv) = u\, dv + v\, du$$

Rearranging this equation,

$$u\, dv = d(uv) - v\, du$$

and integrating both sides of the equation results in

$$\int u\, dv = uv - \int v\, du + C \qquad (20)$$

This is the same as Eq. (19) but with v instead of x as the variable.

Example 12. Find $\int x\epsilon^x\, dx$.

Solution. Let

$$u = x \qquad dv = \epsilon^x\, dx$$
$$du = dx \qquad v = \epsilon^x$$

Making these substitutions in Eq. (20) gives

$$\int x\epsilon^x\, dx = x\epsilon^x - \int \epsilon^x\, dx + C = x\epsilon^x - \epsilon^x + C = \epsilon^x(x - 1) + C \quad Ans.$$

(IX)
$$\int \epsilon^{ax}\, dx = \frac{1}{a}\epsilon^{ax} + C \tag{21}$$

Differentiating,

$$\frac{d}{dx}\left(\frac{1}{a}\epsilon^{ax}\right) = \epsilon^{ax}$$

Hence the above equation must be correct.

Example 13. The current in a circuit is given by the equation

$$i = \frac{E}{R}\left(1 - \epsilon^{-\frac{R}{L}t}\right)$$

What charge of electricity $Q = \int i\, dt$ has passed through the circuit in t seconds?

Solution. Substituting for i,

$$Q = \int \frac{E}{R}\left(1 - \epsilon^{-\frac{R}{L}t}\right) dt$$

Applying Eq. (18),

$$Q = \int \frac{E}{R}\, dt - \int \frac{E}{R}\epsilon^{-\frac{R}{L}t}\, dt$$

$$= \frac{Et}{R} - \frac{E}{R}\left(-\frac{L}{R}\right)\epsilon^{-\frac{R}{L}t} + C$$

$$= \frac{Et}{R} + \frac{EL}{R^2}\epsilon^{-\frac{R}{L}t} + C \quad Ans.$$

To make this a useful engineering answer, other information is needed to evaluate C.

(X)
$$\int \ln x\, dx = x(\ln x - 1) + C \tag{22}$$

To prove this, take the derivative

$$\frac{d}{dx}(x \ln x - 1) = x \cdot x^{-1} + \ln x - 1 = \ln x \quad Check.$$

(XI)
$$\int \sin ax\, dx = \frac{1}{a}\cos ax + C \tag{23}$$

Taking the derivative of the answer,

$$\frac{d}{dx}\left(-\frac{1}{a}\cos ax\right) = -\frac{1}{a}(-a)\sin ax = \sin ax \quad Check.$$

Making $a = 1$ gives the answer for $\int \sin x = -\cos x + C$

(XII) $$\int \cos ax \, dx = \frac{1}{a}\sin ax + C \qquad (24)$$

Similarly, $$\frac{d}{dx}\left(\frac{1}{a}\sin ax\right) = \cos ax \quad Check.$$

(XIII) $$\int \tan ax \, dx = -\frac{1}{a}\ln(\cos ax) + C \qquad (25)$$

To prove this, write

$$\int \tan ax \, dx = \int \frac{\sin ax}{\cos ax}\, dx = \frac{1}{a}\int \frac{d(\cos ax)}{\cos ax}$$

Now, by applying Eq. (17),

$$\frac{1}{a}\int \frac{d(\cos ax)}{\cos ax} = \frac{1}{a}\ln(\cos ax) + C \quad Check.$$

Multiple Integrals.—We have already discussed *partial differentiation* when there were several variables. The inverse process is called *partial integration*. When making a partial integration all variables but one are held constant for the first integration and then in the second integration only one other variable is allowed to vary. This is continued until all the variables are allowed to vary during the integration. When performing multiple integration there are as many integral signs as there are variables to be integrated.

Consider the multiple integral

$$z = \iint (x^2 + y^2) \, dx \, dy \qquad (26)$$

Holding y^2 and dy constant while integrating with respect to x,

$$z = \int[\int(x^2 + y^2)\, dx]\, dy = \int[\int x^2 \, dx + \int y^2 \, dx]\, dy$$
$$= \int[\tfrac{1}{3} x^3 + y^2 x]\, dy$$

Now, holding x^3 and x constant while integrating with respect to y,

$$z = \frac{1}{3} x^3 y + \frac{1}{3} y^3 x + C \qquad (27)$$

Double integrals are useful in determining areas. The general equation for an area is given by the equation

$$A = \iint dy \, dx \tag{28}$$

where the inner integral $\int dy$ gives the total length of the y line by summing up all the little dy bits. Then this line is moved in the x direction by a small amount dx and summed over the total x distance involved.

Another way to visualize this is to consider an elemental area $dy \cdot dx$ as shown in Fig. 89. This elemental area is summed from the x-axis to the curve along the dx strip. Then the strips are summed in the x direction from the y-axis to the end of the area, which is $x = 3$ in this case.

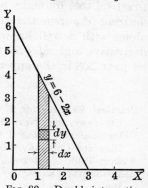

FIG. 89.—Double integration of an area.

Example 14. By double integration, find the shaded area between the line $y = 6 - 2x$, the x and y axes.

Solution. By Eq. (28) the area is,

$$A = \int_{x=0}^{x=3} \int_{y=0}^{y=6-2x} dy \, dx$$
$$= \int_0^3 y \Big|_0^{6-2x} dx = \int_0^3 (6 - 2x) \, dx$$
$$= \int_0^3 6 \, dx - \int_0^3 2x \, dx = 6x \Big|_0^3 - x^2 \Big|_0^3$$
$$= (6 \cdot 3 - 0) - (3^2 - 0) = 9 \quad Ans.$$

This simple example illustrates the process of substituting the limits for a double integral and solving the integral equation for the area.

Triple integrals are useful in determining volumes. The general equation for a volume in Cartesian coordinator is given by

$$V = \iiint dx \, dy \, dz \tag{29}$$

This type of equation is used, for example, to find the electric charge ρ in space. In such a case the equation is written

$$V = \iiint \rho \, dx \, dy \, dz \tag{30}$$

where ρ is the charge density in the increment of volume $dx \, dy \, dz$.

Some of the more elementary ideas of calculus have been presented, to enable the reader to follow better the reasoning of authors who resort to calculus in their technical articles or books. Calculus can be considered as an art that is acquired only by continued study and by solving many problems. It is used as a practical tool by many research and design engineers. To those desiring to pursue the subject further, a few references are given along with a well known table of integrals. A short table of derivative and integral tables for ready reference will be found on page 308 in the appendix.

References

"Practical Calculus for Home Study," by Palmer, McGraw-Hill Book Company, Inc., New York.

"Differential and Integral Calculus," by Granville, Smith and Longley, Ginn and Company, Boston.

"A Short Table of Integrals," by B. O. Peirce, Ginn and Company, Boston.

"Mathematical Tables," by H. B. Dwight, McGraw-Hill Book Company, Inc.

Exercises

1. Determine the average current I_{av} of the sine curve $i = \sin \omega t$ by taking values every 10° up to 90° and using the trapezoidal rule.

2. Determine the average current I_{av} of the sine curve $i = \sin \omega t$ by taking values every 15° up to 90° and using Simpson's rule.

3. Integrate the sine curve $i = \sin \omega t$ from $\omega t = 0$ to $\omega t = \dfrac{\pi}{2}$ radians to determine the average current I_{av}. Compare the accuracy of the three methods used above to four decimal places.

4. Find the value of the series

$$S_n = 1 - \tfrac{1}{2} + \tfrac{1}{3} - \tfrac{1}{4} + \cdots$$

to eight terms.

5. Integrate $\displaystyle\int \frac{dx}{x^5}$ and $\displaystyle\int ax^9\, dx$.

6. Integrate $\int 2(x+1)\, dx$ and $\int 4(x^2+2)(x-1)\, dx$.

7. Integrate $\displaystyle\int a^2\, \frac{dx}{x}$.

8. Integrate $\int x^2 \epsilon^x\, dx$.

9. Integrate $\int \cos 6\omega t\, d(\omega t)$ and $\int 16^{2x}\, dx$.

10. Integrate $\int a \ln (10x)\, dx$.

CHAPTER 15

SERIES AND WAVE FORMS

The use of series makes possible the numerical solution of many problems that would otherwise be extremely difficult.

This chapter will deal with some of the more useful series and wave forms encountered in engineering work. Particular attention will be given to practical applications of power series and the use of Fourier's series to express wave forms.

Definitions.—A *series* is the sum of a sequence of terms. "Sequence" means that the terms are formed according to some fixed rule. Thus, the sequence of terms

$$1, 2, 3, 4, \text{ etc.}$$

can be written into the series

$$S_n = 1 + 2 + 3 + 4 + \cdots + k + \cdots + n = \sum_{k=1}^{k=n} k \quad (1)$$

where S_n = a series of n terms.

k = a general or representative term in the series.

n = the last term.

A finite series has a limited number of terms. For illustration, the series

$$(a + b)^3 = a^3 + 3a^2b + 3ab^2 + b^3 \quad (2)$$

is a finite series containing only four terms.

An *infinite series* has an unlimited number of terms. The fraction

$$\tfrac{1}{3} = 0.3 + 0.03 + 0.003 + 0.0003 + \cdots \quad (3)$$

is a good illustration of an infinite series when the fraction is expressed decimally because no matter how many decimal terms you add the sum will never quite reach the value of $\tfrac{1}{3}$. In other words, an infinite number of terms must be added to give the desired answer.

A convergent series approaches a finite value as the number of terms are increased. Equations (2) and (3) are convergent series. Equation (2) reaches the final finite value with only four terms.

A *divergent series* approaches an infinite value as the number of terms is increased. Equation (1) is a divergent series because the sum of terms becomes increasingly large as the number n is made larger.

Example 1. Write down three more terms and the kth term, and also express as a summation, the series

$$S_n = 2 + 4 + 8 + 16 + \cdots$$

Solution. It is noted that each succeeding term doubles. The second term is the square of the first term and the third term is the cube of the first term. Hence the desired series is

$$S_n = 2 + 4 + 8 + 16 + 32 + 64 + 128 + \cdots$$
$$+ 2^k + \cdots + 2^n = \sum_{k=1}^{k=n} 2^k \quad Ans.$$

Comparison Test for Convergence or Divergence.—Since a converging series has a definite value, it is of far more practical importance than a diverging series. It is therefore important to know if the series is convergent or divergent. One of the simplest ways to test this is to compare the given series with a series that is known to converge. Two series are frequently used to apply this test. The geometric (or power) series

$$S_n = a + ax + ax^2 + \cdots + ax^{n-1}$$
$$= \frac{a(1 - x^n)}{1 - x} = \frac{a(x^n - 1)}{x - 1} \qquad (4)$$

converges when x is less than 1 and diverges when x is equal to or greater than 1. If x is less than 1, then x^n will become very small as n is increased, hence x^n can be neglected, with the result that the series converges to the value

$$S_n = \frac{a}{1 - x} \qquad \text{when} \qquad x < 1 \qquad (5)$$

When x is greater than 1, the term x^n in the last fraction of Eq. (4) becomes increasingly large as n is increased, with the result that no definite value can be given to the fraction. This means that the series is divergent for $x > 1$.

When x equals 1, the series reduces to a sum of a terms. Hence as n is increased the sum will continue to increase. Therefore, the series is divergent when $x = 1$.

The p series which is frequently used in the comparison test is

$$S_n = 1 + \frac{1}{2^p} + \frac{1}{3^p} + \cdots + \frac{1}{k^p} + \cdots + \frac{1}{n^p} = \sum_{k=1}^{k=n} \frac{1}{k^p} \quad (6)$$

which is convergent for $p > 1$ and divergent for $p \leq 1$.

The comparison test states that *a given series converges if corresponding terms are smaller than those of a converging series. Likewise, a given series diverges if corresponding terms are larger than those of a diverging series.*

Applying these rules and Eq. (4), let us see if the following series is convergent:

$$f(x) = 1 + \frac{9}{10} + \left(\frac{9}{10}\right)^2 + \cdots$$

Then $S_n = 1 + x + x^2 + \cdots$ is the value of Eq. (4) when $a = 1$. Equating corresponding terms, $x = \frac{9}{10}$; hence $x < 1$ and the series converges by the comparison test.

Example 2.   Test the following series for convergence or divergence.

$$f(k) = \sum_{k=1}^{k=\infty} 2\left(\frac{1}{k}\right)^k$$

Solution.   Comparing this series with Eq. (4) when $a = 2$ and x is less than 1, we have

test series $S_n = 2 + 2x + 2x^2 + 2x^3 + \cdots + 2x^n$

and given series $f(k) = 2 + 2\left(\frac{1}{2}\right)^2 + 2\left(\frac{1}{3}\right)^3 + 2\left(\frac{1}{4}\right)^2 + \cdots + 2\left(\frac{1}{n}\right)^n$

Comparing term by term, the first terms are equal, the second term of the given series is less than the second term of the test series when x is slightly less than 1, and so on for the rest of the terms, hence the series converges. *Ans.*

Note: The given series could be shifted to the right one place so the exponents would be similar; then the terms of the given series would all be less than corresponding terms of the test series with the exception of the first term of the given series. Since the first term is finite, the series must converge, because the rest of the series converges.

Example 3.　Test for convergence or divergence the following series:

$$Q_n = \sum_{n=1}^{n=\infty} \frac{1}{5n}$$

Solution.　Comparing this with Eq. (6) when $p = 1$ gives

test series $S_n = 1 + \frac{1}{2} + \frac{1}{3} + \cdots + \frac{1}{n}$

and given series $Q_n = \frac{1}{5} + \frac{1}{5 \cdot 2} + \frac{1}{5 \cdot 3} + \cdots + \frac{1}{5 \cdot n}$

$$= \frac{1}{5}\left(1 + \frac{1}{2} + \frac{1}{3} + \cdots + \frac{1}{n}\right)$$

Since the test series diverges for $p = 1$, the given series must also diverge, because, when the factor $\frac{1}{5}$ is removed, the corresponding terms are identical.　*Ans.*

Ratio Test for Convergence or Divergence.—If the test ratio of the $(n + 1)$th term divided by the nth term is less than 1, a series of positive terms is convergent.　If this ratio is greater than 1, the series is divergent.　If the ratio equals 1, the test fails.

In equation language, the *test ratio* for a series of positive terms is

$$\rho = \frac{x_{n+1}}{x_n} \tag{7}$$

when $\rho < 1$ the series is convergent.

　　$\rho > 1$ the series is divergent.

　　$\rho = 1$ the test ratio fails.

Example 4.　Test the following series for convergence or divergence:

$$S_n = \frac{1}{10} + \frac{\underline{2}}{10^2} + \frac{\underline{3}}{10^3} + \cdots + \frac{\underline{n}}{10^n} + \frac{\underline{n+1}}{10^{n+1}}$$

Solution.　By Eq. (7),

$$\rho = \frac{x_{n+1}}{x_n} = \frac{\dfrac{\underline{n+1}}{10^{n+1}}}{\dfrac{\underline{n}}{10^n}} = \frac{n+1}{10} > 1$$

Hence, the series is divergent.　*Ans.*

A good general rule is first to apply the test ratio and then, if $\rho = 1$, to resort to the *comparison test*.

Power Series.—The power series

$$S_n = a_o + a_1x + a_2x^2 + a_3x^3 + \cdots + a_nx^n \qquad (8)$$

Where the a terms are independent of the x terms, the series may converge or diverge depending upon the values of the a and x terms. The above tests should be applied to determine these properties.

The sum of two converging power series is another converging power series. For illustration, add

$$\epsilon^x = 1 + x + \frac{x^2}{\underline{2}} + \frac{x^3}{\underline{3}} + \frac{x^4}{\underline{4}} + \cdots$$

$$\epsilon^{-x} = 1 - x + \frac{x^2}{\underline{2}} - \frac{x^3}{\underline{3}} + \frac{x^4}{\underline{4}} - \cdots$$

$$\epsilon^x + \epsilon^{-x} = 2 + \frac{2x^2}{\underline{2}} + \frac{2x^4}{\underline{4}} + \cdots = 2 \cosh x$$

The product of two converging power series is another converging power series. For example, multiply

$$\sin x = x - \frac{x^3}{\underline{3}} + \frac{x^5}{\underline{5}} - \frac{x^7}{\underline{7}} + \cdots$$

by

$$\cos x = 1 - \frac{x^2}{\underline{2}} + \frac{x^4}{\underline{4}} - \frac{x^6}{\underline{6}} + \cdots$$

Then

$$\sin x \cos x = x - \left(\frac{1}{\underline{2}} + \frac{1}{\underline{3}}\right)x^3 + \left(\frac{1}{\underline{4}} + \frac{1}{\underline{2}\cdot\underline{3}} + \frac{1}{\underline{5}}\right)x^5 - \cdots$$

$$2 \sin x \cos x = 2x - \frac{8}{6}x^3 + \frac{32}{120}x^5 - \cdots$$

$$= 2x - \frac{(2x)^3}{6} + \frac{(2x)^5}{120} - \cdots = \sin 2x$$

If a converging power series is divided by another converging power series, the quotient must be tested for convergence, since it may be divergent. To illustrate, divide the series $\cos x$ by x, thus

$$\cos x = 1 - \frac{x^2}{\underline{2}} + \frac{x^4}{\underline{4}} - \cdots$$

and

$$\frac{\cos x}{x} = \frac{1}{x} - \frac{x}{\underline{2}} + \frac{x^3}{\underline{4}} - \cdots$$

This is not a power series, because the $\frac{1}{x}$ term is present, but the rest of the series after this term is a power series.

Power series are very useful in engineering to express binomials such as

$$(a + x)^n = a^n + na^{n-1}x + \frac{n(n-1)}{\lfloor 2} a^{n-2}x^2 + \cdots \qquad (9)$$

$$= a_o + a_1x + a_2x^2 + \cdots$$

In this equation the a terms are defined thus: $a_o = a^n$, $a_1 = na^{n-1}$, etc.

Example 5. In an artificial transmission line, express the characteristic impedance

$$Z_o = \sqrt{\frac{Z_1}{Z_2} + \left(\frac{Z_1}{2Z_2}\right)^2}$$

by a power series to two terms.

Solution. Let $\frac{Z_1}{Z_2} = a$ and $\left(\frac{Z_1}{2Z_2}\right)^2 = x$, then $n = \frac{1}{2}$ and the above binomial expansion gives

$$Z_o = \left(\frac{Z_1}{Z_2}\right)^{\frac{1}{2}} + \frac{1}{2}\left(\frac{Z_1}{Z_2}\right)^{-\frac{1}{2}}\left(\frac{Z_1}{2Z_2}\right)^2 + \cdots \quad Ans.$$

Maclaurin's Series.—Many functions can be expressed as a power series if the a terms can be evaluated. We have already treated the binomial series method which works in some cases. We will now treat Maclaurin's series, which works in other cases.

Consider the power series

$$f(x) = a_0 + a_1x + a_2x^2 + a_3x^3 + \cdots \qquad (10)$$

The first term a_0 can be determined by letting $x = 0$, thus

$$f(0) = a_0 \qquad (11)$$

Now, if the first derivative is taken and then x is set equal to zero, we have

$$\frac{d}{dx}[f(x)] = f'(x) = 0 + a_1 + 2a_2x + 3a_3x^2 + \cdots$$

Setting $x = 0$ results in $f'(0) = a_1$ \qquad (12)

Taking the second derivative and then setting $x = 0$ gives

$$f''(0) = 2a_2 = \lfloor 2\, a_2 \tag{13}$$

Similarly,
$$f'''(0) = 6a_3 = \lfloor 3\, a_3 \tag{14}$$

In general,
$$f^{(n)}(0) = \lfloor n\, a_n \tag{15}$$

Making these substitutions for the a terms in Eq (10) results in Maclaurin's series

$$f(x) = f(0) + f'(0)\,\frac{x}{\lfloor 1} + f''(0)\,\frac{x^2}{\lfloor 2} + f'''(0)\,\frac{x^3}{\lfloor 3} + \cdots \tag{16}$$

Example 6. Use Maclaurin's series to express the function

$$f(x) = \frac{1}{1 - x} = (1 - x)^{-1}.$$

Solution.

By Eq. (11), $f(x) = (1 - x)^{-1}$ $\qquad f(0) = 1$
By Eq. (12), $f'(x) = (1 - x)^{-2}$ $\qquad f'(0) = 1 = \lfloor 1$
By Eq. (13), $f''(x) = 2(1 - x)^{-3}$ $\qquad f''(0) = 2 = \lfloor 2$
By Eq. (14), $f'''(x) = 6(1 - x)^{-4}$ $\qquad f'''(0) = 6 = \lfloor 3$
By Eq. (15), $f^{(n)}(x) = \lfloor n(1 - x)^{-n-1}$ $\qquad f^{(n)}(0) = \lfloor n$

Substituting these values in Eq. (16),

$$f(x) = 1 + x + x^2 + x^3 + \cdots + x^n \quad Ans.$$

This example can be checked by performing the division $\dfrac{1}{1 - x}$ or by using the binomial expansion of $(1 - x)^{-1}$.

Approximate Formulas by Using Maclaurin's Series.—One of the most common uses of the power series is to evaluate functions. The accuracy of the evaluation depends upon the number of terms taken in the converging series. Such approximate formulas are widely used in engineering. A few cases will be given.

1. When x is small and n is positive,

	First approximation	Second approximation

$$(1 \pm x)^n = \quad 1 \pm nx \quad = 1 \pm nx \pm \frac{n(n-1)}{2}\,x^2 \tag{17}$$

2. When x is small and n is positive,

	First approximation	Second approximation

$$\frac{1}{(1 \pm x)^n} = \quad 1 \mp nx \quad = 1 \mp nx \mp \frac{n(n-1)}{2}\,x^2 \tag{18}$$

3. When x is small,

	First approximation		Second approximation

$$\sin x = \qquad x \qquad = \qquad x - \frac{x^3}{6} \qquad (19)$$

Example 7. State the error by using the second approximation of $\sin x$ when $x = 45° = \frac{\pi}{4}$.

Solution. $\sin x = \frac{\pi}{4} - \frac{\pi^3}{6 \cdot 4^3} = 0.785368 - 0.0807746$
$$= 0.704622$$

From the tables, $\qquad \sin x = 0.707107$

The error is less than 0.002485. *Ans.*

In this example, x was not small enough to give good accuracy.

Taylor's Series.—Sometimes it is desired to evaluate a function near some value other than zero. Taylor's series is a generalization of Maclaurin's series which permits the evaluation of a function near some fixed value such as a. If the power series is written in the form

$$f(x) = b_0 + b_1 (x - a) + b_2 (x - a)^2 + \cdots \qquad (20)$$

Then x can be evaluated for $(x - a)$, as was done in the case of Maclaurin's series, to get

$$b_0 = f(a), \qquad b_1 = f'(a), \qquad b_n = \frac{f^{(n)}(a)}{\lfloor n}$$

Making these substitutions results in Taylor's series

$$f(x) = f(a) + f'(a)(x - a) + \frac{f''(a)(x - a)^2}{\lfloor 2} + \cdots$$
$$+ \frac{f^{(n)}(a)(x - a)^n}{\lfloor n} \qquad (21)$$

Example 8. Evaluate $\cos x$ when $\alpha = \frac{\pi}{4} = 45°$ by Taylor's series.

$$f(x) = \cos x \qquad f(a) = \cos \alpha = \frac{1}{\sqrt{2}}$$

$$f'(x) = - \sin x \qquad f'(a) = - \sin \alpha = - \frac{1}{\sqrt{2}}$$

$$f''(x) = - \cos x \qquad f''(a) = - \cos \alpha = - \frac{1}{\sqrt{2}}$$

$$f'''(x) = \sin x \qquad f'''(a) = \alpha = \frac{1}{\sqrt{2}}$$

Then, by Taylor's series,

$$(x) = \cos x = \cos \alpha - \sin \alpha \frac{(x-\alpha)}{1} - \cos \alpha \frac{(x-\alpha)^2}{\underline{|2}}$$
$$+ \sin \alpha \frac{(x-\alpha)^3}{\underline{|3}} + \cdots$$

$$= \frac{1}{\sqrt{2}} - \frac{1}{\sqrt{2}} \left(x - \frac{\pi}{4} \right) - \frac{1}{\sqrt{2}} \frac{\left(x - \frac{\pi}{4} \right)^2}{\underline{|2}} + \frac{1}{\sqrt{2}} \frac{\left(x - \frac{\pi}{4} \right)^3}{\underline{|3}} + \cdots$$

$$= 0.70711 \left[1 - \left(x - \frac{\pi}{4} \right) - \frac{1}{2} \left(x - \frac{\pi}{4} \right)^2 + \frac{1}{6} \left(x - \frac{\pi}{4} \right)^3 + \cdots \right] \quad Ans.$$

In this answer the angles must be expressed in radians.

Approximate Formulas by Using Taylor's Series.—Taylor's series is particularly useful in evaluating functions for making tables with high accuracy. Much greater accuracy can be secured with a given number of terms than is usually obtained from using Maclaurin's series. To illustrate, a few cases will be given.

1. When x is nearly equal to α,

First approximation

$$\sin x \doteq \sin \alpha + (x - \alpha) \cos \alpha$$

Second approximation

$$\doteq \sin \alpha + (x - \alpha) \cos \alpha - \frac{(x-\alpha)^2}{\underline{|2}} \sin \alpha \tag{22}$$

2. When x is nearly equal to α,

First approximation

$$\cos x \doteq \cos \alpha - (x - \alpha) \sin \alpha$$

Second approximation

$$\doteq \cos \alpha - (x - \alpha) \sin \alpha - \frac{(x-\alpha)^2}{\underline{|2}} \cos \alpha \tag{23}$$

3. When x is nearly equal to α,

First approximation

$$\epsilon^x \doteq \epsilon^\alpha + (x - \alpha)\epsilon^\alpha$$

Second approximation

$$\doteq \epsilon^\alpha + (x - \alpha) \epsilon^\alpha + \frac{(x-\alpha)^2}{\underline{|2}} \epsilon^\alpha \tag{24}$$

Example 9. Calculate cos 50° to the second approximation when $\alpha = 45°$ and indicate the error.

Solution. Substituting 50° in Eq. (23),

$$\cos x = \frac{1}{\sqrt{2}} - \left(\frac{5\pi}{18} - \frac{\pi}{4}\right)\frac{1}{\sqrt{2}} - \frac{\left(\frac{5\pi}{18} - \frac{\pi}{4}\right)^2}{\lfloor 2} \frac{1}{\sqrt{2}}$$

$$= 0.70711\left(1 - \frac{\pi}{36} - \frac{\pi^2}{2 \cdot 36^2}\right) = 0.70711(1 - 0.08727 - 0.00381)$$

$$= 0.70711(0.90892) = 0.64271 \quad Ans.$$

The tables give cos 50° = 0.64279

or an error of $\qquad$ 0.00008 *Ans.*

This example shows an accuracy to four places using a second approximation, as compared to Example 7 which gave an accuracy to only two places. This shows that Taylor's series can be chosen to converge rapidly so only a few terms need be used to give a required accuracy.

Sine and Cosine Integral Functions.—Since some radiation problems are simplified by the use of these functions, a brief treatment is in order.

The sine integral function is defined

$$Si(x) = \int_0^x \frac{\sin \alpha}{\alpha}\, d\alpha = x - \frac{x^3}{3\lfloor 3} + \frac{x^5}{5\lfloor 5} - \cdots \qquad (25)$$

The cosine integral function is defined

$$Ci(x) = \int_\infty^x \frac{\cos \alpha}{\alpha}\, d\alpha = \gamma + \ln x + \int_0^x \frac{\cos \alpha - 1}{\alpha}\, d\alpha$$

$$= \gamma + \ln x - \frac{x^2}{2\lfloor 2} + \frac{x^4}{4\lfloor 4} - \cdots \qquad (26)$$

where,

$$\gamma = \int_0^1 \frac{1 - \epsilon^{-\alpha}}{\alpha}\, d\alpha - \int_1^\infty \frac{\epsilon^{-\alpha}}{\alpha}\, d\alpha$$

$$= 0.796599599 - 0.219383934$$

$$= 0.577215665 \qquad \text{Euler's constant} \quad (27)$$

Euler's constant can also be defined by the series

$$\gamma = \lim_{n \to \infty}\left[1 + \frac{1}{2} + \frac{1}{3} + \cdots + \frac{1}{n} - \log n\right]$$

Example 10. Show that the integral function in Eq. (25) can be written in a series.

Solution. The series for $\dfrac{\sin \alpha}{\alpha}$ is the sin α series divided by α, thus

$$\sin \alpha = \alpha - \frac{\alpha^3}{\underline{|3}} + \frac{\alpha^5}{\underline{|5}} - \frac{\alpha^7}{\underline{|7}} + \cdots$$

and

$$\frac{\sin \alpha}{\alpha} = 1 - \frac{\alpha^2}{\underline{|3}} + \frac{\alpha^4}{\underline{|5}} - \frac{\alpha^6}{\underline{|7}} + \cdots$$

Integrating term by term and substituting the limits results in

$$Si(x) = \int_0^x (1) \, d\alpha - \int_0^x \frac{\alpha^2}{\underline{|3}} \, d\alpha + \int_0^x \frac{\alpha^4}{\underline{|5}} \, d\alpha - \int_0^x \frac{\alpha^6}{\underline{|7}} \, d\alpha + \cdots$$

$$= x - \frac{x^3}{3\underline{|3}} + \frac{x^5}{5\underline{|5}} - \frac{x^7}{7\underline{|7}} + \cdots \quad Ans.$$

Bessel Functions.—These functions often appear in engineering literature to solve practical problems dealing with such things as frequency modulation, acoustics, loading transmission lines, and eddy current loss in the core of a solenoid.

The Bessel functions are solutions to the differential equation

$$x^2 \frac{d^2y}{dx^2} + x \frac{dy}{dx} + (x^2 - n^2)y = 0 \tag{28}$$

The solution of this differential equation is accomplished by evaluating the a terms of a power series,[1] which results in the following series when $n = 0$

$$J_0(x) = 1 - \frac{x^2}{2^2} + \frac{x^4}{2^2 \cdot 4^2} - \frac{x^6}{2^2 \cdot 4^2 \cdot 6^2} + \cdots \tag{29}$$

which is the Bessel function of the first kind of zero order. When n is a positive real number or zero in Eq. (28), we have the more general form

$$J_n(x) = \frac{x^n}{2^n \underline{|n}} \left[1 - \frac{x^2}{2(2n + 2)} + \frac{x^4}{2 \cdot 4(2n + 2)(2n + 4)} \right.$$
$$\left. - \frac{6}{2 \cdot 4 \cdot 6(2n + 2)(2n + 4)(2n + 6)} + \cdots \right]$$
$$= \sum_{k=0}^{k=\infty} \frac{(-1)^k}{\underline{|k}\,\underline{|n+k}} \left(\frac{x}{2}\right)^{n+2k} \tag{30}$$

[1] The solution of this differential equation is beyond the scope of this book. Those interested in the subject might consult Reddick and Miller, "Advanced Mathematics for Engineers," John Wiley and Sons.

which is the Bessel function of order n where n is a positive integer.

Example 11. Show that $\dfrac{d}{dx} J_0(x) = -J_1(x)$.

Solution. Performing the indicated differentiation on successive terms of the series in Eq. (29) gives

$$\frac{d}{dx} J_0(x) = 0 - \frac{2x}{2^2} + \frac{4x^3}{2^2 \cdot 4^2} - \frac{6x^5}{2^2 \cdot 4^2 \cdot 6^2} + \cdots$$

Now substituting $n = 1$ in Eq. (30) gives

$$J_1(x) = \frac{x}{2} - \frac{x^3}{2^3 \lfloor 2} + \frac{x^5}{2^5 \lfloor 2 \lfloor 3} - \cdots$$

A close inspection of each term of these two series reveals that the second series is the negative of the first, hence

$$\frac{d}{dx} J_0(x) = -J_1(x) \quad Ans.$$

Periodic Functions.—A *periodic function* can be represented by a curve that repeats the same shape for each period. Referring to Fig. 90, the sine wave is a simple periodic function that

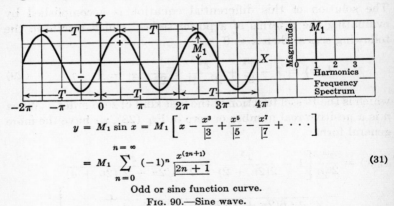

$$y = M_1 \sin x = M_1 \left[x - \frac{x^3}{\lfloor 3} + \frac{x^5}{\lfloor 5} - \frac{x^7}{\lfloor 7} + \cdots \right]$$

$$= M_1 \sum_{n=0}^{n=\infty} (-1)^n \frac{x^{(2n+1)}}{\lfloor 2n+1} \tag{31}$$

Odd or sine function curve.

Fig. 90.—Sine wave.

repeats its shape each period T. The wave starts at $x = 0$, following a definite shape until $x = 2\pi$ is reached. From $x = 2\pi$ to $x = 4\pi$ exactly the same curve is repeated. In other words, each time the curve is ready to repeat itself it has completed a period of $T = 2\pi$. It should be noted that the series as given in Eq. (31) is made up of odd numbered powers of x

which results in a curve that is positive just to the right of the
y-axis and negative just to the left of the y-axis, hence an antisymmetrical function. An antisymmetrical function is a
function that is symmetrical about the origin. To illustrate, the
curve to the right of the origin in Fig. 90 can be swung around
the origin as a hinge point and it will exactly fit the curve to the
left of the origin.

The cosine wave of Fig. 91 is another illustration of a simple
periodic function. It is the same as the sine wave except that

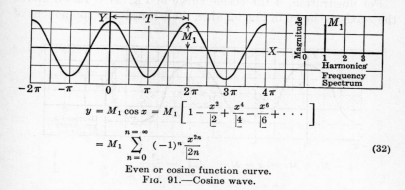

$$y = M_1 \cos x = M_1 \left[1 - \frac{x^2}{\underline{|2}} + \frac{x^4}{\underline{|4}} - \frac{x^6}{\underline{|6}} + \cdots \right]$$

$$= M_1 \sum_{n=0}^{n=\infty} (-1)^n \frac{x^{2n}}{\underline{|2n}} \qquad (32)$$

Even or cosine function curve.
FIG. 91.—Cosine wave.

it is shifted to the left $\pi/2$ radians or 90 degrees to make a function that is symmetrical about the y-axis. A symmetrical
function about the y-axis is a curve such that if the portion to the
right of the y-axis is swung around the y-axis as a hinge it will
exactly fit the curve to the left of the y-axis. In a symmetrical
function the powers of x in the series are even numbers.

The variable x in Eqs. (31) and (32) can be made proportional
to a single frequency by the equation

$$x = \omega t = 2\pi f t \qquad (33)$$

where ω = the angular velocity in radians per second
f = the frequency in cycles per second
t = time in seconds

Since both Eqs. (31) and (32) contain only one frequency, it is
known as the first harmonic or fundamental frequency and can
be plotted in a frequency spectrum as shown in Figs. 90 and 91.
The M_1 is defined as the magnitude of the first harmonic. It

will be noted that both the sine and cosine wave have the same magnitude. The frequency spectrum does not give information as to whether the curve is a sine or a cosine wave.

Constant Component.—If a wave is not balanced about the x-axis—that is, if the area under the curve above the x-axis is not equal to the area above the curve below the x-axis—then there will be a steady or constant component. The sine and cosine wave of Figs. 90 and 91 have a zero steady component; in other words, they are balanced about the x-axis.

For illustration, if the cosine curve of Fig. 91 is raised above the x-axis as shown in Fig. 92, then there is a steady component of

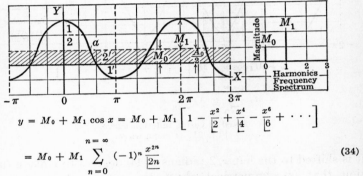

$$y = M_0 + M_1 \cos x = M_0 + M_1 \left[1 - \frac{x^2}{\lfloor 2} + \frac{x^4}{\lfloor 4} - \frac{x^6}{\lfloor 6} + \cdots \right]$$

$$= M_0 + M_1 \sum_{n=0}^{n=\infty} (-1)^n \frac{x^{2n}}{\lfloor 2n} \qquad (34)$$

Fig. 92.—Cosine wave plus a constant component.

magnitude M_0, the height of the shaded area. The cosine wave balances itself about the dashed line as can be seen in the figure. The area marked 1 can be turned around point a as a hinge and fitted in the area marked $1'$. Since the area marked 1 is positive and the area marked $1'$ is negative, they cancel. Now the area marked 2 above the dashed line if turned around point a as a hinge will fit into the area marked $2'$ thus showing that the constant component height is M_0. The frequency spectrum in Fig. 92 shows a zero frequency magnitude M_0 to represent the constant component. Equation (34) also has this constant component.

Example 12. Integrate the curve of Eq. (34) from 0 to π, and show that the average height is M_0.

Solution. The average height is

$$y_0 = \frac{\text{area}}{\text{length}} = \frac{A}{\pi} = \frac{1}{\pi} \int_0^\pi (M_0 + M_1 \cos x)\, dx$$

$$= \frac{1}{\pi} \left(M_0\, x \Big|_0^\pi + M_1 \sin x \Big|_0^\pi \right) = \frac{1}{\pi} (M_0 \pi - M_0 0 + M_1 \sin \pi - M_1 \sin 0)$$

$$= \frac{1}{\pi} (M_0 \pi - 0 + 0 - 0) = M_0 \quad Ans.$$

Harmonic Components.—Any periodic wave can be analyzed in terms of a constant and harmonic components. To do this, the magnitude and phase of each component must be properly selected. To illustrate how a square wave can be synthesized, the magnitude and phase will be properly selected to give the correct result. Later a method of determining the values will be given.

Referring to Fig. 93*a*, we have redrawn one half the sine wave as shown in Fig. 90. The magnitude of this wave is $M_1 = 4E/\pi$, as shown in the figure, which represents the magnitude of the fundamental or first harmonic. If the third harmonic $M_3 \sin 3x$ is added to the first harmonic $M_1 \sin x$ the resulting wave will be as shown in Fig. 93*b*. In this case $M_3 = 4E/3\pi$ which is one third of the magnitude of the fundamental as shown in the frequency spectrum. Since $x = 2\pi f_1 t$ by Eq. (33) where f_1 represents the first harmonic frequency, then

$$3x = 2\pi(3f_1)t = 2\pi f_3 t \tag{35}$$

where $f_3 =$ the third harmonic frequency.

If this process of adding odd harmonics of decreasing magnitude is continued the curve approximates closer and closer to that of a square wave as shown in Fig. 93. A careful inspection of Fig. 93 will reveal how the various harmonics add to make closer approximations to a square wave.

Square Sine and Square Cosine Waves.—The square sine wave of Fig. 93*f* has been redrawn in Fig. 94*a* to show its general shape over more than two periods. It will be noted that this curve is antisymmetrical about the *y*-axis and is made up of sine terms, hence is often referred to as a square sine wave.

If the square sine wave is moved over so that it is symmetrical about the *y*-axis, as shown in Fig. 94*b*, the terms of the series change from sine to cosine as shown in Eq. (42) and the series is often referred to as a square cosine wave. The reason for the terms in Eq. (42) can be visualized if the y-axis of Fig. 93 is imagined shifted to the $\pi/2$ position which makes the fundamental or first harmonic symmetrical about the new y-axis, hence, $\cos x$ which is the first term of Eq. (42). It will be noted in Fig. 93b that the third harmonic is a negative maximum at $\pi/2$, hence is written $-\frac{1}{3}\cos 3x$, which is the second term in Eq. (42). Continuing this process, the fifth harmonic component is a positive maximum at this midpoint in Fig. 93c. It is therefore

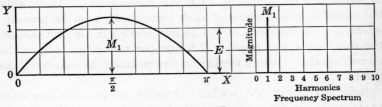

$$y = M_1 \sin x = \frac{4E}{\pi} \sin x \tag{36}$$

a. Fundamental or first harmonic sine wave.

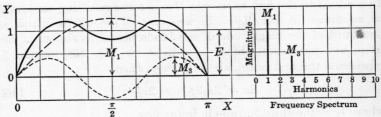

$$y = M_1 \sin x + M_3 \sin 3x = \frac{4E}{\pi}\left(\sin x + \frac{1}{3}\sin 3x\right) \tag{37}$$

b. Fundamental plus third harmonic sine waves.

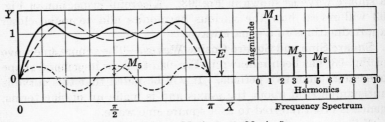

$$y = M_1 \sin x + M_3 \sin 3x + M_5 \sin 5x$$
$$= \frac{4E}{\pi}\left(\sin x + \frac{1}{3}\sin 3x + \frac{1}{5}\sin 5x\right) \tag{38}$$

c. Fundamental plus third and fifth harmonic sine waves.

Fig. 93.—Approximations

written $+\frac{1}{5} \cos 5x$ to make up the third term of the series in Eq. (42).

The frequency spectrum is the same for both the square sine and square cosine waves. This is because the series in Eqs. (41) and (42) both have the same values of M. The fact that they are negative or multiplied by a cosine rather than a sine term does not alter their magnitude, hence the frequency spectrum of Fig. 93f also holds for a square cosine wave.

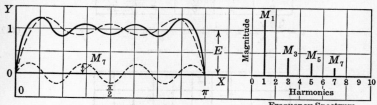

$$y = M_1 \sin x + M_3 \sin 3x + M_5 \sin 5x + M_7 \sin 7x$$
$$= \frac{4E}{\pi} \left(\sin x + \frac{1}{3} \sin 3x + \frac{1}{5} \sin 5x + \frac{1}{7} \sin 7x \right) \quad (39)$$

d. Fundamental plus third, fifth, and seventh harmonic sine waves.

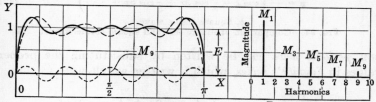

$$y = M_1 \sin x + M_3 \sin 3x + M_5 \sin 5x + M_7 \sin 7x + M_9 \sin 9x$$
$$= \frac{4E}{\pi} \left(\sin x + \frac{1}{3} \sin 3x + \frac{1}{5} \sin 5x + \frac{1}{7} \sin 7x + \frac{1}{9} \sin 9x \right) \quad (40)$$

e. Fundamental plus third, fifth, seventh, and ninth harmonic sine waves.

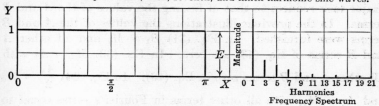

$$y = M_1 \sin x + M_3 \sin 3x + M_5 \sin 5x + \cdots$$
$$= \frac{4E}{\pi} \left(\sin x + \frac{1}{3} \sin 3x + \frac{1}{5} \sin 5x + \cdots \right) \quad (41)$$

f. Square sine wave (fundamental plus all odd harmonics).

for a square sine wave.

Fourier Series.—Thus far, we have examined waves made up of a constant component, harmonic sine components, and harmonic cosine components. Generalizing, the equation for

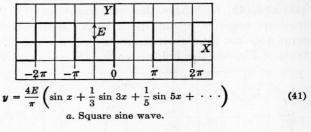

$$y = \frac{4E}{\pi}\left(\sin x + \frac{1}{3}\sin 3x + \frac{1}{5}\sin 5x + \cdots\right) \tag{41}$$

a. Square sine wave.

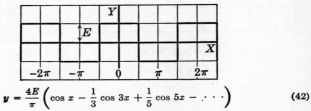

$$y = \frac{4E}{\pi}\left(\cos x - \frac{1}{3}\cos 3x + \frac{1}{5}\cos 5x - \cdots\right) \tag{42}$$

b. Square cosine wave.

FIG. 94.—Comparison of square sine and square cosine waves.

any periodic wave can be written by substituting the proper values in *Fourier's series*, which is written as follows:

$$y = f(x) = \frac{A_0}{2} + A_1 \cos x + A_2 \cos 2x + A_3 \cos 3x + \cdots$$
$$+ B_1 \sin x + B_2 \sin 2x + B_3 \sin 3x + \cdots \tag{43}$$

Since this equation can be used to express any periodic wave, the major task reduces to that of finding the values of the A and B terms. In the previous illustrations the values of the A and B terms were furnished. In Eq. (31) $B_1 = M_1$ and all other A and B terms of Eq. (43) are zero. In Eq. (32) $M_1 = A_1$ with all other A and B terms zero in Eq. (43). In Eq. (34) $\frac{A_0}{2} = M_0$ and $A_1 = M_1$, with all other terms in Fourier's series equal to zero. In Eq. (41) all of the A terms are zero and all of the odd B terms exist.

Then in Eq. (42) all the B terms are zero and all but the A_0 and even A terms exist.

If the shape of the desired curve is known, it is possible to determine the value of the A and B terms by the following definite integrals. The integrals are followed by a word statement of their meaning. The constant or zero frequency component is

$$A_0 = \frac{1}{\pi} \int_0^{2\pi} y \, dx$$

$$= 2 \begin{pmatrix} \text{average value of } y \\ \text{taken over one period} \\ \text{or cycle} \end{pmatrix} \tag{44}$$

The nth cosine term of the nth harmonic is

$$A_n = \frac{1}{\pi} \int_0^{2\pi} y \cos nx \, dx$$

$$= 2 \begin{pmatrix} \text{average value of } y \cos nx \\ \text{taken over one period or} \\ \text{cycle} \end{pmatrix} \tag{45}$$

The nth sine term of the nth harmonic is

$$B_n = \frac{1}{\pi} \int_0^{2\pi} y \sin nx \, dx$$

$$= 2 \begin{pmatrix} \text{average value of } y \sin nx \\ \text{taken over one period or} \\ \text{cycle} \end{pmatrix} \tag{46}$$

If $n = 0$ in Eq. (45), $\cos 0 \cdot x = 1$ and the equation reduces to Eq. (44). If $n = 0$ in Eq. (46), $\sin 0 \cdot x = 0$ and the value is zero. That is the reason for the absence of the B_0 term in Eq. (43).

Example 13. Determine the A and B terms for the wave illustrated in Fig. 92.

Solution. Substituting in Eq. (44) the value of y given in Eq. (34) for the cosine wave above the x-axis, we have for the A_0 term

$$A_0 = \frac{1}{\pi} \int_0^{2\pi} y \, dx = \frac{1}{\pi} \int_0^{2\pi} (M_0 + M_1 \cos x) \, dx$$

$$= \frac{1}{\pi} \int_0^{2\pi} M_0 \, dx + \frac{1}{\pi} \int_0^{2\pi} M_1 \cos x \, dx = \frac{1}{\pi} M_0 x \Big|_0^{2\pi} + \frac{1}{\pi} M_1 \sin x \Big|_0^{2\pi}$$

$$= \frac{1}{\pi} (M_0 \cdot 2\pi - M_0 \cdot 0) + \frac{1}{\pi} (0 - 0) = 2M_0 \quad Ans.$$

For the A_1 term we have

$$A_1 = \frac{1}{\pi} \int_0^{2\pi} y \cos x \, dx = \frac{1}{\pi} \int_0^{2\pi} (M_0 + M_1 \cos x) \cos x \, dx$$

$$= \frac{1}{\pi} \int_0^{2\pi} M_0 \cos x \, dx + \frac{1}{\pi} \int_0^{2\pi} M_1 \cos^2 x \, dx$$

$$= \frac{1}{\pi} M_0 \sin x \Big|_0^{2\pi} + \frac{1}{\pi} \int_0^{2\pi} M_1 \frac{1}{2} (1 + \cos 2x) \, dx$$

$$= \frac{1}{\pi} M_0 (0 - 0) + \frac{1}{\pi} M_1 \frac{1}{2} \left(\int_0^{2\pi} dx + \int_0^{2\pi} \cos 2x \, dx \right)$$

$$= \frac{1}{\pi} M_1 \frac{1}{2} \left[(2\pi - 0) - \frac{1}{2} \sin 2x \Big|_0^{2\pi} \right] = M_1 \quad Ans.$$

All other A and B terms are zero, so these substitutions can be made in Eq. (43) to get the complete equation of the wave, thus

$$y = \frac{A_0}{2} + A_1 \cos x = \frac{2M_0}{2} + M_1 \cos x = M_0 + M_1 \cos x \quad Ans.$$

The value of y can often be expressed by a simple equation over various portions of the period. In such cases the integration can be added over these various portions. This is illustrated in the following example:

Example 14.   Determine two A and three B terms for a square sine wave of amplitude E.

Solution.   Referring to Fig. 94a, $y = E$ from $x = 0$ to $x = \pi$ and $y = -E$ from $x = \pi$ to $x = 2\pi$.

Substituting these values in Eq. (44) for A_0,

$$A_0 = \frac{1}{\pi} \int_0^{\pi} E \cos 0 \cdot x \, dx + \frac{1}{\pi} \int_{\pi}^{2\pi} (-E \cos 0 \cdot x) \, dx$$

$$= \frac{1}{\pi} Ex \Big|_0^{\pi} - \frac{1}{\pi} Ex \Big|_{\pi}^{2\pi}$$

$$= \frac{1}{\pi} E\pi - \frac{1}{\pi} E(2\pi - \pi) = 0 \quad Ans.$$

This means that the wave is balanced around the x-axis. Substituting the above values in Eq. (45) for A_1,

$$A_1 = \frac{1}{\pi} \int_0^{\pi} E \cos x \, dx + \frac{1}{\pi} \int_{\pi}^{2\pi} (-E \cos x) \, dx$$

$$= \frac{1}{\pi} E \sin x \Big|_0^{\pi} - \frac{1}{\pi} E \sin x \Big|_{\pi}^{2\pi}$$

$$= \frac{1}{\pi} E(0 - 0) - \frac{1}{\pi} E(0 - 0) = 0 \quad Ans.$$

Since the sign of any multiple of π is zero, all the rest of the A_n terms in Eq. (43) will be zero.

Substituting the above values in Eq. (46) for B_1,

$$B_1 = \frac{1}{\pi} \int_0^{2\pi} y \sin x \, dx = \frac{1}{\pi} \int_0^{\pi} E \sin x \, dx + \frac{1}{\pi} \int_{\pi}^{2\pi} (-E \sin x) \, dx$$

$$= \frac{E}{\pi} (-\cos x)\Big|_0^{\pi} + \frac{E}{\pi} \cos x \Big|_{\pi}^{2\pi}$$

$$= \frac{E}{\pi} (1 + 1) + \frac{E}{\pi} (1 + 1) = \frac{4E}{\pi} \quad Ans.$$

Substituting the above values in Eq. (46) for B_2,

$$B_2 = \frac{1}{\pi} \int_0^{2\pi} y \sin 2x \, dx = \frac{1}{\pi} \int_0^{\pi} E \sin 2x \, dx + \frac{1}{\pi} \int_{\pi}^{2\pi} (-E \sin 2x) \, dx$$

$$= \frac{E}{2\pi} (-\cos 2x)\Big|_0^{\pi} + \frac{E}{2\pi} (\cos 2x)\Big|_{\pi}^{2\pi} = \frac{E}{2\pi} (-1 + 1) + \frac{E}{2\pi} (1 - 1) = 0$$

$$Ans.$$

Since the cosine of any even multiple of π results in zero over these limits, all the rest of the even B_n terms in Eq. (43) will be zero.

Substituting the above values in Eq. (46) for B_3,

$$B_3 = \frac{1}{\pi} \int_0^{2\pi} y \sin 2x \, dx = \frac{1}{\pi} \int_0^{\pi} E \sin 3x \, dx + \frac{1}{\pi} \int_{\pi}^{2\pi} (-E \sin 3x) \, dx$$

$$= \frac{E}{3\pi} (-\cos 3x)\Big|_0^{\pi} - \frac{E}{3\pi} (-\cos 3x)\Big|_{\pi}^{2\pi}$$

$$= \frac{E}{3\pi} (+1 + 1) - \frac{E}{3\pi} (-1 - 1) = \frac{4E}{3\pi} \quad Ans.$$

This indicates that only odd B terms will have values in Eq. (43). Now, substituting the above values in Eq. (43) gives two terms of the series, thus

$$y = \frac{4E}{\pi} \left(\sin x + \frac{1}{3} \sin 3x + \cdots \right) \quad Ans.$$

Magnitude and Phase of Harmonic Components.—The corresponding terms in Fourier's series of Eq. (43) can be combined into single terms, by using the equation

$$M_n \sin (n\omega t + \psi_n) = A_n \cos n\omega t + B_n \sin n\omega t \qquad (47)$$

where, as shown in Fig. 95,

$$M_n = \sqrt{A_n^2 + B_n^2} \qquad (48)$$

$$\cos \psi_n = \frac{B_n}{M_n} \qquad (49)$$

$$\sin \psi_n = \frac{A_n}{M_n} \qquad (50)$$

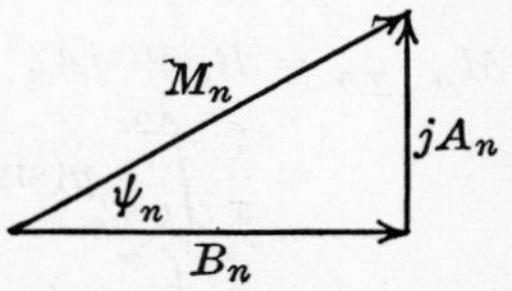

FIG. 95.—Relation of phase and magnitude of an nth harmonic component.

To prove Eq. (47), consider the trigonometric identity

$$\sin (a + b) = \sin b \cos a + \cos b \sin a,$$

and let $a = n\omega t$, $b = \psi_n$; then

$$\sin (n\omega t + \psi_n) = \sin \psi_n \cos n\omega t + \cos \psi_n \sin n\omega t$$

Now substituting the value of $\sin \psi_n$ and $\cos \psi_n$ as given in Eqs. (49) and (50) and multiplying both sides by M_n results in Eq. (47) and completes the proof.

Fourier's series of Eq. (43) can, with the use of Eq. (47), be converted to read

$$y = f(x) = M_0 + M_1 \sin (\omega t + \psi_1) + M_2 \sin (2\omega t + \psi_2 + \cdots$$

$$= M_0 + \sum_{n=1}^{n=\infty} M_n \sin (n\omega t + \psi_n) \quad (51)$$

Since M_0 of this series equals $\dfrac{A_0}{2}$ of the original series, it can be evaluated by converting the definite integral of Eq. (44) to read

$$M_0 = \frac{1}{2\pi} \int_0^{2\pi} y \, dx$$

$$= \begin{pmatrix} \text{average value of } y \text{ taken} \\ \text{over one period or cycle} \end{pmatrix} \quad (52)$$

In this equation the integral gives the area under the curve from 0 to 2π. This area can be converted to an equivalent rectangle having a base of 2π and an altitude of M_0, hence as given in Eq. (52), the altitude of the rectangle is

$$M_0 = \frac{\text{area of equivalent rectangle}}{\text{base of rectangle}} \quad (53)$$

By using the vectors of Fig. 95, it is possible to express the magnitude (M) term and phase angle (ψ) term by a definite integral. Multiplying both sides of Eq. (45) by j and adding to Eq. (46) gives, for $n = 1, 2, 3 \ldots ,$

$$M_n \underline{/\psi_n} = B_n + jA_n$$

$$= \frac{1}{\pi} \int_0^{2\pi} y(\sin nx + j \cos nx) \, dx$$

$$= \frac{j}{\pi} \int_0^{2\pi} y(\cos nx - j \sin nx) \, dx$$

$$= \frac{j}{\pi} \int_0^{2\pi} y\epsilon^{-inx} \, dx$$

$$= 2 \begin{pmatrix} \text{average value of } y\epsilon^{-inx} \\ \text{taken over one period} \\ \text{or cycle} \end{pmatrix} \begin{pmatrix} \text{phase angle of} \\ n\text{th harmonic} \end{pmatrix} \quad (54)$$

In other words, this equation states that

$$M_n \underline{/\psi_n} = 2 \left(\frac{\text{area of}}{\text{equivalent rectangle}} \middle/ \text{base of rectangle} \right) \left(\text{phase angle of } n\text{th harmonic} \right) \tag{55}$$

The area of the equivalent rectangle is given by the integral, which also gives an angle. The base of the rectangle is 2π, hence M_n is twice the altitude of the rectangle. The angle given by the integral when multiplied by j gives the phase term.

Example 15. Determine the first harmonic term for a square sine wave of amplitude E.

Solution. Dividing the integral of Eq. (54) into two parts, the first from 0 to π and the second from π to 2π, results in

$$M_1\underline{/\psi_1} = \frac{j}{\pi} \int_0^\pi E\epsilon^{-jx}\, dx + \frac{j}{\pi} \int_\pi^{2\pi} - E\epsilon^{-jx}\, dx$$

$$= -\frac{E}{\pi} \epsilon^{-jx}\Big|_0^\pi + \frac{E}{\pi} \epsilon^{-jx}\Big|_\pi^{2\pi}$$

$$= -\frac{E}{\pi} \epsilon^{-j\pi} + \frac{E}{\pi} \epsilon^0 + \frac{E}{\pi} \epsilon^{-j2\pi} - \frac{E}{\pi} \epsilon^{-j\pi}$$

$$= \frac{E}{\pi} \underline{/0°} + \frac{E}{\pi} \underline{/0°} + \frac{E}{\pi} \underline{/0°} + \frac{E}{\pi} \underline{/0°} = \frac{4E}{\pi} \underline{/0°}$$

The second term in Eq. (51) is then

$$M_1 \sin (\omega t + \psi_1) = \frac{4E}{\pi} \sin (\omega t + 0) = \frac{4E}{\pi} \sin \omega t \quad Ans.$$

This checks the solution for the first harmonic term in Example 14, which used x in place of ωt. Since $\psi_1 = 0°$, the j component is absent and the B_n term of Eq. (54) is equal to $\frac{4E}{\pi}$.

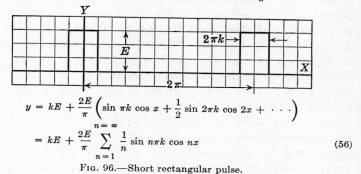

$$y = kE + \frac{2E}{\pi} \left(\sin \pi k \cos x + \frac{1}{2} \sin 2\pi k \cos 2x + \cdots \right)$$

$$= kE + \frac{2E}{\pi} \sum_{n=1}^{n=\infty} \frac{1}{n} \sin n\pi k \cos nx \tag{56}$$

Fig. 96.—Short rectangular pulse.

Example 16. Evaluate the first two terms for a *short rectangular pulse* as shown in Fig. 96.

Solution. By Eq. (52),

$$M_0 = \frac{1}{2\pi} \int_{-\pi k}^{+\pi k} E\, dx = \frac{E}{2\pi} x \Big|_{-\pi k}^{\pi k} = kE \quad Ans.$$

Checking by Eq. (53),

$$M_0 = \frac{(2\pi k)(E)}{2\pi} = kE \quad Check.$$

By Eq. (54),

$$M_1\underline{/\psi_1} = \frac{j}{\pi} \int_{-\pi k}^{+\pi k} E\epsilon^{-ix}\, dx = \frac{-E}{\pi} \epsilon^{-ix} \Big|_{-\pi k}^{+\pi k}$$

$$= \frac{2Ej}{\pi} \frac{\epsilon^{i\pi k} - \epsilon^{-i\pi k}}{2j} = \frac{2E}{\pi} \sin \pi k \underline{/90°}$$

Hence, substituting in Eq. (51),

$$M_1 \sin (x + \psi_1) = \frac{2E}{\pi} \sin \pi k \sin (x + 90°)$$

$$= \frac{2E}{\pi} \sin \pi k \cos x \quad Ans.$$

A square cosine wave was illustrated in Fig. 94*b*. It is a special case of the short rectangular pulse of Fig. 96. If $k = \frac{1}{2}$ and the M_0 term is made zero, Eq. (56) reduces to Eq. (42).

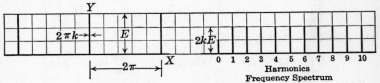

$$y = kE + 2kE(\cos x + \cos 2x + \cos 3x + \cdots) \tag{57}$$

Fig. 97.—Thin line pulse.

Thin Line Pulse.—Another case of interest is to narrow the width of the rectangular pulse until it is essentially a single line pulse. As the pulse width of Fig. 96 is made narrow k becomes very small, with the result that for small values of n the term $\sin n\pi k \doteq n\pi k$ in Eq. (56). With this substitution Eq. (56) can be expressed as Eq. (57), which is illustrated in Fig. 97. It is interesting to note that the harmonics have the same magnitude, hence giving a frequency spectrum as shown in Fig. 97. If this series is carried to a very large number of terms, the pulse width must be very small for the above approximation to hold with reasonable accuracy. Also, the value of each harmonic component will be very small. The height of the pulse will be approximately the sum of the harmonic components. It is of importance to note that all harmonics are present and of equal amplitude in the frequency spectrum of Fig. 97.

Exercises

1. Write the nth term for the series

$$S_n = x + \frac{x^2}{1} + \frac{x^3}{1 \cdot 2} + \frac{x^4}{1 \cdot 2 \cdot 3} + \cdots$$

and test the series for convergence or divergence.

2. Test the series $S_n = \frac{1}{1} + \frac{1}{(\sqrt{2})^3} + \frac{1}{(\sqrt{3})^3} + \cdots$

for convergence or divergence and write the nth term.

3. Test ratio the series $S_n = 1 + \frac{1}{\lfloor 1} + \frac{1}{\lfloor 2} + \frac{1}{\lfloor 3} + \cdots$

4. Find the approximate value of $\sqrt{37}$ by applying the binomial series.

5. Expand the function $\sin x$ into a series.

6. What is the third approximation value of $\dfrac{\sin x}{1 - x}$?

7. Give the second approximation value of $\epsilon^{2.1}$ when $\epsilon^2 = 7.3891$ and note the error.

8. Determine the third harmonic term for a square sine wave of amplitude E.

9. Evaluate the second harmonic of a scanning voltage when the wave form is

$$y = \frac{E}{\pi} x \text{ from } -\pi \text{ to } +\pi.$$

10. An antisymmetrical sawtooth wave has the following wave form:

$$y = \frac{2E}{\pi} x \text{ from } -\frac{\pi}{2} \text{ to } +\frac{\pi}{2}$$

$$y = 2E - \frac{2E}{\pi} x \text{ from } \frac{\pi}{2} \text{ to } \frac{3\pi}{2}$$

Determine the first harmonic term in the series.

APPENDIX

1. GREEK ALPHABET

Letters		Name	Pronunciation	Equivalent
Capital	Small			
A	α	Alpha	ăl′fȧ	a
B	β	Beta	bē′tȧ or bā′tȧ	b
Γ	γ	Gamma	găm′ȧ	g
Δ	δ	Delta	dĕl′tȧ	d
E	ε	Epsilon	ĕp′sĭ-lŏn	e (short)
Z	ζ	Zeta	zē′tȧ or zā′tȧ	z
H	η	Eta	ē′tȧ or ā′tȧ	e (long)
Θ	θ	Theta	thē′tȧ or thā′tȧ	th
I	ι	Iota	ī-ō′tȧ	i
K	κ	Kappa	kăp′ȧ	k, c
Λ	λ	Lambda	lăm′dȧ	l
M	μ	Mu	mū, mōō, or mü	m
N	ν	Nu	nū or nü	n
Ξ	ξ	Xi	zī or ksē	x
O	o	Omicron	ŏm′ĭ-krŏn or ŏ-mī′krŏn	o (short)
Π	π	Pi	pī or pē	p
P	ρ	Rho	rō	r
Σ	σ	Sigma	sĭg′mȧ	s
T	τ	Tau	tô or tou	t
Υ	υ	Upsilon	ūp′sĭ-lŏn	u, y
Φ	φ	Phi	fī or fē	ph
X	χ	Chi	kī, kē, or κē	kh, ch
Ψ	ψ	Psi	psē or sī	ps
Ω	ω	Omega	ŏ-mē′gȧ ŏ-mĕg′ȧ, or ō′mĕ-gȧ	o (long)

ăt, āte, operȧ;
nĕt, mē, pĭn, pīne;
nŏt, ôrb, nōte, fōōd, ŭp, lūte, menü;
κ-ch, in German *ach.*

2. MATHEMATICAL SYMBOLS AND ABBREVIATIONS

Symbol	Name	Uses
1, 2, 3, 4, 5, 6, 7, 8, 9, 0	Arabic numerals	The numerals used in mathematics
∞	Infinity	A quantity larger than any number
.	Decimal point	A period used to point off numbers
$+$	Plus	Addition, positive
$-$	Minus	Subtraction, negative
$\pm$	Plus or minus	Addition or subtraction
$\mp$	Minus or plus	Subtraction or addition
$\times$	Multiply by	Multiplication
$a \cdot b$	a is multiplied by b	Multiplication
$(2 \cdot 1)(3 \cdot 4)$	2·1 multiplied by 3·4	Quantity multiplication
$\div$	Divided by	Division
a/b	a is divided by b	Division (fraction form), or per
$\dfrac{a}{b}$	a is divided by b	Division (fraction or ratio form)
$a{:}b$	a is to b	Ratio form of division
$=$	Equal to	Equality in equation form
$\equiv$	Identical to	Identity in equation form
$\doteq$	Approximately equal to	Approximate equality in equations (sometimes used for approaches)
$\neq$	Not equal to	Inequality in equation form
$<$	Less than	Inequality in equation form
$>$	Greater than	Inequality in equation form
$\leqq$	Equal or less than	Equality or inequality in equation form
$\geqq$	Equal or greater than	Equality or inequality in equation form
$\propto$	Proportional to	Proportionality used in equation form
$::$	Proportional to	Proportionality used in equation form
$\rightarrow$	Approaches	To express that a quantity approaches in equation form
$\perp$	Perpendicular	Geometry
$\parallel$	Parallel to, or in parallel with	Geometry, or parallel electrical circuits
$\underline{\angle}$	Positive angle sign	Geometry, vector quantities
$\overline{\angle}$	Negative angle sign	Geometry, vector quantities
$\triangle$	Triangle	Geometry
$\odot$	Circle	Geometry
$\therefore$	Therefore	Geometry
#	Number	When placed before figures
%	Per cent	Placed after number expressing per cent
$\cdots$	Continued	To indicate the continuation of a number or series
π	Pi	$\pi = 3.1416 \cdots$ radians, the circumference of a circle divided by its diameter

Symbol	Name	Uses
ϵ	Epsilon	$\epsilon = 2.71828 \cdots$, the base of natural logarithms
3! or $\lfloor 3$	Factorial	To express the fact that a number is multiplied by all smaller numbers, thus $3! = \lfloor 3 = 3 \times 2 \times 1 = 6$
Σ	Summation	To add a series of terms
$\sum\limits_{o}^{n}$	Summation from o to n	To add a series of terms from o to n
$(\ \ )$	Parentheses	A sign placed at both ends of a grouping
$[\ \ ]$	Brackets	A sign placed at both ends of a grouping
$\{\ \ \}$	Braces	A sign placed at both ends of a grouping
—	Vinculum	A line placed over a grouping
$\sqrt{}$	Radical	Extract the root of a number
$\sqrt{}$	Radical and vinculum	Extract the square root of a quantity or number
$\sqrt[3]{A}$ or $A^{\frac{1}{3}}$	3 is the root of the quantity A	Expressing the root to be extracted, or $\frac{1}{3}$ is the power to which it must be raised
A^2	2 is the exponent of the quantity A	Expressing the power to which a quantity is to be raised
$|A|$	A has a magnitude only	To express only the magnitude of a quantity
$\mathbf{A}$ or $\dot{\mathrm{A}}$ or $\bar{\mathrm{A}}$	A is a vector	To express a quantity that has both magnitude and direction
A	A is a vector	When the magnitude is expressed $|A|$, the A can be used to express a vector quantity
A_x	x is a subscript	To identify the quantity A, as, for example, lying along the x-axis
j	Operator j	To express quantities in the direction of the y-axis. (In pure mathematics, i is used for this operator and is called an imaginary number.)
$\circ$	Degree sign	To express angles in degrees
$\prime$	Minute sign	To express angles in minutes
$\prime\prime$	Second sign	To express angles in seconds
$\begin{vmatrix} a & b \\ c & d \end{vmatrix}$	Determinate sign	To express the solution of simultaneous equations
Δx	Increment of x	Small changes, in calculus
dx	Differential of x	Differential, in calculus
∂x	Partial differential of x	Partial differential, in calculus
∇	Del	Differential operator, in differential calculus

Symbol	Name	Uses
$\int$	Integral	Integral calculus
$\int_b^a$	Integral between the limits of a and b	Integration between limits
$F(x)$ or $f(x)$	Function of x	Algebra or calculus
$J_n(x)$	Bessel function of the first kind of order n	Higher mathematics—Frequency modulation
$K_n(x)$	Bessel function of second kind of order n	Higher mathematics
Γ	Gamma function	Higher mathematics

Abbreviation	Name	Uses
ln, log	Logarithm	Express the natural and common logarithm of a quantity, respectively
log or $\log_{10}$	Logarithm to base 10	This is the common base and is usually written log
ln or $\log_\epsilon$	Logarithm to base ϵ	This is the natural base and is usually expressed ln (sometimes called "Napierian")
colog	Cologarithm	The logarithm of the reciprocal of a number
antilog	Antilogarithm	To express a number in terms of its logarithm (the reverse operation of taking the logarithm of a number)
sin	Sine of	Circular trigonometry
$\sin^{-1}$	Arc whose sine is	Antisine of, inverse of sine (circular trigonometry)
sinh	Hyperbolic sine of	Hyperbolic trigonometry
$\sinh^{-1}$	Inverse hyperbolic sine of	Hyperbolic trigonometry
cos	Cosine of	Circular trigonometry
$\cos^{-1}$	Arc whose cosine is	Anticosine of, inverse cosine of (circular trigonometry)
cosh	Hyperbolic cosine of	Hyperbolic trigonometry
$\cosh^{-1}$	Inverse hyperbolic cosine of	Hyperbolic trigonometry
tan	Tangent of	Circular trigonometry
$\tan^{-1}$	Arc whose tangent is	Antitangent of, inverse of tangent (circular trigonometry)
tanh	Hyperbolic tangent of	Hyperbolic trigonometry

Abbreviation	Name	Uses
tanh⁻¹	Inverse hyperbolic tangent of	Hyperbolic trigonometry
cot	Cotangent of	Circular trigonometry
cot⁻¹	Arc whose tangent is	Anticotangent of, inverse of cotangent (circular trigonometry)
coth	Hyperbolic cotangent of	Hyperbolic trigonometry
coth⁻¹	Inverse hyperbolic cotangent of	Hyperbolic trigonometry
csc	Cosecant of	Circular trigonometry
csc⁻¹	Arc whose cosecant is	Anticosecant of, inverse of cosecant (circular trigonometry)
csch	Hyperbolic cosecant of	Hyperbolic trigonometry
csch⁻¹	Inverse hyperbolic cosecant of	Hyperbolic trigonometry
sec	Secant of	Circular trigonometry
sec⁻¹	Arc whose secant is	Antisecant of, inverse of secant (circular trigonometry)
sech	Hyperbolic secant of	Hyperbolic trigonometry
sech⁻¹	Inverse hyperbolic secant of	Hyperbolic trigonometry
vers	Versed sine	vers $\beta = 1 - \cos \beta$ (circular trigonometry)
covers	Coversed sine	covers $\beta = 1 - \sin \beta$ (circular trigonometry)
hyp	hypotenuse	Trigonometry
opp	opposite side	Trigonometry
adj	adjacent side	Trigonometry
L.C.D.	least common denominator	Algebra

3. ENGINEERING SYMBOLS AND ABBREVIATIONS

a. Greek alphabet symbols:

α Angles, attenuation factor, radiation

β Angles, wave length constant, radiation

Γ Complex Hertzian vector

γ Angles, propagation constant, conductivity, radiation, Euler's constant

Δ Increments, variation

δ Decrement, density

ϵ Base natural logarithms, very small quantity, inductivity, permittivity

η Efficiency, elliptic coordinate

Θ   Angles, temperature
θ   Angles, elevation angle, time constant, phase displacement
κ   Boltzmann's constant, dielectric constant
Λ, λ   Wave length of electric waves
μ   Amplification factor, permeability, prefix micro
ν   Frequency of radiation
ξ   Elliptic coordinate
Π   Hertz vector
π   Circumference of a circle divided by its diameter
ρ   Resistivity, specific resistivity, charge density
Σ   Summation
σ   Conductivity
τ   angles, tangent vector, surface density
Φ   Scalar velocity potential, magnetic flux
φ   Angles, flux, power factor angle, true azimuth, electric potential
χ   Magnetic susceptibilities
Ψ   Angles, phase difference, scalar function
Ω   Resistance in ohms
ω   Resistance in ohms, angular velocity

b. English alphabet symbols:

A   Area, current electromagnetic vector potential
a   Dimensions, amperes
B   Susceptance, magnetic inductance, magnetic flux density
b   Susceptance
C   Capacity, centigrade
c   Constant, velocity of light
D   Electric displacement, electrostatic flux density
d   Distance, diameter
E   Effective voltage, emf, electric field intensity
e   Instantaneous voltage
F   Force, electrostatic field intensity
f   Frequency, force, farad
G   Conductance measured in mho
g   Conductance, acceleration due to gravity, gram
H   Magnetic field intensity
h   Height, Plank's constant, henry
I   Effective current
i   Instantaneous current
J   Poynting's vector, current density vector, intensity of magnetization
j   Operator
K   Constant, dielectric constant, stacking factor
k   Susceptibility, prefix "kilo-"
L   Self inductance
l   Length
M   Mutual inductance, meters, induced polarization, prefix "mega-"
m   Mass, prefix "milli-"
N   Number of conductors or turns, Avogadro's number
n   Number, velocity of rotation

O Origin of coordinate system
o Origin of coordinate system
P Power
p Sound pressure, instantaneous power
Q Quantity of electricity, ratio of reactance to resistance
q Electric charge
R Resistance, reluctance
r Resistance, radius
S Sensitivity, surface area
s Transconductance
T Absolute temperature, periodic time, absolute temperature, tension
t Time
U Energy
u Particle velocity
V Voltage, volume, reluctivity
v Velocity
W Energy
w Watts
X Coordinates, reactance
x Coordinates, reactance
Y Coordinates, admittance
y Coordinates, admittance
Z Coordinates, impedance
z Coordinates, impedance

c. **Quantitative electrical abbreviations:**

Capacitance

$\mu\mu f$ Micromicrofarad (one-millionth of a millionth part of a farad)

μf Microfarad (one-millionth of a farad) NOTE: In some cases, mfd or mf are used instead of μf to indicate one millionth of a farad. It is always safe to assume that mfd or mf means microfarad and not millifarads.

f   Farad NOTE: The letter f is rarely used alone. It is preferable to spell the word out when it is used.

Current

μa Microampere (one-millionth of an ampere)
ma   Milliampere (one-thousandth of an ampere)
a or amp   Ampere

Frequency

cps   Cycles per second
kc   Kilocycles per second
Mc   Megacycles per second

Inductance

μh Microhenry (one-millionth of a henry)
mh   Millihenry (one-thousandth of a henry)
h   Henry

Power

μw	Microwatt (one-millionth of a watt)
mw	Milliwatt (one-thousandth of a watt)
w	Watt
kw	Kilowatt (one thousand watts)
Mw	Megawatt (one million watts)
kva	Kilovolt ampere—apparent power
kwhr	Kilowatt hour

Resistance

Ω	Ohms NOTE: In some cases ω is used to express ohms.
kΩ	Kilohm (one thousand ohms)
MΩ	Megohm (one million ohms) NOTE: In some cases Meg is used to express megohms.

Voltage

μv	Microvolt (one-millionth of a volt)
mv	Millivolt (one-thousandth of a volt)
v	Volt
kv	Kilovolt (one thousand volts)

d. **Circuit Symbols:**

Admittance

Y	Admittance in mhos
B	Susceptance in mhos
B_C	Capacitive susceptance in mhos
B_L	Inductive susceptance in mhos

Constants

G	Conductance in mhos
C	Capacitance in farads
L	Inductance in henrys
M	Mutual inductance in henrys
R	Resistance in ohms
G	Conductance in mhos

Current

I	Effective (or rms) current in amperes
I_m	Maximum (or peak) current in amperes[1]
I_{av}	Average current in amperes[2]
i	Instantaneous current in amperes

Impedance

Z	Impedance in ohms
X	Reactance in ohms
X_C	Capacitive reactance in ohms
X_L	Inductive reactance in ohms
R	Resistance in ohms

Miscellaneous

Ant	Antenna
Gnd	Ground
Mod	Modulator
Spkr	Loud speaker

[1,2] See footnotes on page 241.

Power supply

A	Filament power supply
B	Plate power supply
C	Grid-bias power supply

Tube

Fil	Filament
K or k	Cathode
H or h	Heater
G or g	Grid
S_g	Screen grid
P or p	Plate

Voltage

E	Effective (or rms) voltage in volts
E_m	Maximum (or peak) voltage in volts[1]
E_{av}	Average voltage in volts[2]
e	Instantaneous voltage in volts

***e*. Abbreviations:[3]**

Current

ac	Alternating current
dc	Direct current

Frequency

af	Audio frequency
if	Intermediate frequency
rf	Radio frequency
trf	Tuned radio frequency
bf	Beat frequency
bfo	Beat-frequency oscillator
lf	Low-frequency (30 to 300 kc band)
mf	Medium-frequency (300 to 3,000 kc band)
hf	High-frequency (3,000 kc to 30 Mc band)
vhf	Very-high-frequency (30 to 300 Mc band)
uhf	Ultra-high-frequency (300 to 3,000 Mc band)

Miscellaneous

cw	Continuous wave
icw	Interrupted continuous wave
am	Amplitude modulation
fm	Frequency modulation

[1] In some cases the subscript "max" is used to indicate maximum or peak current or voltage. For example, when the subscript "min" is used to indicate minimum current or voltage, the subscript "max" will probably be used for maximum current or voltage.

[2] In some cases the subscript "avg" is used to express average current or voltage.

[3] The abbreviations as given here are used as nouns. When they are used as adjectives, it is common practice to use a hyphen, thus

ac Alternating current (noun)

a-c alternating-current (adjective)

pm   Phase modulation
ptm   Pulse time modulation
emf   Electromotive force in volts
mmf   Magnetomotive force in gilberts
avc   Automatic volume control
davc   Delayed automatic volume control
mopa   Master-oscillator power-amplifier

f. **Measurement abbreviations:**

Metric prefixes

μ Micro- (one-millionth)
m   Milli- (one-thousandth)
c   Centi- (one-hundredth)
d   Deci- (one-tenth)
        Uni- (one) NOTE: This prefix is usually omitted.
dk   Deka- (ten)
h   Hekto- (one hundred)
k   Kilo- (one thousand)
M   Mega- (one million)

Metric measure

mm   Millimeter (one-thousandth of a meter)
cm   Centimeter (one-hundredth of a meter)
km   Kilometer (one thousand meters)
sq cm   Square centimeter or cm^2
sq cm   Square meter or m^2
sq km   Square kilometer or km^3
cu cm   Cubic meter or m^3
cgs   Centimeter-gram-second system of units
mks   Meter-kilogram-second system of units

English measure

in.   Inch
ft   Foot
yd   Yard
mile   Mile NOTE: This unit is always spelled out.
sq in   Square inch
sq ft   Square foot
cu in   Cubic inch
cu ft   Cubic foot
sec   Second
min   Minute
hr   Hour
yr   Year
lb   Pound
rps   Revolutions per second
rpm   Revolutions per minute
mph   Miles per hour

g. **Miscellaneous abbreviations:**

A.W.G. or B.&S.   American wire gauge or Brown and Sharpe wire
                  gauge. NOTE: These gauges are commonly used
                  for copper, aluminum, and resistance wire.

db	Decibel
deg	Degree
diam	Diameter
dcc	Double cotton covered
dsc	Double silk covered
ec	Enamel covered
mlt	Mean length of turn
p., pp.	Page, pages
rms	Root mean square
rss	Root sum square
temp	Temperature
vol	Volume
vs.	Versus
wt	Weight

4. CONVERSION TABLE

Multiply number of — by — to obtain	$\mu\mu$ units micro-micro units	μ units micro units	m units milli units	units	k units kilo units	M units mega units
$\mu\mu$ units micromicro units	1	10^6	10^9	10^{12}	10^{15}	10^{18}
μ units micro units	10^{-6}	1	10^3	10^6	10^9	10^{12}
m units milli units	10^{-9}	10^{-3}	1	10^3	10^6	10^9
units	10^{-12}	10^{-6}	10^{-3}	1	10^3	10^6
k units kilo units	10^{-15}	10^{-9}	10^{-6}	10^{-3}	1	10^3
M units mega units	10^{-18}	10^{-12}	10^{-9}	10^{-6}	10^{-3}	1

5. LOGARITHMS OF NUMBERS FROM 1 TO 100

n	log n	n	log n	n	log n	n	log n	n	log n
1	0.000000	21	1.322219	41	1.612784	61	1.785330	81	1.908485
2	0.301030	22	1.342423	42	1.623249	62	1.792392	82	1.913814
3	0.477121	23	1.361728	43	1.633468	63	1.799341	83	1.919078
4	0.602060	24	1.380211	44	1.643453	64	1.806180	84	1.924279
5	0.698970	25	1.397940	45	1.653213	65	1.812913	85	1.929419
6	0.778151	26	1.414973	46	1.662758	66	1.819544	86	1.934498
7	0.845098	27	1.431364	47	1.672098	67	1.826075	87	1.939519
8	0.903090	28	1.447158	48	1.681241	68	1.832509	88	1.944483
9	0.954243	29	1.462398	49	1.690196	69	1.838849	89	1.949390
10	1.000000	30	1.477121	50	1.698970	70	1.845098	90	1.954243
11	1.041393	31	1.491362	51	1.707570	71	1.851258	91	1.959041
12	1.079181	32	1.505150	52	1.716003	72	1.857332	92	1.963788
13	1.113943	33	1.518514	53	1.724276	73	1.863323	93	1.968483
14	1.146128	34	1.531479	54	1.732394	74	1.869232	94	1.973128
15	1.176091	35	1.544068	55	1.740363	75	1.875061	95	1.977724
16	1.204120	36	1.556303	56	1.748188	76	1.880814	96	1.982271
17	1.230449	37	1.568202	57	1.755875	77	1.886491	97	1.986772
18	1.255273	38	1.579784	58	1.763428	78	1.892095	98	1.991226
19	1.278754	39	1.591065	59	1.770852	79	1.897627	99	1.995635
20	1.301030	40	1.602060	60	1.778151	80	1.903090	100	2.000000

6. BRIEF TABLE OF TRIGONOMETRIC FUNCTIONS

Degrees	Sine	Cosine	Tangent	Cotangent
0	0.0000	1.0000	0.0000	∞
10	0.1736	0.9848	0.1763	5.6713
20	0.3420	0.9397	0.3640	2.7475
30	0.5000	0.8660	0.5774	1.7321
40	0.6428	0.7660	0.8391	1.1918
50	0.7660	0.6428	1.1918	0.8391
60	0.8660	0.5000	1.7321	0.5774
70	0.9397	0.3420	2.7475	0.3640
80	0.9848	0.1736	5.6713	0.1763
90	1.0000	0.0000	∞	0.0000

7. TABLE OF NATURAL LOGARITHMS*

These four pages give the natural logarithms of numbers between 0.1 and 10, correct to four places. Moving the decimal point n places to the right in the number, i.e., multiplying the number by 10^n, requires the addition of n times 2.3026 to the logarithm; values are given in the accompanying tables. Since the numbers in the first two pages are less than 1, the logarithms are all *negative* and should be preceded by a minus sign. The base is $e = 2.71828$.

$$\log_e x = \log_e 10 \, \log_{10} x = 2.3026 \log_{10} x$$
$$\log_{10} x = \log_{10} e \, \log_e x = 0.4343 \log_e x$$

n	$(n \cdot 2.3026)$	$n(0.6974-3)$
1	2.3026	0.6974-3
2	4.6052	0.3948-5
3	6.9078	0.0922-7
4	9.2103	0.7897-10
5	11.5129	0.4871-12
6	13.8155	0.1845-14
7	16.1181	0.8819-17
8	18.4207	0.5793-19
9	20.7233	0.2767-21

Number	0	1	2	3	4	5	6	7	8	9	Avg. diff.
.10	2.3026	2926	2828	2730	2634	2538	2443	2349	2256	2164	95
.11	.2073	1982	1893	1804	1716	1628	1542	1456	1371	1286	87
.12	.1203	1120	1037	0956	0875	0794	0715	0636	0557	0479	80
.13	.0402	0326	0250	0174	0099	0025	9951	9878	9805	9733	74
.14	1.9661	9590	9519	9449	9379	9310	9241	9173	9105	9038	69
.15	1.8971	8905	8839	8773	8708	8643	8579	8515	8452	8389	65
.16	8326	8264	8202	8140	8079	8018	7958	7898	7838	7779	61
.17	7720	7661	7603	7545	7487	7430	7373	7316	7260	7204	57
.18	7148	7093	7037	6983	6928	6874	6820	6766	6713	6660	54
.19	6607	6555	6503	6451	6399	6348	6296	6246	6195	6145	51
.20	1.6094	6045	5995	5945	5896	5847	5799	5750	5702	5654	49
.21	5606	5559	5512	5465	5418	5371	5325	5279	5233	5187	47
.22	5141	5096	5051	5006	4961	4917	4872	4828	4784	4740	44
.23	4697	4653	4610	4567	4524	4482	4439	4397	4355	4313	43
.24	4271	4230	4188	4147	4106	4065	4024	3984	3943	3903	41
.25	1.3863	3823	3783	3744	3704	3665	3626	3587	3548	3509	39
.26	3471	3432	3394	3356	3318	3280	3243	3205	3168	3130	38
.27	3093	3056	3020	2983	2946	2910	2874	2837	2801	2765	36
.28	2730	2694	2658	2623	2588	2553	2518	2483	2448	2413	36
.29	2379	2344	2310	2276	2242	2208	2174	2140	2107	2073	34
.30	1.2040	2006	1973	1940	1907	1874	1842	1809	1777	1744	33
.31	1712	1680	1648	1616	1584	1552	1520	1489	1457	1426	32
.32	1394	1363	1332	1301	1270	1239	1209	1178	1147	1117	31
.33	1087	1056	1026	0996	0966	0936	0906	0877	0847	0818	30
.34	0788	0759	0729	0700	0671	0642	0613	0584	0556	0527	29
.35	1.0498	0470	0441	0413	0385	0356	0328	0300	0272	0244	28
.36	0217	0189	0161	0134	0106	0079	0051	0024	9997	9970	27
.37	0.9943	9916	9889	9862	9835	9808	9782	9755	9729	9702	27
.38	9676	9650	9623	9597	9571	9545	9519	9493	9467	9442	26
.39	9416	9390	9365	9339	9314	9289	9263	9238	9213	9188	25
.40	0.9163	9138	9113	9088	9063	9039	9014	8989	8965	8940	25
.41	8916	8892	8867	8843	8819	8795	8771	8747	8723	8699	24
.42	8675	8651	8627	8604	8580	8557	8533	8510	8486	8463	23
.43	8440	8416	8393	8370	8347	8324	8301	8278	8255	8233	23
.44	8210	8187	8164	8142	8119	8097	8074	8052	8030	8007	22
.45	0.7985	7963	7941	7919	7897	7875	7853	7831	7809	7787	22
.46	7765	7744	7722	7700	7679	7657	7636	7614	7593	7572	21
.47	7550	7529	7508	7487	7465	7444	7423	7402	7381	7361	21
.48	7340	7319	7298	7277	7257	7236	7215	7195	7174	7154	20
.49	7133	7113	7093	7072	7052	7032	7012	6992	6972	6951	20

* This page and the following are from Allen's "Six-Place Tables," published by the McGraw-Hill Book Company, Inc., New York.

Number	0	1	2	3	4	5	6	7	8	9	Avg. diff.
.50	0.6931	6911	6892	6872	6852	6832	6812	6792	6773	6753	20
.51	6733	6714	6694	6675	6655	6636	6616	6597	6578	6559	19
.52	6539	6520	6501	6482	6463	6444	6425	6406	6387	6368	19
.53	6349	6330	6311	6292	6274	6255	6236	6218	6199	6180	18
.54	6162	6143	6125	6106	6088	6070	6051	6033	6015	5997	18
.55	0.5978	5960	5942	5924	5906	5888	5870	5852	5834	5816	18
.56	5798	5780	5763	5745	5727	5709	5692	5674	5656	5639	18
.57	5621	5604	5586	5569	5551	5534	5516	5499	5482	5465	17
.58	5447	5430	5413	5396	5379	5361	5344	5327	5310	5293	17
.59	5276	5259	5243	5226	5209	5192	5175	5158	5142	5125	17
.60	0.5108	5092	5075	5058	5042	5025	5009	4992	4976	4959	16
.61	4943	4927	4910	4894	4878	4861	4845	4829	4813	4796	16
.62	4780	4764	4748	4732	4716	4700	4684	4668	4652	4636	16
.63	4620	4604	4589	4573	4557	4541	4526	4510	4494	4479	16
.64	4463	4447	4432	4416	4401	4385	4370	4354	4339	4323	15
.65	0.4308	4292	4277	4262	4246	4231	4216	4201	4186	4170	15
.66	4155	4140	4125	4110	4095	4080	4065	4050	4035	4020	15
.67	4005	3990	3975	3960	3945	3930	3916	3901	3886	3871	15
.68	3857	3842	3827	3813	3798	3783	3769	3754	3740	3725	15
.69	3711	3696	3682	3667	3653	3638	3624	3610	3595	3581	14
.70	0.3567	3552	3538	3524	3510	3496	3481	3467	3453	3439	14
.71	3425	3411	3397	3383	3369	3355	3341	3327	3313	3299	14
.72	3285	3271	3257	3243	3230	3216	3202	3188	3175	3161	14
.73	3147	3133	3120	3106	3092	3079	3065	3052	3038	3025	13
.74	3011	2998	2984	2971	2957	2944	2930	2917	2904	2890	13
.75	0.2877	2863	2850	2837	2824	2810	2797	2784	2771	2758	13
.76	2744	2731	2718	2705	2692	2679	2666	2653	2640	2627	13
.77	2614	2601	2588	2575	2562	2549	2536	2523	2510	2497	13
.78	2485	2472	2459	2446	2433	2421	2408	2395	2383	2370	13
.79	2357	2345	2332	2319	2307	2294	2282	2269	2256	2244	12
.80	0.2231	2219	2206	2194	2182	2169	2157	2144	2132	2120	12
.81	2107	2095	2083	2070	2058	2046	2033	2021	2009	1997	12
.82	1985	1972	1960	1948	1936	1924	1912	1900	1888	1875	12
.83	1863	1851	1839	1827	1815	1803	1791	1779	1767	1755	12
.84	1744	1732	1720	1708	1696	1684	1672	1661	1649	1637	12
.85	0.1625	1613	1602	1590	1578	1567	1555	1543	1532	1520	12
.86	1508	1497	1485	1473	1462	1450	1439	1427	1416	1404	12
.87	1393	1381	1370	1358	1347	1335	1324	1312	1301	1290	11
.88	1278	1267	1256	1244	1233	1222	1210	1199	1188	1177	11
.89	1166	1154	1143	1132	1120	1109	1098	1087	1076	1065	11
.90	0.1054	1043	1031	1020	1009	0998	0987	0976	0965	0954	11
.91	0943	0932	0921	0910	0899	0888	0877	0866	0856	0845	11
.92	0834	0823	0812	0801	0790	0780	0769	0758	0747	0736	11
.93	0726	0715	0704	0694	0683	0672	0661	0651	0640	0629	11
.94	0619	0608	0598	0587	0576	0566	0555	0545	0534	0523	11
.95	0.0513	0502	0492	0481	0471	0460	0450	0440	0429	0419	10
.96	0408	0398	0387	0377	0367	0356	0346	0336	0325	0315	10
.97	0305	0294	0284	0274	0263	0253	0243	0233	0222	0212	10
.98	0202	0192	0182	0171	0161	0151	0141	0131	0121	0111	10
.99	0101	0090	0080	0070	0060	0050	0040	0030	0020	0010	10

Number	0	1	2	3	4	5	6	7	8	9	Avg. diff.
1.0	0.0000	0100	0198	0296	0392	0488	0583	0677	0770	0862	95
1.1	0953	1044	1133	1222	1310	1398	1484	1570	1655	1740	87
1.2	1823	1906	1989	2070	2151	2231	2311	2390	2469	2546	80
1.3	2624	2700	2776	2852	2927	3001	3075	3148	3221	3293	74
1.4	3365	3436	3507	3577	3646	3716	3784	3853	3920	3988	69
1.5	0.4055	4121	4187	4253	4318	4383	4447	4511	4574	4637	65
1.6	4700	4762	4824	4886	4947	5008	5068	5128	5188	5247	61
1.7	5306	5365	5423	5481	5539	5596	5653	5710	5766	5822	57
1.8	5878	5933	5988	6043	6098	6152	6206	6259	6313	6366	54
1.9	6419	6471	6523	6575	6627	6678	6729	6780	6831	6881	51
2.0	0.6931	6981	7031	7080	7129	7178	7227	7275	7324	7372	49
2.1	7419	7467	7514	7561	7608	7655	7701	7747	7793	7839	47
2.2	7885	7930	7975	8020	8065	8109	8154	8198	8242	8286	44
2.3	8329	8372	8416	8459	8502	8544	8587	8629	8671	8713	43
2.4	8755	8796	8838	8879	8920	8961	9002	9042	9083	9123	41
2.5	0.9163	9203	9243	9282	9322	9361	9400	9439	9478	9517	39
2.6	9555	9594	9632	9670	9708	9746	9783	9821	9858	9895	38
2.7	0.9933	9969	0006	0043	0080	0116	0152	0188	0225	0260	36
2.8	1.0296	0332	0367	0403	0438	0473	0508	0543	0578	0613	35
2.9	0647	0682	0716	0750	0784	0818	0852	0886	0919	0953	34
3.0	1.0986	1019	1053	1086	1119	1151	1184	1217	1249	1282	33
3.1	1314	1346	1378	1410	1442	1474	1506	1537	1569	1600	32
3.2	1632	1663	1694	1725	1756	1787	1817	1848	1878	1909	31
3.3	1939	1969	2000	2030	2060	2090	2119	2149	2179	2208	30
3.4	2238	2267	2296	2326	2355	2384	2413	2442	2470	2499	29
3.5	1.2528	2556	2585	2613	2641	2669	2698	2726	2754	2782	28
3.6	2809	2837	2865	2892	2920	2947	2975	3002	3029	3056	27
3.7	3083	3110	3137	3164	3191	3218	3244	3271	3297	3324	27
3.8	3350	3376	3403	3429	3455	3481	3507	3533	3558	3584	26
3.9	3610	3635	3661	3686	3712	3737	3762	3788	3813	3838	25
4.0	1.3863	3888	3913	3938	3962	3987	4012	4036	4061	4085	25
4.1	4110	4134	4159	4183	4207	4231	4255	4279	4303	4327	24
4.2	4351	4375	4398	4422	4446	4469	4493	4516	4540	4563	23
4.3	4586	4609	4633	4656	4679	4702	4725	4748	4770	4793	23
4.4	4816	4839	4861	4884	4907	4929	4951	4974	4996	5019	22
4.5	1.5041	5063	5085	5107	5129	5151	5173	5195	5217	5239	22
4.6	5261	5282	5304	5326	5347	5369	5390	5412	5433	5454	21
4.7	5476	5497	5518	5539	5560	5581	5602	5623	5644	5665	21
4.8	5686	5707	5728	5748	5769	5790	5810	5831	5851	5872	20
4.9	5892	5913	5933	5953	5974	5994	6014	6034	6054	6074	20
5.0	1.6094	6114	6134	6154	6174	6194	6214	6233	6253	6273	20
5.1	6292	6312	6332	6351	6371	6390	6409	6429	6448	6467	19
5.2	6487	6506	6525	6544	6563	6582	6601	6620	6639	6658	19
5.3	6677	6696	6715	6734	6752	6771	6790	6808	6827	6845	18
5.4	6864	6882	6901	6919	6938	6956	6974	6993	7011	7029	18
5.5	1.7047	7066	7084	7102	7120	7138	7156	7174	7192	7210	18
5.6	7228	7246	7263	7281	7299	7317	7334	7352	7370	7387	18
5.7	7405	7422	7440	7457	7475	7492	7509	7527	7544	7561	17
5.8	7579	7596	7613	7630	7647	7664	7681	7699	7716	7733	17
5.9	7750	7766	7783	7800	7817	7834	7851	7867	7884	7901	17

[1] Pages 247 and 248 are taken from Marks' "Mechanical Engineers' Handbook," published by the McGraw-Hill Book Company, Inc., New York.

Number	0	1	2	3	4	5	6	7	8	9	Avg. diff.
6.0	1.7918	7934	7951	7967	7984	8001	8017	8034	8050	8066	16
6.1	8083	8099	8116	8132	8148	8165	8181	8197	8213	8229	16
6.2	8245	8262	8278	8294	8310	8326	8342	8358	8374	8390	16
6.3	8405	8421	8437	8453	8469	8485	8500	8516	8532	8547	16
6.4	8563	8579	8594	8610	8625	8641	8656	8672	8687	8703	15
6.5	1.8718	8733	8749	8764	8779	8795	8810	8825	8840	8856	15
6.6	8871	8886	8901	8916	8931	8946	8961	8976	8991	9006	15
6.7	9021	9036	9051	9066	9081	9095	9110	9125	9140	9155	15
6.8	9169	9184	9199	9213	9228	9242	9257	9272	9286	9301	15
6.9	9315	9330	9344	9359	9373	9387	9402	9416	9430	9445	14
7.0	1.9459	9473	9488	9502	9516	9530	9544	9559	9573	9587	14
7.1	9601	9615	9629	9643	9657	9671	9685	9699	9713	9727	14
7.2	9741	9755	9769	9782	9796	9810	9824	9838	9851	9865	14
7.3	1.9879	9892	9906	9920	9933	9947	9961	9974	9988	0001	13
7.4	2.0015	0028	0042	0055	0069	0082	0096	0109	0122	0136	13
7.5	2.0149	0162	0176	0189	0202	0215	0229	0242	0255	0268	13
7.6	0281	0295	0308	0321	0334	0347	0360	0373	0386	0399	13
7.7	0412	0425	0438	0451	0464	0477	0490	0503	0516	0528	13
7.8	0541	0554	0567	0580	0592	0605	0618	0631	0643	0656	13
7.9	0669	0681	0694	0707	0719	0732	0744	0757	0769	0782	12
8.0	2.0794	0807	0819	0832	0844	0857	0869	0882	0894	0906	12
8.1	0919	0931	0943	0956	0968	0980	0992	1005	1017	1029	12
8.2	1041	1054	1066	1078	1090	1102	1114	1126	1138	1150	12
8.3	1163	1175	1187	1199	1211	1223	1235	1247	1258	1270	12
8.4	1282	1294	1306	1318	1330	1342	1353	1365	1377	1389	12
8.5	2.1401	1412	1424	1436	1448	1459	1471	1483	1494	1506	12
8.6	1518	1529	1541	1552	1564	1576	1587	1599	1610	1622	12
8.7	1633	1645	1656	1668	1679	1691	1702	1713	1725	1736	11
8.8	1748	1759	1770	1782	1793	1804	1815	1827	1838	1849	11
8.9	1861	1872	1883	1894	1905	1917	1928	1939	1950	1961	11
9.0	2.1972	1983	1994	2006	2017	2028	2039	2050	2061	2072	11
9.1	2083	2094	2105	2116	2127	2138	2148	2159	2170	2181	11
9.2	2192	2203	2214	2225	2235	2246	2257	2268	2279	2289	11
9.3	2300	2311	2322	2332	2343	2354	2364	2375	2386	2396	11
9.4	2407	2418	2428	2439	2450	2460	2471	2481	2492	2502	11
9.5	2.2513	2523	2534	2544	2555	2565	2576	2586	2597	2607	10
9.6	2618	2628	2638	2649	2659	2670	2680	2690	2701	2711	10
9.7	2721	2732	2742	2752	2762	2773	2783	2793	2803	2814	10
9.8	2824	2834	2844	2854	2865	2875	2885	2895	2905	2915	10
9.9	2925	2935	2946	2956	2966	2976	2986	2996	3006	3016	10
10.0	2.3026										

8. TABLE OF EXPONENTIAL AND HYPERBOLIC FUNCTIONS IN TERMS OF NEPERS*

x	e^x	e^{-x}	sinh x	cosh x	tanh x
.00	1.0000	1.0000	0.0000	1.0000	0.0000
.01	.0101	0.9900	.0100	.0001	.0100
.02	.0202	.9802	.0200	.0002	.0200
.03	.0305	.9704	.0300	.0005	.0300
.04	.0408	.9608	.0400	.0008	.0400
.05	.0513	.9512	.0500	.0013	.0500
.06	.0618	.9418	.0600	.0018	.0599
.07	.0725	.9324	.0701	.0025	.0699
.08	.0833	.9231	.0801	.0032	.0798
.09	.0942	.9139	.0901	.0041	.0898
.10	1.1052	0.9048	0.1002	1.0050	0.0997
.11	.1163	.8958	.1102	.0061	.1096
.12	.1275	.8869	.1203	.0072	.1194
.13	.1388	.8781	.1304	.0085	.1293
.14	.1503	.8694	.1405	.0098	.1391
.15	.1618	.8607	.1506	.0113	.1489
.16	.1735	.8521	.1607	.0128	.1587
.17	.1853	.8437	.1708	.0145	.1684
.18	.1972	.8353	.1810	.0162	.1781
.19	.2092	.8270	.1911	.0181	.1878
.20	1.2214	0.8187	0.2013	1.0201	0.1974
.21	.2337	.8106	.2115	.0221	.2070
.22	.2461	.8025	.2218	.0243	.2165
.23	.2586	.7945	.2320	.0266	.2260
.24	.2712	.7866	.2423	.0289	.2355
.25	.2840	.7788	.2526	.0314	.2449
.26	.2969	.7711	.2629	.0340	.2543
.27	.3100	.7634	.2733	.0367	.2636
.28	.3231	.7558	.2837	.0395	.2729
.29	.3364	.7483	.2941	.0423	.2821
.30	1.3499	0.7408	0.3045	1.0453	0.2913
.31	.3634	.7334	.3150	.0484	.3004
.32	.3771	.7261	.3255	.0516	.3095
.33	.3910	.7189	.3360	.0549	.3185
.34	.4049	.7118	.3466	.0584	.3275
.35	.4191	.7047	.3572	.0619	.3364
.36	.4333	.6977	.3678	.0655	.3452
.37	.4477	.6907	.3785	.0692	.3540
.38	.4623	.6839	.3892	.0731	.3627
.39	.4770	.6771	.4000	.0770	.3714
.40	1.4918	0.6703	0.4108	1.0811	0.3800
.41	.5068	.6637	.4216	.0852	.3885
.42	.5220	.6570	.4325	.0895	.3969
.43	.5373	.6505	.4434	.0939	.4053
.44	.5527	.6440	.4543	.0984	.4136
.45	.5683	.6376	.4653	.1030	.4219
.46	.5841	.6313	.4764	.1077	.4301
.47	.6000	.6250	.4875	.1125	.4382
.48	.6161	.6188	.4986	.1174	.4462
.49	.6323	.6126	.5098	.1225	.4542
.50	1.6487	0.6065	0.5211	1.1276	0.4621
.51	.6653	.6005	.5324	.1329	.4700
.52	.6820	.5945	.5438	.1383	.4777
.53	.6989	.5886	.5552	.1438	.4854
.54	.7160	.5827	.5666	.1494	.4930

* From Allen's "Six-Place Tables," published by the McGraw-Hill Book Company, Inc., New York.

x	e^x	e^{-x}	sinh x	cosh x	tanh x
.55	.7333	.5769	.5782	.1551	.5005
.56	.7507	.5712	.5897	.1609	.5080
.57	.7683	.5655	.6014	.1669	.5154
.58	.7860	.5599	.6131	.1730	.5227
.59	.8040	.5543	.6248	.1792	.5299
.60	1.8221	0.5488	0.6367	1.1855	0.5370
.61	.8404	.5434	.6485	.1919	.5441
.62	.8589	.5379	.6605	.1984	.5511
.63	.8776	.5326	.6725	.2051	.5581
.64	.8965	.5273	.6846	.2119	.5649
.65	.9155	.5220	.6967	.2188	.5717
.66	.9348	.5169	.7090	.2258	.5784
.67	.9542	.5117	.7213	.2330	.5850
.68	.9739	.5066	.7336	.2402	.5915
.69	.9937	.5016	.7461	.2476	.5980
.70	2.0138	0.4966	0.7586	1.2552	0.6044
.71	.0340	.4916	.7712	.2628	.6107
.72	.0544	.4868	.7838	.2706	.6169
.73	.0751	.4819	.7966	.2785	.6231
.74	.0959	.4771	.8094	.2865	.6291
.75	.1170	.4724	.8223	.2947	.6352
.76	.1383	.4677	.8353	.3030	.6411
.77	.1598	.4630	.8484	.3114	.6469
.78	.1815	.4584	.8615	.3199	.6527
.79	.2034	.4538	.8748	.3286	.6584
.80	2.2255	0.4493	0.8881	1.3374	0.6640
.81	.2479	.4449	.9015	.3464	.6696
.82	.2705	.4404	.9150	.3555	.6751
.83	.2933	.4360	.9286	.3647	.6805
.84	.3164	.4317	.9423	.3740	.6858
.85	.3396	.4274	.9561	.3835	.6911
.86	.3632	.4232	.9700	.3932	.6963
.87	.3869	.4190	.9840	.4029	.7014
.88	.4109	.4148	.9981	.4128	.7064
.89	.4351	.4107	1.0122	.4229	.7114
.90	2.4596	0.4066	1.0265	1.4331	0.7163
.91	.4843	.4025	.0409	.4434	.7211
.92	.5093	.3985	.0554	.4539	.7259
.93	.5345	.3946	.0700	.4645	.7306
.94	.5600	.3906	.0847	.4753	.7352
.95	.5857	.3867	.0995	.4862	.7398
.96	.6117	.3829	.1144	.4973	.7443
.97	.6379	.3791	.1294	.5085	.7487
.98	.6645	.3753	.1446	.5199	.7531
.99	.6912	.3716	.1598	.5314	.7574
1.00	2.7183	0.3679	1.1752	1.5431	0.7616
.05	.8577	.3499	.2539	.6038	.7818
.10	3.0042	.3329	.3356	.6685	.8005
.15	.1582	.3166	.4208	.7374	.8178
.20	.3201	.3012	.5095	.8107	.8337
.25	.4903	.2865	.6019	.8884	.8483
.30	.6693	.2725	.6984	.9709	.8617
.35	.8574	.2592	.7991	2.0583	.8741
.40	4.0552	.2466	.9043	.1509	.8854
.45	.2631	.2346	2.0143	.2488	.8957

x	e^x	e^{-x}	$\sinh x$	$\cosh x$	$\tanh x$
1.50	4.4817	0.2231	2.1293	2.3524	0.9052
.55	.7115	.2122	.2496	.4619	.9138
.60	.9530	.2019	.3756	.5775	.9217
.65	5.2070	.1920	.5075	.6995	.9289
.70	.4739	.1827	.6456	.8283	.9354
.75	.7546	.1738	.7904	.9642	.9414
.80	6.0496	.1653	.9422	3.1075	.9468
.85	.3598	.1572	3.1013	.2585	.9518
.90	.6859	.1496	.2682	.4177	.9562
.95	7.0287	.1423	.4432	.5855	.9603
2.00	7.3891	0.1353	3.6269	3.7622	0.9640
.05	.7679	.1287	.8196	.9483	.9674
.10	8.1662	.1225	4.0219	4.1443	.9705
.15	.5848	.1165	.2342	.3507	.9732
.20	9.025	.1108	.457	.568	.9757
.25	.488	.1054	.691	.797	.9780
.30	.974	.1003	.937	5.037	.9801
.35	10.486	.0954	5.195	.290	.9820
.40	11.023	.0907	.466	.557	.9837
.5	12.182	.0821	6.050	6.132	.9866
.6	13.464	.0743	.695	.769	.9890
.7	14.880	.0672	7.406	7.473	.9910
.8	16.445	.0608	8.192	8.253	.9926
.9	18.174	.0550	9.060	9.115	.9940
3.0	20.086	.0498	10.018	10.068	.9951
.1	22.198	.0450	11.076	11.121	.9959
.2	24.533	.0408	12.246	12.287	.9967
.3	27.113	.0369	13.538	13.575	.9973
.4	29.964	.0334	14.965	14.999	.9978
.5	33.115	.0302	16.543	16.573	.9982
.6	36.598	.0273	18.285	18.313	.9985
.7	40.447	.0247	20.211	20.236	.9988
.8	44.701	.0224	22.339	22.362	.9990
.9	49.402	.0202	24.691	24.711	.9992
4.0	54.60	.0183	27.29	27.31	.999
4.1	60.34	.0166	30.16	30.18	.999
4.2	66.69	.0150	33.34	33.35	1.000
4.3	73.70	.0136	36.84	36.86	1.000
4.4	81.45	.0123	40.72	40.73	1.000
4.5	90.02	.0111	45.00	45.01	1.000
4.6	99.48	.0101	49.74	49.75	1.000
4.7	109.95	.0091	54.97	54.98	1.000
4.8	121.51	.0082	60.75	60.76	1.000
4.9	134.29	.0074	67.14	67.15	1.000
5.0	148.41	.0067	74.20	74.21	1.000
6.0	403.4	.0025	201.7		1.000
7.0	1096.6	.00091	548.3		1.000
8.0	2981.0	.00034	1490.5		1.000
9.0	8103.1	.00012	4051.5		1.000
10.0	22026.5	.000045	11013.2		1.000

In the compilation of this table, extensive use was made of Kennelly's Tables of Complex Hyperbolic and Circular Functions.

9. TABLE OF EXPONENTIAL AND HYPERBOLIC FUNCTIONS IN TERMS OF DECIBELS

N_{db}	Nepers α	k ϵ^α	$\dfrac{1}{k}$ $\epsilon^{-\alpha}$	k^2 $\epsilon^{2\alpha}$	$\dfrac{k^2-1}{2k}$ $\sinh \alpha$	$\dfrac{k^2+1}{2k}$ $\cosh \alpha$	$\dfrac{k^2-1}{k^2+1}$ $\tanh \alpha$	$\dfrac{k-1}{k+1}$ $\tanh \dfrac{\alpha}{2}$
0.05	0.005757	1.00577	0.99426	1.01158	0.005756	1.00002	0.005756	0.002878
0.1	0.011513	1.01158	0.98855	1.02330	0.011513	1.00007	0.011512	0.005756
0.2	0.023024	1.02329	0.97724	1.04713	0.023028	1.00027	0.023022	0.011512
0.3	0.034539	1.03514	0.96605	1.07152	0.034546	1.00060	0.034525	0.017268
0.4	0.046052	1.04713	0.95499	1.09648	0.046067	1.00106	0.046019	0.023022
0.5	0.057565	1.05925	0.94406	1.12202	0.057597	1.00166	0.057502	0.028774
0.6	0.069078	1.07152	0.93325	1.14815	0.069131	1.00238	0.068968	0.034525
0.7	0.080591	1.08393	0.92257	1.17490	0.080679	1.00325	0.080418	0.040274
0.8	0.092103	1.09648	0.91201	1.20227	0.092236	1.00425	0.091846	0.046019
0.9	0.103626	1.10917	0.90157	1.23027	0.103797	1.00538	0.103249	0.051763
1.0	0.11513	1.12202	0.89125	1.25893	0.11539	1.00664	0.11463	0.057502
1.1	0.12664	1.13501	0.88105	1.28825	0.12697	1.00803	0.12597	0.063237
1.2	0.13816	1.14815	0.87096	1.31826	0.13860	1.00956	0.13728	0.068968
1.3	0.14967	1.16145	0.86099	1.34896	0.15023	1.01122	0.14956	0.074695
1.4	0.16118	1.17490	0.85114	1.38038	0.16188	1.01301	0.15979	0.080418
1.5	0.17269	1.18850	0.84139	1.41254	0.17356	1.01495	0.17100	0.086132
1.6	0.18421	1.20227	0.83176	1.44544	0.18525	1.01701	0.18215	0.091846
1.7	0.19572	1.21618	0.82224	1.47911	0.19697	1.01922	0.19326	0.097551
1.8	0.20723	1.23027	0.81283	1.51356	0.20872	1.02155	0.20432	0.103249
1.9	0.21876	1.24452	0.80353	1.54882	0.22050	1.02402	0.21532	0.108939
2.0	0.23026	1.25893	0.79433	1.58489	0.23230	1.02662	0.22627	0.11463
2.2	0.25328	1.28825	0.77625	1.65959	0.25600	1.03225	0.24800	0.12597
2.4	0.27631	1.31826	0.75858	1.73780	0.27984	1.03841	0.26948	0.13728
2.5	0.28782	1.33352	0.74989	1.77828	0.29181	1.04171	0.28013	0.14293
2.6	0.29934	1.34896	0.74131	1.81970	0.30383	1.04514	0.29071	0.14856
2.8	0.32236	1.38038	0.72444	1.90546	0.32798	1.05241	0.31164	0.15980
3.0	0.34539	1.41254	0.70795	1.99526	0.35230	1.06024	0.33228	0.17100
3.2	0.36841	1.44544	0.69183	2.08930	0.37681	1.06864	0.35261	0.18215
3.4	0.39144	1.47911	0.67608	2.18776	0.40151	1.07759	0.37260	0.19326
3.5	0.40295	1.49623	0.66834	2.23870	0.41394	1.08229	0.38246	0.19879
3.6	0.41447	1.51356	0.66069	2.29086	0.42645	1.08714	0.39226	0.20432
3.8	0.43749	1.54882	0.64565	2.39884	0.45157	1.09722	0.41156	0.21532
4.0	0.46052	1.58489	0.63096	2.51188	0.47697	1.10793	0.43051	0.22627
4.5	0.51808	1.67880	0.59566	2.81837	0.54158	1.13724	0.47622	0.25340
5.0	0.57565	1.77828	0.56234	3.16228	0.60798	1.17032	0.51950	0.28013

N_{db}	Nepers α	k ϵ^{α}	$\dfrac{1}{k}$ $\epsilon^{-\alpha}$	k^2 $\epsilon^{2\alpha}$	$\dfrac{k^2-1}{2k}$ $\sinh \alpha$	$\dfrac{k^2+1}{2k}$ $\cosh \alpha$	$\dfrac{k^2-1}{k^2+1}$ $\tanh \alpha$	$\dfrac{k-1}{k+1}$ $\tanh \dfrac{\alpha}{2}$
5.5	0.63321	1.88365	0.53088	3.5481	0.67637	1.20726	0.56026	0.30643
6.0	0.69078	1.99526	0.50119	3.9811	0.74705	1.24823	0.59848	0.33228
6.5	0.74834	2.11349	0.47315	4.4668	0.82016	1.29331	0.63415	0.35764
7.0	0.80591	2.23872	0.44668	5.0119	0.89603	1.34272	0.66732	0.38246
7.5	0.86347	2.37137	0.42170	5.6234	0.97483	1.39652	0.69804	0.40677
8.0	0.92103	2.5119	0.39811	6.3096	1.05689	1.45500	0.72639	0.43051
8.5	0.97860	2.6607	0.37584	7.0795	1.14246	1.51830	0.75246	0.45366
9.0	1.03616	2.8184	0.35481	7.9433	1.23178	1.58659	0.77637	0.47622
9.5	1.09373	2.9854	0.33497	8.9125	1.32520	1.66016	0.79823	0.49817
10.0	1.15129	3.1623	0.31623	10.0000	1.42302	1.73924	0.81818	0.51950
10.5	1.20886	3.3497	0.29854	11.220	1.52551	1.82404	0.83633	0.54020
11.0	1.26642	3.5481	0.28184	12.589	1.63313	1.91497	0.85282	0.56026
11.5	1.32399	3.7584	0.26607	14.125	1.74609	2.01216	0.86777	0.57969
12.0	1.38155	3.9811	0.25119	15.849	1.86494	2.11612	0.88130	0.59848
12.5	1.43912	4.2170	0.23714	17.783	1.98992	2.22706	0.89352	0.61664
13.0	1.49668	4.4668	0.22387	19.953	2.12154	2.34542	0.90455	0.63416
13.5	1.55425	4.7315	0.21135	22.387	2.26007	2.47142	0.91448	0.65105
14.0	1.61181	5.0119	0.19953	25.119	2.40617	2.60570	0.92343	0.66733
14.5	1.66937	5.3088	0.18836	28.184	2.56028	2.74864	0.93147	0.68298
15.0	1.72694	5.6234	0.17783	31.623	2.72282	2.90065	0.93869	0.69804
15.5	1.78450	5.9566	0.16788	35.481	2.89435	3.06223	0.94517	0.71250
16.0	1.84207	6.3096	0.15849	39.811	3.07555	3.23404	0.95099	0.72639
16.5	1.89963	6.6834	0.14962	44.668	3.26690	3.41653	0.95621	0.73970
17.0	1.95720	7.0795	0.14125	50.119	3.46910	3.61035	0.96088	0.75246
17.5	2.01476	7.4989	0.13335	56.234	3.68281	3.81616	0.96506	0.76468
18.0	2.07233	7.9433	0.12589	63.096	3.90870	4.03460	0.96880	0.77637
18.5	2.12989	8.4139	0.11885	70.795	4.14760	4.26645	0.97214	0.78755
19.0	2.18746	8.9125	0.11220	79.433	4.40017	4.51237	0.97514	0.79823
19.5	2.24502	9.4406	0.10593	89.125	4.66734	4.77327	0.97781	0.80844
20.0	2.30259	10.0000	0.10000	100.000	4.95000	5.05000	0.98020	0.81818
21.0	2.41771	11.2202	8912.5*	125.893	5.56554	5.65467	0.98424	0.83634
22.0	2.53284	12.5893	7943.3*	158.490	6.25506	6.33450	0.98746	0.85282
23.0	2.64797	14.1254	7079.5*	199.527	7.02761	7.09841	0.99003	0.86777
24.0	2.76310	15.8489	6309.6*	251.188	7.89293	7.95602	0.99207	0.88130
25.0	2.87823	17.7828	5623.4*	316.228	8.86324	8.91947	0.99370	0.89352

* Multiply by 10^{-5}.

N_{db}	Nepers α	k ϵ^{α}	$\dfrac{1}{k}$ $\epsilon^{-\alpha}$	k^2 $\epsilon^{2\alpha}$	$\dfrac{k^2-1}{2k}$ $\sinh \alpha$	$\dfrac{k^2+1}{2k}$ $\cosh \alpha$	$\dfrac{k^2-1}{k^2+1}$ $\tanh \alpha$	$\dfrac{k-1}{k+1}$ $\tanh \dfrac{\alpha}{2}$
26.0	2.99336	19.953	5011.9*	398.11	9.951	10.001	0.99499	0.90455
27.0	3.10849	22.387	4466.8*	501.19	11.171	11.216	0.99602	0.91448
28.0	3.22362	25.119	3981.1*	630.96	12.540	12.579	0.99684	0.92343
29.0	3.33875	28.184	3548.1*	794.33	14.074	14.110	0.99749	0.93147
30.0	3.45388	31.623	3162.3*	1000.00	15.795	15.827	0.99800	0.93869
31.0	3.56901	35.481	2818.4*	1258.9	17.726	17.754	0.99841	0.94518
32.0	3.68414	39.811	2511.9*	1584.9	19.893	19.918	0.99874	0.95099
33.0	3.79927	44.668	2238.7*	1995.3	22.324	22.346	0.99900	0.95621
34.0	3.91439	50.119	1995.3*	2511.9	25.049	25.069	0.99920	0.96088
35.0	4.02952	56.234	1778.3*	3162.3	28.108	28.126	0.99937	0.96506
36.0	4.14465	63.096	1584.9*	3981.1	⨍ 31.540	31.556	0.99950	0.96880
37.0	4.25978	70.795	1412.5*	5011.9	35.390	35.404	0.99960	0.97214
38.0	4.37491	79.433	1258.9*	6309.6	39.710	39.723	0.99968	0.97513
39.0	4.49004	89.125	1122.0*	7943.3	44.557	44.568	0.99975	0.97781
40.0	4.60517	100.000	1000.0*	10000.0	49.995	50.005	0.99980	0.98020
41.0	4.72030	112.20	891.25*	12589.	56.095	56.104	0.99984	0.98233
42.0	4.83543	125.89	794.33*	15849.	62.944	62.956	0.99987	0.98424
43.0	4.95056	141.25	707.95*	19953.	70.627	70.634	0.99990	0.98594
44.0	5.06569	158.49	630.96*	25119.	79.242	79.248	0.99992	0.98746
45.0	5.18081	177.83	562.34*	31623.	88.911	88.916	0.99994	0.98887
46.0	5.29595	199.53	501.19*	39811.	99.77	99.76	0.99995	0.99003
47.0	5.41107	223.87	446.68*	50119.	111.94	111.94	0.99996	0.99111
48.0	5.52620	251.19	398.11*	63096.	125.59	125.60	0.99997	0.99207
49.0	5.64133	281.84	354.81*	79433.	140.92	140.92	0.99997	0.99293
50.0	5.75646	316.23	316.23*	100000.	158.11	158.11	0.99998	0.99370
55.0	6.33211	562.3	177.83*	3.162†	281.17	281.17	0.99999	0.99645
60.0	6.90776	1000.0	100.00*	10.000†	500.00	500.00	0.99999	0.99800
65.0	7.48340	1778.3	56.23*	31.623†	889.14	889.14	0.99999	0.99888
70.0	8.05905	3162.3	31.62*	100.000†	1581.13	1581.13	1.00000	0.99937
75.0	8.63469	5623.4	17.78*	316.228†	2811.71	2811.71	1.00000	0.99964
80.0	9.21034	10000.	10.000*	1000.†	0.5000†	0.5000†	1.00000	0.99980
85.0	9.78599	17783.	5.623*	3162.†	0.8891†	0.8891†	1.00000	0.99989
90.0	10.36163	31623.	3.162*	10000.†	1.5811†	1.5811†	1.00000	0.99994
95.0	10.93728	56234.	1.778*	31623.†	2.8117†	2.8117†	1.00000	0.99996
100.0	11.51293	100000.	1.000*	100000.†	5.0000†	5.0000†	1.00000	0.99998

* Multiply by 10^{-5}.
† Multiply by 10^{+5}.

10. CURVES AND TABLES OF BESSEL FUNCTIONS

a. Bessel function curves:

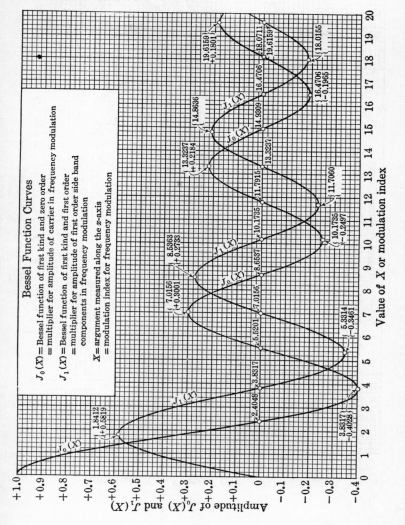

Bessel Function Curves

$J_0(X)$ = Bessel function of first kind and zero order
= multiplier for amplitude of carrier in frequency modulation

$J_1(X)$ = Bessel function of first kind and first order
= multiplier for amplitude of first order side band
components in frequency modulation

X = argument measured along the x-axis
= modulation index for frequency modulation

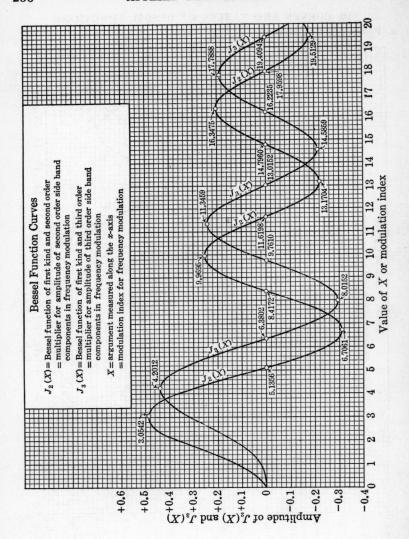

Bessel Function Curves

$J_2(X)$ = Bessel function of first kind and second order
= multiplier for amplitude of second order side band components in frequency modulation

$J_3(X)$ = Bessel function of first kind and third order
= multiplier for amplitude of third order side band components in frequency modulation

X = argument measured along the x-axis
= modulation index for frequency modulation

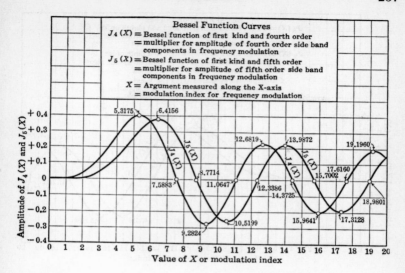

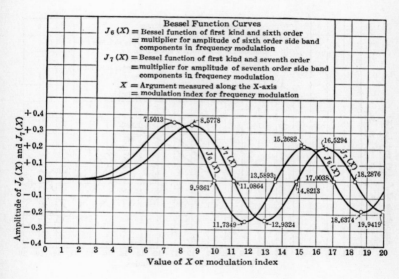

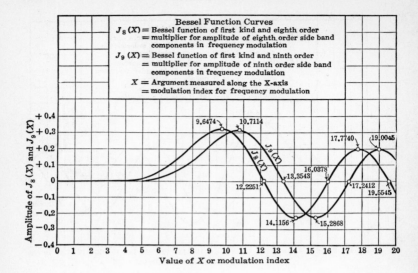

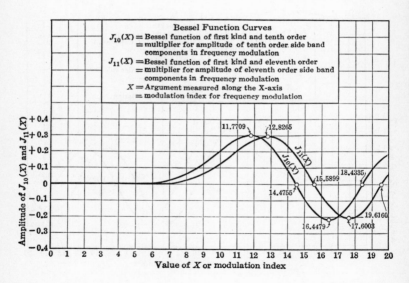

b. Table of Bessel functions, $J_0(x)$ and $J_1(x)$:*

x	$J_0(x)$	$-J_1(x)$	x	$J_0(x)$	$-J_1(x)$
0.00	1.000000	0.000000	0.25	0.984436	−0.124026
0.01	0.999975	−0.005000	0.26	0.983171	−0.128905
0.02	0.999900	−0.010000	0.27	0.981858	−0.133774
0.03	0.999775	−0.014998	0.28	0.980496	−0.138632
0.04	0.999600	−0.019996	0.29	0.979085	−0.143481
0.05	0.999375	−0.024992	0.30	0.977626	−0.148319
0.06	0.999100	−0.029987	0.31	0.976119	−0.153146
0.07	0.998775	−0.034979	0.32	0.974563	−0.157961
0.08	0.998401	−0.039968	0.33	0.972960	−0.162764
0.09	0.997976	−0.044954	0.34	0.971308	−0.167555
0.10	0.997502	−0.049938	0.35	0.969609	−0.172334
0.11	0.996977	−0.054917	0.36	0.967861	−0.177100
0.12	0.996403	−0.059892	0.37	0.966067	−0.181852
0.13	0.995779	−0.064863	0.38	0.964224	−0.186591
0.14	0.995106	−0.069829	0.39	0.962335	−0.191316
0.15	0.994383	−0.074789	0.40	0.960398	−0.196027
0.16	0.993610	−0.079744	0.41	0.958414	−0.200723
0.17	0.992788	−0.084693	0.42	0.956384	−0.205403
0.18	0.991916	−0.089636	0.43	0.954306	−0.210069
0.19	0.990995	−0.094572	0.44	0.952183	−0.214719
0.20	0.990025	−0.099501	0.45	0.950012	−0.219353
0.21	0.989005	−0.104422	0.46	0.947796	−0.223970
0.22	0.987937	−0.109336	0.47	0.945533	−0.228571
0.23	0.986819	−0.114241	0.48	0.943224	−0.233154
0.24	0.985652	−0.119138	0.49	0.940870	−0.237720
0.25	0.984436	−0.124026	0.50	0.938470	−0.242268

* This table is a simplification of Dr. Meissel's "Tafel der Bessel'schen Functionen," originally published in Berlin, 1888. These twelve place tables have been reprinted in "Bessel Functions" by Gray, Mathews, and Macrobert, published by Macmillan & Company, Ltd., in 1931.

x	$J_0(x)$	$-J_1(x)$	x	$J_0(x)$	$-J_1(x)$
0.50	0.938470	−0.242268	0.80	0.846287	−0.368842
0.51	0.936024	−0.246799	0.81	0.842580	−0.372681
0.52	0.933534	−0.251310	0.82	0.838834	−0.376492
0.53	0.930998	−0.255803	0.83	0.835050	−0.380275
0.54	0.928418	−0.260277	0.84	0.831228	−0.384029
0.55	0.925793	−0.264732	0.85	0.827369	−0.387755
0.56	0.923123	−0.269166	0.86	0.823473	−0.391453
0.57	0.920410	−0.273581	0.87	0.819541	−0.395121
0.58	0.917652	−0.277975	0.88	0.815571	−0.398760
0.59	0.914850	−0.282349	0.89	0.811565	−0.402370
0.60	0.912005	−0.286719	0.90	0.807524	−0.405950
0.61	0.909116	−0.291032	0.91	0.803447	−0.409499
0.62	0.905184	−0.295341	0.92	0.799334	−0.413018
0.63	0.903209	−0.299628	0.93	0.795186	−0.416507
0.64	0.900192	−0.303893	0.94	0.791004	−0.419965
0.65	0.897132	−0.308135	0.95	0.786787	−0.423392
0.66	0.894029	−0.312355	0.96	0.782536	−0.426787
0.67	0.890885	−0.316551	0.97	0.778251	−0.430151
0.68	0.887698	−0.320723	0.98	0.773933	−0.433483
0.69	0.884470	−0.324871	0.99	0.769582	−0.436783
0.70	0.881201	−0.328996	1.00	0.765198	−0.440051
0.71	0.877890	−0.333096	1.01	0.760781	−0.443286
0.72	0.874539	−0.337170	1.02	0.756332	−0.446488
0.73	0.871147	−0.341220	1.03	0.751851	−0.449658
0.74	0.867715	−0.345245	1.04	0.747339	−0.452794
0.75	0.864242	−0.349244	1.05	0.742796	−0.455897
0.76	0.860730	−0.353216	1.06	0.738221	−0.458966
0.77	0.857178	−0.357163	1.07	0.733616	−0.462001
0.78	0.853587	−0.361083	1.08	0.728981	−0.465003
0.79	0.849956	−0.364976	1.09	0.724316	−0.467970
0.80	0.846287	−0.368842	1.10	0.719622	−0.470902

x	$J_0(x)$	$-J_1(x)$	x	$J_0(x)$	$-J_1(x)$
1.10	0.719622	−0.470902	1.40	0.566855	−0.541948
1.11	0.714898	−0.473800	1.41	0.561427	−0.543726
1.12	0.710146	−0.476663	1.42	0.555981	−0.545464
1.13	0.705365	−0.479491	1.43	0.550518	−0.547162
1.14	0.700556	−0.482284	1.44	0.545038	−0.548821
1.15	0.695720	−0.485041	1.45	0.539541	−0.550441
1.16	0.690856	−0.487763	1.46	0.534029	−0.552020
1.17	0.685965	−0.490449	1.47	0.528501	−0.553559
1.18	0.681047	−0.493098	1.48	0.522958	−0.555059
1.19	0.676103	−0.495712	1.49	0.517400	−0.556518
1.20	0.671133	−0.498289	1.50	0.511828	−0.557937
1.21	0.666137	−0.500830	1.51	0.506241	−0.559315
1.22	0.661116	−0.503334	1.52	0.500642	−0.560653
1.23	0.656071	−0.505801	1.53	0.495028	−0.561951
1.24	0.651000	−0.508231	1.54	0.489403	−0.563208
1.25	0.645906	−0.510623	1.55	0.483764	−0.564424
1.26	0.640788	−0.512979	1.56	0.478114	−0.565600
1.27	0.635647	−0.515296	1.57	0.472453	−0.566735
1.28	0.630482	−0.517577	1.58	0.466780	−0.567830
1.29	0.625295	−0.519819	1.59	0.461096	−0.568883
1.30	0.620086	−0.522023	1.60	0.455402	−0.569896
1.31	0.614855	−0.524189	1.61	0.449698	−0.570868
1.32	0.609602	−0.526317	1.62	0.443985	−0.571798
1.33	0.604329	−0.528407	1.63	0.438262	−0.572688
1.34	0.599034	−0.530458	1.64	0.432531	−0.573537
1.35	0.593720	−0.532470	1.65	0.426792	−0.574344
1.36	0.588385	−0.534444	1.66	0.421045	−0.575111
1.37	0.583031	−0.536379	1.67	0.415290	−0.575836
1.38	0.577658	−0.538274	1.68	0.409528	−0.576520
1.39	0.572266	−0.540131	1.69	0.403760	−0.577163
1.40	0.566855	−0.541948	1.70	0.397985	−0.577765

x	$J_0(x)$	$-J_1(x)$	x	$J_0(x)$	$-J_1(x)$
1.70	0.397985	−0.577765	2.00	0.223891	−0.576725
1.71	0.392204	−0.578326	2.01	0.218127	−0.576060
1.72	0.386418	−0.578845	2.02	0.212370	−0.575355
1.73	0.380628	−0.579323	2.03	0.206620	−0.574611
1.74	0.374832	−0.579760	2.04	0.200878	−0.573827
1.75	0.369033	−0.580156	2.05	0.195143	−0.573003
1.76	0.363229	−0.580511	2.06	0.189418	−0.572139
1.77	0.357422	−0.580824	2.07	0.183701	−0.571236
1.78	0.351613	−0.581096	2.08	0.177993	−0.570294
1.79	0.345801	−0.581327	2.09	0.172295	−0.569313
1.80	0.339986	−0.581517	2.10	0.166607	−0.568292
1.81	0.334170	−0.581666	2.11	0.160929	−0.567233
1.82	0.328353	−0.581773	2.12	0.155262	−0.566134
1.83	0.322535	−0.581840	2.13	0.149607	−0.564997
1.84	0.316717	−0.581865	2.14	0.143963	−0.563821
1.85	0.310898	−0.581849	2.15	0.138330	−0.562607
1.86	0.305080	−0.581793	2.16	0.132711	−0.561354
1.87	0.299262	−0.581695	2.17	0.127104	−0.560063
1.88	0.293446	−0.581557	2.18	0.121509	−0.558735
1.89	0.287631	−0.581377	2.19	0.115929	−0.557368
1.90	0.281819	−0.581157	2.20	0.110362	−0.555963
1.91	0.276008	−0.580896	2.21	0.104810	−0.554521
1.92	0.270201	−0.580595	2.22	0.099272	−0.553041
1.93	0.264397	−0.580252	2.23	0.093749	−0.551524
1.94	0.258596	−0.579870	2.24	0.088242	−0.549970
1.95	0.252799	−0.579446	2.25	0.082750	−0.548378
1.96	0.247007	−0.578983	2.26	0.077274	−0.546750
1.97	0.241220	−0.578478	2.27	0.071815	−0.545085
1.98	0.235438	−0.577934	2.28	0.066373	−0.543384
1.99	0.229661	−0.577349	2.29	0.060947	−0.541646
2.00	0.223891	−0.576725	2.30	0.055540	−0.539873

x	$J_0(x)$	$-J_1(x)$	x	$J_0(x)$	$-J_1(x)$
2.30	0.055540	−0.539873	2.60	−0.096805	−0.470818
2.31	0.050150	−0.538063	2.61	−0.101499	−0.468025
2.32	0.044779	−0.536217	2.62	−0.106165	−0.465202
2.33	0.039426	−0.534336	2.63	−0.110803	−0.462350
2.34	0.034092	−0.532419	2.64	−0.115412	−0.459470
2.35	0.028778	−0.530467	2.65	−0.119992	−0.456561
2.36	0.023483	−0.528480	2.66	−0.124543	−0.453625
2.37	0.018208	−0.526458	2.67	−0.129064	−0.450660
2.38	0.012954	−0.524402	2.68	−0.133557	−0.447668
2.39	0.007720	−0.522311	2.69	−0.138018	−0.444648
2.40	0.002508	−0.520185	2.70	−0.142449	−0.441601
2.41	−0.002683	−0.518026	2.71	−0.146850	−0.438528
2.42	−0.007853	−0.515833	2.72	−0.151220	−0.435428
2.43	−0.013000	−0.513606	2.73	−0.155559	−0.432302
2.44	−0.018125	−0.511346	2.74	−0.159866	−0.429150
2.45	−0.023227	−0.509052	2.75	−0.164141	−0.425972
2.46	−0.028306	−0.506726	2.76	−0.168385	−0.422769
2.47	−0.033361	−0.504366	2.77	−0.172597	−0.419541
2.48	−0.038393	−0.501974	2.78	−0.176776	−0.416288
2.49	−0.043401	−0.499550	2.79	−0.180922	−0.413011
2.50	−0.048384	−0.497094	2.80	−0.185036	−0.409709
2.51	−0.053342	−0.494606	2.81	−0.189117	−0.406384
2.52	−0.058276	−0.492086	2.82	−0.193164	−0.403035
2.53	−0.063184	−0.489535	2.83	−0.197177	−0.399662
2.54	−0.068066	−0.486953	2.84	−0.201157	−0.396267
2.55	−0.072923	−0.484340	2.85	−0.205102	−0.392849
2.56	−0.077753	−0.481696	2.86	−0.209014	−0.389408
2.57	−0.082557	−0.479021	2.87	−0.212890	−0.385945
2.58	−0.087333	−0.476317	2.88	−9.216732	−0.382461
2.59	−0.092083	−0.473582	2.89	−0.220540	−0.378955
2.60	−0.096805	−0.470818	2.90	−0.224312	−0.375427

x	$J_0(x)$	$-J_1(x)$	x	$J_0(x)$	$-J_1(x)$
2.90	−0.224312	−0.375427	3.20	−0.320188	−0.261343
2.91	−0.228048	−0.371879	3.21	−0.322781	−0.257319
2.92	−0.231749	−0.368311	3.22	−0.325335	−0.253284
2.93	−0.235414	−0.364722	3.23	−0.327847	−0.249239
2.94	−0.239043	−0.361113	3.24	−0.330319	−0.245184
2.95	−0.242636	−0.357485	3.25	−0.332751	−0.241120
2.96	−0.246193	−0.353837	3.26	−0.335142	−0.237046
2.97	−0.249713	−0.350170	3.27	−0.337492	−0.232963
2.98	−0.253196	−0.346485	3.28	−0.339801	−0.228871
2.99	−0.256643	−0.342781	3.29	−0.342069	−0.224771
3.00	−0.260052	−0.339059	3.30	−0.344296	−0.220663
3.01	−0.263424	−0.335319	3.31	−0.346482	−0.216548
3.02	−0.266758	−0.331563	3.32	−0.348627	−0.212425
3.03	−0.270055	−0.327789	3.33	−0.350731	−0.208296
3.04	−0.273314	−0.323998	3.34	−6.352793	−0.204160
3.05	−0.276535	−0.320191	3.35	−0.354814	−0.200018
3.06	−0.279718	−0.316368	3.36	−0.356793	−0.195870
3.07	−0.282862	−0.312529	3.37	−0.358731	−0.191716
3.08	−0.285968	−0.308675	3.38	−0.360628	−0.187557
3.09	−0.289036	−0.304805	3.39	−0.362482	−0.183394
3.10	−0.292064	−0.300921	3.40	−0.364296	−0.179226
3.11	−0.295054	−0.297023	3.41	−0.366067	−0.175054
3.12	−0.298005	−0.293110	3.42	−0.367797	−0.170878
3.13	−0.300916	−0.289184	3.43	−0.369485	−0.166699
3.14	−0.303788	−0.285244	3.44	−0.371131	−0.162516
3.15	−0.306621	−0.281291	3.45	−0.372735	−0.158331
3.16	−0.309414	−0.277326	3.46	−0.374297	−0.154144
3.17	−0.312168	−0.273348	3.47	−0.375818	−0.149954
3.18	−0.314881	−0.269358	3.48	−0.377296	−0.145763
3.19	−0.317555	−0.265356	3.49	−0.378733	−0.141571
3.20	−0.320188	−0.261343	3.50	−0.380128	−0.137378

x	$J_0(x)$	$-J_1(x)$	x	$J_0(x)$	$-J_1(x)$
3.50	−0.380128	−0.137378	3.80	−0.402556	−0.012821
3.51	−0.381481	−0.133183	3.81	−0.402664	−0.008766
3.52	−0.382791	−0.128989	3.82	−0.402732	−0.004722
3.53	−0.384060	−0.124795	3.83	−0.402759	−0.000687
3.54	−0.385287	−0.120601	3.84	−0.402746	+0.003337
3.55	−0.386472	−0.116408	3.85	−0.402692	+0.007350
3.56	−0.387615	−0.112216	3.86	−0.402599	+0.011352
3.57	−0.388717	−0.108025	3.87	−0.402465	+0.015343
3.58	−0.389776	−0.103836	3.88	−0.402292	+0.019322
3.59	−0.390793	−0.099650	3.89	−0.402079	+0.023289
3.60	−0.391769	−0.095466	3.90	−0.401826	+0.027244
3.61	−0.392703	−0.091284	3.91	−0.401534	+0.031186
3.62	−0.393595	−0.087106	3.92	−0.401202	+0.035115
3.63	−0.394445	−0.082931	3.93	−0.400832	+0.039031
3.64	−0.395253	−0.078760	3.94	−0.400422	+0.042933
3.65	−0.396020	−0.074593	3.95	−0.399973	+0.046821
3.66	−0.396745	−0.070431	3.96	−0.399485	+0.050695
3.67	−0.397429	−0.066274	3.97	−0.398959	+0.054555
3.68	−0.398071	−0.062122	3.98	−0.398394	+0.058400
3.69	−0.398671	−0.057975	3.99	−0.397791	+0.062229
3.70	−0.399230	−0.053834	4.00	−0.397150	+0.066043
3.71	−0.399748	−0.049699	4.01	−0.396470	+0.069842
3.72	−0.400224	−0.045571	4.02	−0.395753	+0.073624
3.73	−0.400659	−0.041450	4.03	−0.394998	+0.077390
3.74	−0.401053	−0.037336	4.04	−0.394205	+0.081140
3.75	−0.401406	−0.033229	4.05	−0.393375	+0.084873
3.76	−0.401718	−0.029131	4.06	−0.392508	+0.088588
3.77	−0.401989	−0.025040	4.07	−0.391603	+0.092286
3.78	−0.402219	−0.020958	4.08	−0.390662	+0.095967
3.79	−0.402408	−0.016885	4.09	−0.389684	+0.099629
3.80	−0.402556	−0.012821	4.10	−0.388670	+0.103273

x	$J_0(x)$	$-J_1(x)$	x	$J_0(x)$	$-J_1(x)$
4.10	−0.388670	+0.103273	4.40	−0.342257	+0.202776
4.11	−0.387619	+0.106899	4.41	−0.340214	+0.205724
4.12	−0.386532	+0.110505	4.42	−0.338142	+0.208647
4.13	−0.385409	+0.114093	4.43	−0.336041	+0.211543
4.14	−0.384250	+0.117661	4.44	−0.333912	+0.214412
4.15	−0.383056	+0.121209	4.45	−0.331753	+0.217255
4.16	−0.381826	+0.124738	4.46	−0.329567	+0.220071
4.17	−0.380561	+0.128246	4.47	−0.327352	+0.222860
4.18	−0.379261	+0.131734	4.48	−0.325110	+0.225621
4.19	−0.377926	+0.135201	4.49	−0.322840	+0.228355
4.20	−0.376557	+0.138647	4.50	−0.320543	+0.231060
4.21	−0.375153	+0.142072	4.51	−0.318218	+0.233738
4.22	−0.373716	+0.145475	4.52	−0.315868	+0.236388
4.23	−0.372244	+0.148857	4.53	−0.313491	+0.239010
4.24	−0.370739	+0.152216	4.54	−0.311088	+0.241603
4.25	−0.369200	+0.155553	4.55	−0.308659	+0.244167
4.26	−0.367628	+0.158868	4.56	−0.306204	+0.246703
4.27	−0.366022	+0.162160	4.57	−0.303725	+0.249209
4.28	−0.364385	+0.165429	4.58	−0.301220	+0.251686
4.29	−0.362714	+0.168674	4.59	−0.298691	+0.254134
4.30	−0.361011	+0.171897	4.60	−0.296138	+0.256553
4.31	−0.359276	+0.175095	4.61	−0.293560	+0.258942
4.32	−0.357509	+0.178269	4.62	−0.290959	+0.261301
4.33	−0.355711	+0.181420	4.63	−0.288334	+0.263630
4.34	−0.353881	+0.184546	4.64	−0.285687	+0.265928
4.35	−0.352020	+0.187647	4.65	−0.283016	+0.268197
4.36	−0.350128	+0.190723	4.66	−0.280323	+0.270435
4.37	−0.348206	+0.193775	4.67	−0.277607	+0.272643
4.38	−0.346253	+0.196800	4.68	−0.274870	+0.274820
4.39	−0.344270	+0.199801	4.69	−0.272111	+0.276966
4.40	−0.342257	+0.202776	4.70	−0.269331	+0.279081

x	$J_0(x)$	$-J_1(x)$	x	$J_0(x)$	$-J_1(x)$
4.70	-0.269331	$+0.279081$	5.00	-0.177597	$+0.327579$
4.71	-0.266530	$+0.281165$	5.01	-0.174315	$+0.328683$
4.72	-0.263708	$+0.283217$	5.02	-0.171023	$+0.329753$
4.73	-0.260865	$+0.285239$	5.03	-0.167720	$+0.330790$
4.74	-0.258003	$+0.287229$	5.04	-0.164408	$+0.331792$
4.75	-0.255121	$+0.289187$	5.05	-0.161085	$+0.332761$
4.76	-0.252219	$+0.291113$	5.06	-0.157752	$+0.333696$
4.77	-0.249299	$+0.293008$	5.07	-0.154411	$+0.334597$
4.78	-0.246359	$+0.294871$	5.08	-0.151061	$+0.335465$
4.79	-0.243401	$+0.296701$	5.09	-0.147702	$+0.336298$
4.80	-0.240425	$+0.298500$	5.10	-0.144335	$+0.337097$
4.81	-0.237431	$+0.300266$	5.11	-0.140960	$+0.337863$
4.82	-0.234420	$+0.302000$	5.12	-0.137578	$+0.338594$
4.83	-0.231392	$+0.303701$	5.13	-0.134188	$+0.339292$
4.84	-0.228346	$+0.305370$	5.14	-0.130792	$+0.339955$
4.85	-0.225284	$+0.307006$	5.15	-0.127389	$+0.340585$
4.86	-0.222206	$+0.308610$	5.16	-0.123980	$+0.341180$
4.87	-0.219112	$+0.310180$	5.17	-0.120566	$+0.341742$
4.88	-0.216003	$+0.311718$	5.18	-0.117146	$+0.342269$
4.89	-0.212878	$+0.313223$	5.19	-0.113720	$+0.342763$
4.90	-0.209738	$+0.314695$	5.20	-0.110290	$+0.343223$
4.91	-0.206584	$+0.316133$	5.21	-0.106856	$+0.343649$
4.92	-0.203416	$+0.317539$	5.22	-0.103418	$+0.344041$
4.93	-0.200233	$+0.318911$	5.23	-0.099975	$+0.344399$
4.94	-0.197038	$+0.320250$	5.24	-0.096530	$+0.344723$
4.95	-0.193829	$+0.321555$	5.25	-0.093081	$+0.345014$
4.96	-0.190607	$+0.322827$	5.26	-0.089630	$+0.345271$
4.97	-0.187372	$+0.324065$	5.27	-0.086176	$+0.345494$
4.98	-0.184125	$+0.325270$	5.28	-0.082720	$+0.345683$
4.99	-0.180867	$+0.326441$	5.29	-0.079262	$+0.345839$
5.00	-0.177597	$+0.327579$	5.30	-0.075803	$+0.345961$

x	$J_0(x)$	$-J_1(x)$	x	$J_0(x)$	$-J_1(x)$
5.30	−0.075803	+0.345961	5.60	+0.026971	+0.334333
5.31	−0.072343	+0.346049	5.61	+0.030310	+0.333451
5.32	−0.068882	+0.346104	5.62	+0.033640	+0.332538
5.33	−0.065421	+0.346126	5.63	+0.036961	+0.331595
5.34	−0.061960	+0.346114	5.64	+0.040272	+0.330621
5.35	−0.058499	+0.346069	5.65	+0.043573	+0.329617
5.36	−0.055039	+0.345990	5.66	+0.046864	+0.328583
5.37	−0.051579	+0.345879	5.67	+0.050144	+0.327518
5.38	−0.048121	+0.345734	5.68	+0.053414	+0.326424
5.39	−0.044665	+0.345556	5.69	+0.056673	+0.325301
5.40	−0.041210	+0.345345	5.70	+0.059920	+0.324148
5.41	−0.037758	+0.345101	5.71	+0.063156	+0.322965
5.42	−0.034308	+0.344824	5.72	+0.066380	+0.321753
5.43	−0.030861	+0.344515	5.73	+0.069591	+0.320513
5.44	−0.027418	+0.344173	5.74	+0.072789	+0.319243
5.45	−0.023978	+0.343798	5.75	+0.075975	+0.317945
5.46	−0.020542	+0.343390	5.76	+0.079148	+0.316618
5.47	−0.017110	+0.342951	5.77	+0.082308	+0.315262
5.48	−0.013683	+0.342479	5.78	+0.085453	+0.313879
5.49	−0.010261	+0.341975	5.79	+0.088585	+0.312467
5.50	−0.006844	+0.341438	5.80	+0.091703	+0.311028
5.51	−0.003432	+0.340870	5.81	+0.094806	+0.309561
5.52	−0.000027	+0.340270	5.82	+0.097894	+0.308066
5.53	+0.003373	+0.339638	5.83	+0.100967	+0.306544
5.54	+0.006766	+0.338974	5.84	+0.104024	+0.304995
5.55	+0.010152	+0.338279	5.85	+0.107067	+0.303419
5.56	+0.013532	+0.337552	5.86	+0.110093	+0.301817
5.57	+0.016903	+0.336794	5.87	+0.113103	+0.300187
5.58	+0.020267	+0.336004	5.88	+0.116096	+0.298532
5.59	+0.023623	+0.335184	5.89	+0.119073	+0.296850
5.60	+0.026971	+0.334333	5.90	+0.122033	+0.295142

x	$J_0(x)$	$-J_1(x)$	x	$J_0(x)$	$-J_1(x)$
5.90	+0.122033	+0.295142	6.20	+0.201747	+0.232917
5.91	+0.124976	+0.293409	6.21	+0.204064	+0.230514
5.92	+0.127901	+0.291650	6.22	+0.206357	+0.228093
5.93	+0.130809	+0.289866	6.23	+0.208626	+0.225654
5.94	+0.133699	+0.288056	6.24	+0.210870	+0.223196
5.95	+0.136570	+0.286222	6.25	+0.213090	+0.220721
5.96	+0.139423	+0.284363	6.26	+0.215285	+0.218228
5.97	+0.142257	+0.282479	6.27	+0.217455	+0.215718
5.98	+0.145072	+0.280572	6.28	+0.219599	+0.213191
5.99	+0.147869	+0.278640	6.29	+0.221718	+0.210647
6.00	+0.150645	+0.276684	6.30	+0.223812	+0.208087
6.01	+0.153402	+0.274704	6.31	+0.225880	+0.205510
6.02	+0.156139	+0.272702	6.32	+0.227922	+0.202918
6.03	+0.158856	+0.270676	6.33	+0.229938	+0.200310
6.04	+0.161553	+0.268627	6.34	+0.231928	+0.197686
6.05	+0.164229	+0.266555	6.35	+0.233892	+0.195048
6.06	+0.166884	+0.264461	6.36	+0.235829	+0.192394
6.07	+0.169518	+0.262345	6.37	+0.237740	+0.189726
6.08	+0.172131	+0.260207	6.38	+0.239624	+0.187044
6.09	+0.174722	+0.258046	6.39	+0.241481	+0.184348
6.10	+0.177291	+0.255865	6.40	+0.243311	+0.181638
6.11	+0.179839	+0.253662	6.41	+0.245113	+0.178914
6.12	+0.182365	+0.251438	6.42	+0.246889	+0.176177
6.13	+0.184868	+0.249193	6.43	+0.248637	+0.173427
6.14	+0.187348	+0.246927	6.44	+0.250357	+0.170665
6.15	+0.189806	+0.244642	6.45	+0.252050	+0.167890
6.16	+0.192241	+0.242336	6.46	+0.253715	+0.165104
6.17	+0.194653	+0.240010	6.47	+0.255352	+0.162305
6.18	+0.197041	+0.237665	6.48	+0.256961	+0.159495
6.19	+0.199406	+0.235300	6.49	+0.258542	+0.156674
6.20	+0.201747	+0.232917	6.50	+0.260095	+0.153841

x	$J_0(x)$	$-J_1(x)$	x	$J_0(x)$	$-J_1(x)$
6.50	+0.260095	+0.153841	6.80	+0.293096	+0.065219
6.51	+0.261619	+0.150998	6.81	+0.293733	+0.062191
6.52	+0.263115	+0.148145	6.82	+0.294339	+0.059161
6.53	+0.264582	+0.145282	6.83	+0.294916	+0.056131
6.54	+0.266020	+0.142409	6.84	+0.295462	+0.053099
6.55	+0.267430	+0.139526	6.85	+0.295978	+0.050066
6.56	+0.268811	+0.136634	6.86	+0.296463	+0.047033
6.57	+0.270162	+0.133733	6.87	+0.296919	+0.044000
6.58	+0.271485	+0.130824	6.88	+0.297343	+0.040967
6.59	+0.272779	+0.127906	6.89	+0.297738	+0.037934
6.60	+0.274043	+0.124980	6.90	+0.298102	+0.034902
6.61	+0.275279	+0.122047	6.91	+0.298436	+0.031871
6.62	+0.276484	+0.119105	6.92	+0.298739	+0.028841
6.63	+0.277661	+0.116157	6.93	+0.299013	+0.025813
6.64	+0.278807	+0.113202	6.94	+0.299256	+0.022787
6.65	+0.279925	+0.110204	6.95	+0.299468	+0.019762
6.66	+0.281012	+0.107272	6.96	+0.299651	+0.016740
6.67	+0.282070	+0.104298	6.97	+0.299803	+0.013721
6.68	+0.283098	+0.101318	6.98	+0.299925	+0.010705
6.69	+0.284096	+0.098333	6.99	+0.300017	+0.007692
6.70	+0.285065	+0.095342	7.00	+0.300079	+0.004683
6.71	+0.286003	+0.092347	7.01	+0.300111	+0.001677
6.72	+0.286912	+0.089347	7.02	+0.300113	−0.001324
6.73	+0.287790	+0.086343	7.03	+0.300085	−0.004321
6.74	+0.288638	+0.083335	7.04	+0.300026	−0.007313
6.75	+0.289457	+0.080323	7.05	+0.299938	−0.010301
6.76	+0.290245	+0.077308	7.06	+0.299820	−0.013283
6.77	+0.291003	+0.074289	7.07	+0.299673	−0.016259
6.78	+0.291731	+0.071268	7.08	+0.299495	−0.019230
6.79	+0.292428	+0.068245	7.09	+0.299288	−0.022195
6.80	+0.293096	+0.065219	7.10	+0.299051	−0.025153

x	$J_0(x)$	$-J_1(x)$	x	$J_0(x)$	$-J_1(x)$
7.10	+0.299051	−0.025153	7.40	+0.278596	−0.109625
7.11	+0.298785	−0.028105	7.41	+0.277487	−0.112256
7.12	+0.298489	−0.031050	7.42	+0.276351	−0.114872
7.13	+0.298164	−0.033987	7.43	+0.275189	−0.117473
7.14	+0.297810	−0.036918	7.44	+0.274002	−0.120059
7.15	+0.297426	−0.039840	7.45	+0.272788	−0.122630
7.16	+0.297013	−0.042755	7.46	+0.271549	−0.125186
7.17	+0.296571	−0.045661	7.47	+0.270285	−0.127726
7.18	+0.296100	−0.048559	7.48	+0.268995	−0.130249
7.19	+0.295600	−0.051448	7.49	+0.267680	−0.132757
7.20	+0.295071	−0.054327	7.50	+0.266340	−0.135248
7.21	+0.294513	−0.057198	7.51	+0.264975	−0.137723
7.22	+0.293927	−0.060059	7.52	+0.263585	−0.140181
7.23	+0.293312	−0.062910	7.53	+0.262171	−0.142622
7.24	+0.292669	−0.065751	7.54	+0.260733	−0.145046
7.25	+0.291997	−0.068582	7.55	+0.259270	−0.147452
7.26	+0.291297	−0.071402	7.56	+0.257784	−0.149840
7.27	+0.290569	−0.074211	7.57	+0.256274	−0.152211
7.28	+0.289813	−0.077009	7.58	+0.254740	−0.154564
7.29	+0.289029	−0.079795	7.59	+0.253182	−0.156898
7.30	+0.288217	−0.082570	7.60	+0.251602	−0.159214
7.31	+0.287377	−0.085334	7.61	+0.249998	−0.161511
7.32	+0.286510	−0.088084	7.62	+0.248372	−0.163789
7.33	+0.285616	−0.090823	7.63	+0.246722	−0.166048
7.34	+0.284694	−0.093549	7.64	+0.245051	−0.168288
7.35	+0.283745	−0.096262	7.65	+0.243357	−0.170509
7.36	+0.282769	−0.098962	7.66	+0.241641	−0.172710
7.37	+0.281766	−0.101648	7.67	+0.239903	−0.174891
7.38	+0.280736	−0.104321	7.68	+0.238143	−0.177052
7.39	+0.279679	−0.106980	7.69	+0.236362	−0.179192
7.40	+0.278596	−0.109625	7.70	+0.234559	−0.181313

x	$J_0(x)$	$-J_1(x)$	x	$J_0(x)$	$-J_1(x)$
7.70	+0.234559	−0.181313	8.00	+0.171651	−0.234636
7.71	+0.232735	−0.183413	8.01	+0.169297	−0.236047
7.72	+0.230891	−0.185492	8.02	+0.166930	−0.237433
7.73	+0.229026	−0.187550	8.03	+0.164549	−0.238794
7.74	+0.227140	−0.189587	8.04	+0.162154	−0.240129
7.75	+0.225234	−0.191603	8.05	+0.159746	−0.241439
7.76	+0.223308	−0.193597	8.06	+0.157325	−0.242724
7.77	+0.221362	−0.195570	8.07	+0.154892	−0.243983
7.78	+0.219397	−0.197521	8.08	+0.152446	−0.245217
7.79	+0.217412	−0.199450	8.09	+0.149988	−0.246425
7.80	+0.215408	−0.201357	8.10	+0.147517	−0.247608
7.81	+0.213385	−0.203242	8.11	+0.145036	−0.248764
7.82	+0.211343	−0.205104	8.12	+0.142542	−0.249895
7.83	+0.209283	−0.206944	8.13	+0.140038	−0.251000
7.84	+0.207204	−0.208761	8.14	+0.137522	−0.252078
7.85	+0.205108	−0.210555	8.15	+0.134996	−0.253131
7.86	+0.202993	−0.212327	8.16	+0.132460	−0.254157
7.87	+0.200861	−0.214015	8.17	+0.129913	−0.255157
7.88	+0.198712	−0.215800	8.18	+0.127357	−0.256131
7.89	+0.196545	−0.217501	8.19	+0.124791	−0.257078
7.90	+0.194362	−0.219179	8.20	+0.122215	−0.257999
7.91	+0.192162	−0.220834	8.21	+0.119631	−0.258893
7.92	+0.189945	−0.222464	8.22	+0.117038	−0.259761
7.93	+0.187713	−0.224071	8.23	+0.114436	−0.260602
7.94	+0.185464	−0.225653	8.24	+0.111826	−0.261416
7.95	+0.183200	−0.227212	8.25	+0.109207	−0.262204
7.96	+0.180920	−0.228746	8.26	+0.106582	−0.262964
7.97	+0.178625	−0.230255	8.27	+0.103948	−0.263698
7.98	+0.176315	−0.231740	8.28	+0.101308	−0.264406
7.99	+0.173990	−0.233201	8.29	+0.098660	−0.265086
8.00	+0.171651	−0.234636	8.30	+0.096006	−0.265739

x	$J_0(x)$	$-J_1(x)$	x	$J_0(x)$	$-J_1(x)$
8.30	+0.096006	−0.265739	8.60	+0.014623	−0.272755
8.31	+0.093346	−0.266366	8.61	+0.011896	−0.272571
8.32	+0.090679	−0.266965	8.62	+0.009172	−0.272360
8.33	+0.088006	−0.267538	8.63	+0.006449	−0.272122
8.34	+0.085328	−0.268083	8.64	+0.003729	−0.271858
8.35	+0.082645	−0.268601	8.65	+0.001012	−0.271567
8.36	+0.079956	−0.269092	8.66	−0.001702	−0.271250
8.37	+0.077263	−0.269557	8.67	−0.004413	−0.270907
8.38	+0.074565	−0.269994	8.68	−0.007120	−0.270537
8.39	+0.071863	−0.270403	8.69	−0.009823	−0.270141
8.40	+0.069157	−0.270786	8.70	−0.012523	−0.269719
8.41	+0.066448	−0.271142	8.71	−0.015218	−0.269271
8.42	+0.063735	−0.271470	8.72	−0.017908	−0.268796
8.43	+0.061018	−0.271772	8.73	−0.020594	−0.268296
8.44	+0.058299	−0.272046	8.74	−0.023274	−0.267770
8.45	+0.055577	−0.272293	8.75	−0.025949	−0.267218
8.46	+0.052853	−0.272513	8.76	−0.028618	−0.266640
8.47	+0.050127	−0.272706	8.77	−0.031282	−0.266037
8.48	+0.047399	−0.272872	8.78	−0.033939	−0.265408
8.49	+0.044670	−0.273010	8.79	−0.036590	−0.264753
8.50	+0.041939	−0.273122	8.80	−0.039234	−0.264074
8.51	+0.039208	−0.273207	8.81	−0.041871	−0.263369
8.52	+0.036475	−0.273264	8.82	−0.044501	−0.262638
8.53	+0.033742	−0.273295	8.83	−0.047124	−0.261883
8.54	+0.031009	−0.273298	8.84	−0.049739	−0.261103
8.55	+0.028277	−0.273275	8.85	−0.052346	−0.260298
8.56	+0.025544	−0.273224	8.86	−0.054945	−0.259468
8.57	+0.022812	−0.273147	8.87	−0.057535	−0.258613
8.58	+0.020081	−0.273043	8.88	−0.060117	−0.257734
8.59	+0.017351	−0.272912	8.89	−0.062690	−0.256830
8.60	+0.014623	−0.272755	8.90	−0.065253	−0.255902

x	$J_0(x)$	$-J_1(x)$	x	$J_0(x)$	$-J_1(x)$
8.90	-0.065253	-0.255902	9.20	-0.136748	-0.217409
8.91	-0.067808	-0.254950	9.21	-0.138914	-0.215795
8.92	-0.070352	-0.253974	9.22	-0.141064	-0.214162
8.93	-0.072887	-0.252974	9.23	-0.143198	-0.212509
8.94	-0.075412	-0.251950	9.24	-0.145314	-0.210837
8.95	-0.077926	-0.250902	9.25	-0.147414	-0.209147
8.96	-0.080430	-0.249831	9.26	-0.149497	-0.207437
8.97	-0.082922	-0.248736	9.27	-0.151563	-0.205709
8.98	-0.085404	-0.247618	9.28	-0.153611	-0.203962
8.99	-0.087875	-0.246476	9.29	-0.155642	-0.202197
9.00	-0.090334	-0.245312	9.30	-0.157655	-0.200414
9.01	-0.092781	-0.244124	9.31	-0.159650	-0.198613
9.02	-0.095216	-0.242914	9.32	-0.161627	-0.196794
9.03	-0.097639	-0.241682	9.33	-0.163586	-0.194958
9.04	-0.100050	-0.240426	9.34	-0.165526	-0.193105
9.05	-0.102447	-0.239149	9.35	-0.167448	-0.191234
9.06	-0.104832	-0.237849	9.36	-0.169351	-0.189347
9.07	-0.107204	-0.236527	9.37	-0.171235	-0.187443
9.08	-0.109563	-0.235183	9.38	-0.173100	-0.185522
9.09	-0.111908	-0.233818	9.39	-0.174945	-0.183585
9.10	-0.114239	-0.232431	9.40	-0.176772	-0.181632
9.11	-0.116557	-0.231022	9.41	-0.178578	-0.179663
9.12	-0.118860	-0.229592	9.42	-0.180365	-0.177679
9.13	-0.121148	-0.228142	9.43	-0.182132	-0.175679
9.14	-0.123422	-0.226670	9.44	-0.183878	-0.173664
9.15	-0.125682	-0.225177	9.45	-0.185605	-0.171633
9.16	-0.127926	-0.223664	9.46	-0.187311	-0.169588
9.17	-0.130155	-0.222130	9.47	-0.188997	-0.167529
9.18	-0.132368	-0.220577	9.48	-0.190661	-0.165455
9.19	-0.134566	-0.219003	9.49	-0.192306	-0.163367
9.20	-0.136748	-0.217409	9.50	-0.193929	-0.161264

x	$J_0(x)$	$-J_1(x)$	x	$J_0(x)$	$-J_1(x)$
9.50	−0.193929	−0.161264	9.80	−0.232276	−0.092840
9.51	−0.195531	−0.159149	9.81	−0.233192	−0.090419
9.52	−0.197112	−0.157019	9.82	−0.234084	−0.087992
9.53	−0.198671	−0.154877	9.83	−0.234952	−0.085558
9.54	−0.200209	−0.152721	9.84	−0.235796	−0.083119
9.55	−0.201726	−0.150552	9.85	−0.236615	−0.080674
9.56	−0.203220	−0.148371	9.86	−0.237409	−0.078223
9.57	−0.204693	−0.146178	9.87	−0.238179	−0.075767
9.58	−0.206144	−0.143972	9.88	−0.238924	−0.073306
9.59	−0.207572	−0.141754	9.89	−0.239645	−0.070840
9.60	−0.208979	−0.139525	9.90	−0.240341	−0.068370
9.61	−0.210363	−0.137284	9.91	−0.241012	−0.065895
9.62	−0.211724	−0.135032	9.92	−0.241659	−0.063417
9.63	−0.213063	−0.132769	9.93	−0.242281	−0.060934
9.64	−0.214380	−0.130495	9.94	−0.242878	−0.058448
9.65	−0.215673	−0.128211	9.95	−0.243450	−0.055959
9.66	−0.216944	−0.125916	9.96	−0.243997	−0.053467
9.67	−0.218192	−0.123611	9.97	−0.244519	−0.050972
9.68	−0.219416	−0.121296	9.98	−0.245016	−0.048474
9.69	−0.220617	−0.118972	9.99	−0.245489	−0.045975
9.70	−0.221795	−0.116639	10.00	−0.245936	−0.043473
9.71	−0.222950	−0.114296	10.01	−0.246358	−0.040969
9.72	−0.224081	−0.111944	10.02	−0.246755	−0.038464
9.73	−0.225189	−0.109584	10.03	−0.247127	−0.035957
9.74	−0.226273	−0.107215	10.04	−0.247474	−0.033450
9.75	−0.227333	−0.104839	10.05	−0.247796	−0.030941
9.76	−0.228370	−0.102454	10.06	−0.248093	−0.028432
9.77	−0.229382	−0.100061	10.07	−0.248365	−0.025923
9.78	−0.230371	−0.097661	10.08	−0.248612	−0.023414
9.79	−0.231336	−0.095254	10.09	−0.248833	−0.020904
9.80	−0.232276	−0.092840	10.10	−0.249030	−0.018396

x	$J_0(x)$	$-J_1(x)$	x	$J_0(x)$	$-J_1(x)$
10.10	−0.249030	−0.018396	10.40	−0.243372	+0.055473
10.11	−0.249201	−0.015887	10.41	−0.242805	+0.057849
10.12	−0.249347	−0.013380	10.42	−0.242215	+0.060218
10.13	−0.249469	−0.010874	10.43	−0.241601	+0.062578
10.14	−0.249565	−0.008369	10.44	−0.240963	+0.064930
10.15	−0.249636	−0.005866	10.45	−0.240302	+0.067273
10.16	−0.249682	−0.003365	10.46	−0.239618	+0.069607
10.17	−0.249703	−0.000866	10.47	−0.238910	+0.071932
10.18	−0.249700	+0.001631	10.48	−0.238179	+0.074248
10.19	−0.249671	+0.004121	10.49	−0.237425	+0.076554
10.20	−0.249617	+0.006616	10.50	−0.236648	+0.078850
10.21	−0.249538	+0.009104	10.51	−0.235848	+0.081136
10.22	−0.249435	+0.011589	10.52	−0.235026	+0.083413
10.23	−0.249307	+0.014070	10.53	−0.234180	+0.085678
10.24	−0.249154	+0.016547	10.54	−0.233312	+0.087933
10.25	−0.248976	+0.019020	10.55	−0.232421	+0.090178
10.26	−0.248773	+0.021489	10.56	−0.231508	+0.092411
10.27	−0.248546	+0.023954	10.57	−0.230573	+0.094633
10.28	−0.248294	+0.026414	10.58	−0.229616	+0.096843
10.29	−0.248018	+0.028868	10.59	−0.228636	+0.099042
10.30	−0.247717	+0.031318	10.60	−0.227635	+0.101229
10.31	−0.247391	+0.033762	10.61	−0.226612	+0.103403
10.32	−0.247042	+0.036200	10.62	−0.225567	+0.105566
10.33	−0.246667	+0.038632	10.63	−0.224501	+0.107716
10.34	−0.246269	+0.041059	10.64	−0.223413	+0.109853
10.35	−0.245846	+0.043478	10.65	−0.222304	+0.111978
10.36	−0.245399	+0.045891	10.66	−0.221173	+0.114089
10.37	−0.244928	+0.048298	10.67	−0.220022	+0.116187
10.38	−0.244433	+0.050697	10.68	−0.218850	+0.118272
10.39	−0.243915	+0.053089	10.69	−0.217656	+0.120342
10.40	−0.243372	+0.055473	10.70	−0.216443	+0.122399

x	$J_0(x)$	$-J_1(x)$	x	$J_0(x)$	$-J_1(x)$
10.70	−0.216443	+0.122399	11.00	−0.171190	+0.176785
10.71	−0.215209	+0.124442	11.01	−0.169415	+0.178327
10.72	−0.213954	+0.126471	11.02	−C.167624	+0.179850
10.73	−0.212679	+0.128485	11.03	−0.165818	+0.181353
10.74	−0.211384	+0.130485	11.04	−0.163997	+0.182837
10.75	−0.210069	+0.132470	11.05	−0.162161	+0.184302
10.76	−0.208735	+0.134440	11.06	−0.160311	+0.185747
10.77	−0.207381	+0.136395	11.07	−0.158446	+0.187172
10.78	−0.206007	+0.138334	11.08	−0.156567	+0.188577
10.79	−0.204614	+0.140258	11.09	−0.154675	+0.189963
10.80	−0.203202	+0.142167	11.10	−0.152768	+0.191328
10.81	−0.201771	+0.144059	11.11	−0.150848	+0.192673
10.82	−0.200321	+0.145935	11.12	−0.148915	+0.193998
10.83	−0.198852	+0.147796	11.13	−0.146968	+0.195303
10.84	−0.197365	+0.149639	11.14	−0.145009	+0.196587
10.85	−0.195859	+0.151467	11.15	−0.143037	+0.197850
10.86	−0.194336	+0.153277	11.16	−0.141052	+0.199093
10.87	−0.192794	+0.155071	11.17	−0.139055	+0.200314
10.88	−0.191234	+0.156848	11.18	−0.137046	+0.201515
10.89	−0.189657	+0.158607	11.19	−0.135025	+0.202695
10.90	−0.188062	+0.160350	11.20	−0.132992	+0.203853
10.91	−0.186450	+0.162074	11.21	−0.130948	+0.204990
10.92	−0.184821	+0.163782	11.22	−0.128892	+0.206106
10.93	−0.183175	+0.165471	11.23	−0.126826	+0.207201
10.94	−0.181511	+0.167142	11.24	−0.124748	+0.208274
10.95	−0.179832	+0.168795	11.25	−0.122660	+0.209325
10.96	−0.178136	+0.170430	11.26	−0.120562	+0.2103●5
10.97	−0.176423	+0.172047	11.27	−0.118453	+0.211363
10.98	−0.174695	+0.173645	11.28	−0.116335	+0.212349
10.99	−0.172950	+0.175225	11.29	−0.114206	+0.213313
11.00	−0.171190	+0.176785	11.30	−0.112068	+0.214255

x	$J_0(x)$	$-J_1(x)$	x	$J_0(x)$	$-J_1(x)$
11.30	−0.112068	+0.214255	11.60	−0.044616	+0.232000
11.31	−0.109921	+0.215175	11.61	−0.042294	+0.232235
11.32	−0.107765	+0.216073	11.62	−0.039971	+0.232446
11.33	−0.105600	+0.216949	11.63	−0.037646	+0.232634
11.34	−0.103426	+0.217802	11.64	−0.035138	+0.232799
11.35	−0.101244	+0.218633	11.65	−0.032990	+0.232941
11.36	−0.099054	+0.219442	11.66	−0.030660	+0.233059
11.37	−0.096855	+0.220228	11.67	−0.028329	+0.233154
11.38	−0.094649	+0.220991	11.68	−0.025997	+0.233226
11.39	−0.092435	+0.221732	11.69	−0.023664	+0.233275
11.40	−0.090215	+0.222451	11.70	−0.021331	+0.233300
11.41	−0.087986	+0.223146	11.71	−0.018998	+0.233303
11.42	−0.085752	+0.223819	11.72	−0.016665	+0.233282
11.43	−0.083510	+0.224469	11.73	−0.014333	+0.233238
11.44	−0.081262	+0.225097	11.74	−0.012001	+0.233171
11.45	−0.079008	+0.225701	11.75	−0.009669	+0.233081
11.46	−0.076748	+0.226282	11.76	−0.007339	+0.232967
11.47	−0.074483	+0.226841	11.77	−0.005010	+0.232831
11.48	−0.072211	+0.227377	11.78	−0.002683	+0.232672
11.49	−0.069935	+0.227889	11.79	−0.000357	+0.232490
11.50	−0.067654	+0.228379	11.80	+0.001967	+0.232285
11.51	−0.065368	+0.228845	11.81	+0.004289	+0.232057
11.52	−0.063077	+0.229288	11.82	+0.006608	+0.231806
11.53	−0.060782	+0.229708	11.83	+0.008925	+0.231532
11.54	−0.058483	+0.230106	11.84	+0.011239	+0.231236
11.55	−0.056180	+0.230479	11.85	+0.013550	+0.230917
11.56	−0.053874	+0.230830	11.86	+0.015857	+0.230575
11.57	−0.051564	+0.231157	11.87	+0.018161	+0.230211
11.58	−0.049250	+0.231462	11.88	+0.020461	+0.229824
11.59	−0.046934	+0.231743	11.89	+0.022757	+0.229415
11.60	−0.044616	+0.232000	11.90	+0.025049	+0.228983

x	$J_0(x)$	$-J_1(x)$	x	$J_0(x)$	$-J_1(x)$
11.90	+0.025049	+0.228983	12.20	+0.090770	+0.205982
11.91	+0.027337	+0.228529	12.21	+0.092825	+0.204896
11.92	+0.029620	+0.228053	12.22	+0.094868	+0.203790
11.93	+0.031898	+0.227554	12.23	+0.096900	+0.202665
11.94	+0.034171	+0.227033	12.24	+0.098921	+0.201521
11.95	+0.036439	+0.226490	12.25	+0.100931	+0.200357
11.96	+0.038701	+0.225926	12.26	+0.102928	+0.199175
11.97	+0.040957	+0.225339	12.27	+0.104914	+0.197974
11.98	+0.043207	+0.224730	12.28	+0.106888	+0.196754
11.99	+0.045452	+0.224099	12.29	+0.108849	+0.195516
12.00	+0.047689	+0.223447	12.30	+0.110798	+0.194259
12.01	+0.049920	+0.222773	12.31	+0.112734	+0.192984
12.02	+0.052145	+0.222078	12.32	+0.114658	+0.191691
12.03	+0.054362	+0.221361	12.33	+0.116568	+0.190380
12.04	+0.056572	+0.220623	12.34	+0.118465	+0.189051
12.05	+0.058774	+0.219863	12.35	+0.120349	+0.187704
12.06	+0.060969	+0.219082	12.36	+0.122219	+0.186340
12.07	+0.063156	+0.218280	12.37	+0.124076	+0.184958
12.08	+0.065335	+0.217457	12.38	+0.125918	+0.183559
12.09	+0.067505	+0.216614	12.39	+0.127747	+0.182143
12.10	+0.069667	+0.215749	12.40	+0.129561	+0.180710
12.11	+0.071820	+0.214864	12.41	+0.131361	+0.179261
12.12	+0.073964	+0.213958	12.42	+0.133146	+0.177794
12.13	+0.076099	+0.213031	12.43	+0.134917	+0.176311
12.14	+0.078225	+0.212085	12.44	+0.136672	+0.174812
12.15	+0.080341	+0.211118	12.45	+0.138413	+0.173297
12.16	+0.082447	+0.210130	12.46	+0.140138	+0.171766
12.17	+0.084543	+0.209123	12.47	+0.141848	+0.170219
12.18	+0.086629	+0.208096	12.48	+0.143543	+0.168656
12.19	+0.088705	+0.207049	12.49	+0.145221	+0.167077
12.20	+0.090770	+0.205982	12.50	+0.146884	+0.165484

x	$J_0(x)$	$-J_1(x)$	x	$J_0(x)$	$-J_1(x)$
12.50	+0.146884	+0.165484	12.80	+0.188701	+0.111432
12.51	+0.148531	+0.163875	12.81	+0.189806	+0.109453
12.52	+0.150162	+0.162251	12.82	+0.190890	+0.107465
12.53	+0.151776	+0.160613	12.83	+0.191955	+0.105467
12.54	+0.153374	+0.158959	12.84	+0.193000	+0.103461
12.55	+0.154955	+0.157292	12.85	+0.194024	+0.101446
12.56	+0.156519	+0.155610	12.86	+0.195029	+0.099423
12.57	+0.158067	+0.153914	12.87	+0.196013	+0.097391
12.58	+0.159598	+0.152204	12.88	+0.196976	+0.095351
12.59	+0.161111	+0.150480	12.89	+0.197920	+0.093304
12.60	+0.162607	+0.148742	12.90	+0.198842	+0.091248
12.61	+0.164086	+0.146992	12.91	+0.199745	+0.089185
12.62	+0.165547	+0.145228	12.92	+0.200626	+0.087115
12.63	+0.166990	+0.143451	12.93	+0.201487	+0.085038
12.64	+0.168416	+0.141661	12.94	+0.202327	+0.082954
12.65	+0.169824	+0.139858	12.95	+0.203146	+0.080863
12.66	+0.171213	+0.138043	12.96	+0.203944	+0.078766
12.67	+0.172584	+0.136216	12.97	+0.204721	+0.076663
12.68	+0.173937	+0.134376	12.98	+0.205477	+0.074554
12.69	+0.175272	+0.132525	12.99	+0.206212	+0.072439
12.70	+0.176588	+0.130662	13.00	+0.206926	+0.070318
12.71	+0.177885	+0.128788	13.01	+0.207619	+0.068192
12.72	+0.179164	+0.126902	13.02	+0.208290	+0.066061
12.73	+0.180423	+0.125005	13.03	+0.208940	+0.063925
12.74	+0.181664	+0.123097	13.04	+0.209568	+0.061784
12.75	+0.182885	+0.121179	13.05	+0.210176	+0.059639
12.76	+0.184087	+0.119249	13.06	+0.210761	+0.057489
12.77	+0.185270	+0.117310	13.07	+0.211325	+0.055336
12.78	+0.186433	+0.115360	13.08	+0.211868	+0.053178
12.79	+0.187577	+0.113401	13.09	+0.212389	+0.051017
12.80	+0.188701	+0.111432	13.10	+0.212888	+0.048852

x	$J_0(x)$	$-J_1(x)$	x	$J_0(x)$	$-J_1(x)$
13.10	+0.212888	+0.048852	13.40	+0.217725	−0.016599
13.11	+0.213366	+0.046685	13.41	+0.217548	−0.018762
13.12	+0.213822	+0.044514	13.42	+0.217350	−0.020922
13.13	+0.214256	+0.042341	13.43	+0.217130	−0.023078
13.14	+0.214669	+0.040164	13.44	+0.216888	−0.025230
13.15	+0.215059	+0.037986	13.45	+0.216625	−0.027378
13.16	+0.215428	+0.035806	13.46	+0.216341	−0.029522
13.17	+0.215776	+0.033623	13.47	+0.216035	−0.031661
13.18	+0.216101	+0.031439	13.48	+0.215708	0.033795
13.19	+0.216404	+0.029254	13.49	+0.215359	−0.035925
13.20	+0.216686	+0.027067	13.50	+0.214989	−0.038049
13.21	+0.216946	+0.024879	13.51	+0.214598	−0.040168
13.22	+0.217183	+0.022690	13.52	+0.214186	−0.042282
13.23	+0.217399	+0.020501	13.53	+0.213752	−0.044389
13.24	+0.217594	+0.018311	13.54	+0.213298	−0.046491
13.25	+0.217766	+0.016121	13.55	+0.212823	−0.048587
13.26	+0.217916	+0.013932	13.56	+0.212326	−0.050676
13.27	+0.218044	+0.011742	13.57	+0.211809	−0.052758
13.28	+0.218151	+0.009553	13.58	+0.211271	−0.054834
13.29	+0.218235	+0.007365	13.59	+0.210713	−0.056903
13.30	+0.218298	+0.005177	13.60	+0.210133	−0.058965
13.31	+0.218339	+0.002991	13.61	+0.209533	−0.061019
13.32	+0.218357	+0.000806	13.62	+0.208913	−0.063065
13.33	+0.218355	−0.001377	13.63	+0.208272	−0.065104
13.34	+0.218330	−0.003559	13.64	+0.207611	−0.067135
13.35	+0.218284	−0.005738	13.65	+0.206929	−0.069158
13.36	+0.218216	−0.007916	13.66	+0.206228	−0.071173
13.37	+0.218126	−0.010091	13.67	+0.205506	−0.073178
13.38	+0.218014	−0.012263	13.68	+0.204764	−0.075176
13.39	+0.217880	−0.014433	13.69	+0.204002	−0.077164
13.40	+0.217725	−0.016599	13.70	+0.203221	−0.079143

x	$J_0(x)$	$-J_1(x)$	x	$J_0(x)$	$-J_1(x)$
13.70	+0.203221	−0.079143	14.00	+0.171073	−0.133375
'13.71	+0.202420	−0.081113	14.01	+0.169732	−0.134983
13.72	+0.201599	−0.083073	14.02	+0.168374	−0.136577
13.73	+0.200758	−0.085023	14.03	+0.167000	−0.138156
13.74	+0.199898	−0.086964	14.04	+0.165611	−0.139720
13.75	+0.199019	−0.088895	14.05	+0.164206	−0.141269
13.76	+0.198120	−0.090815	14.06	+0.162785	−0.142803
13.77	+0.197203	−0.092725	14.07	+0.161350	−0.144322
13.78	+0.196266	−0.094624	14.08	+0.159899	−0.145825
13.79	+0.195310	−0.096513	14.09	+0.158433	−0.147312
13.80	+0.194336	−0.098391	14.10	+0.156953	−0.148784
13.81	+0.193342	−0.100257	14.11	+0.155458	−0.150240
13.82	+0.192331	−0.102112	14.12	+0.153948	−0.151681
13.83	+0.191300	−0.103956	14.13	+0.152424	−0.153104
13.84	+0.190251	−0.105788	14.14	+0.150886	−0.154512
13.85	+0.189184	−0.107608	14.15	+0.149334	−0.155904
13.86	+0.188099	−0.109416	14.16	+0.147768	−0.157279
13.87	+0.186996	−0.111212	14.17	+0.146188	−0.158637
13.88	+0.185875	−0.112995	14.18	+0.144595	−0.159978
13.89	+0.184736	−0.114767	14.19	+0.142989	−0.161303
13.90	+0.183580	−0.116525	14.20	+0.141369	−0.162611
13.91	+0.182406	−0.118270	41.21	+0.139737	−0.163901
13.92	+0.181214	−0.120003	14.22	+0.138091	−0.165175
13.93	+0.180006	−0.121722	14.23	+0.136433	−0.166431
13.94	+0.178780	−0.123428	14.24	+0.134763	−0.167669
13.95	+0.177537	−0.125121	14.25	+0.133080	−0.168891
13.96	+0.176278	−0.126800	14.26	+0.131385	−0.170094
13.97	+0.175001	−0.128465	14.27	+0.129678	−0.171280
13.98	+0.173708	−0.130116	14.28	+0.127960	−0.172447
13.99	+0.172399	−0.131753	14.29	+0.126229	−0.173597
14.00	+0.171073	−0.133375	14.30	+0.124488	−0.174729

x	$J_0(x)$	$-J_1(x)$	x	$J_0(x)$	$-J_1(x)$
14.30	+0.124488	−0.174729	14.60	+0.067864	−0.199853
14.31	+0.122735	−0.175843	14.61	+0.065863	−0.200384
14.32	+0.120971	−0.176938	14.62	+0.063856	−0.200896
14.33	+0.119196	−0.178015	14.63	+0.061845	−0.201387
14.34	+0.117411	−0.179073	14.64	+0.059829	−0.201857
14.35	+0.115615	−0.180113	14.65	+0.057808	−0.202307
14.36	+0.113808	−0.181135	14.66	+0.055783	−0.202737
14.37	+0.111992	−0.182137	14.67	+0.053753	−0.203146
14.38	+0.110166	−0.183121	14.68	+0.051720	−0.203535
14.39	+0.108330	−0.184086	14.69	+0.049683	−0.203904
14.40	+0.106484	−0.185032	14.70	+0.047642	−0.204251
14.41	+0.104629	−0.185958	14.71	+0.045598	−0.204578
14.42	+0.102765	−0.186866	14.72	+0.043550	−0.204885
14.43	+0.100892	−0.187755	14.73	+0.041500	−0.205171
14.44	+0.099010	−0.188624	14.74	+0.039447	−0.205436
14.45	+0.097119	−0.189473	14.75	+0.037391	−0.205681
14.46	+0.095221	−0.190304	14.76	+0.035333	−0.205905
14.47	+0.093313	−0.191115	14.77	+0.033273	−0.206109
14.48	+0.091398	−0.191906	14.78	+0.031211	−0.206292
14.49	+0.089475	−0.192678	14.79	+0.029148	−0.206454
14.50	+0.087545	−0.193429	14.80	+0.027082	−0.206596
14.51	+0.085607	−0.194162	14.81	+0.025016	−0.206716
14.52	+0.083662	−0.194874	14.82	+0.022948	−0.206817
14.53	+0.081709	−0.195566	14.83	+0.020879	−0.206896
14.54	+0.079750	−0.196239	14.84	+0.018810	−0.206955
14.55	+0.077785	−0.196891	14.85	+0.016740	−0.206994
14.56	+0.075813	−0.197524	14.86	+0.014670	−0.207011
14.57	+0.073834	−0.198136	14.87	+0.012600	−0.207008
14.58	+0.071850	−0.198729	14.88	+0.010530	−0.206985
14.59	+0.069860	−0.199301	14.89	+0.008461	−0.206941
14.60	+0.067864	−0.199853	14.90	+0.006392	−0.206876

x	$J_0(x)$	$-J_1(x)$	x	$J_0(x)$	$-J_1(x)$
14.90	+0.006392	−0.206876	15.20	−0.054421	−0.195545
41.91	+0.004323	−0.206791	15.21	−0.056372	−0.194863
14.92	+0.002256	−0.206685	15.22	−0.058317	−0.194162
14.93	+0.000190	−0.206559	15.23	−0.060256	−0.193442
14.94	−0.001875	−0.206412	15.24	−0.062187	−0.192703
14.95	−0.003939	−0.206245	15.25	−0.064110	−0.191945
14.96	−0.006000	−0.206058	15.26	−0.066025	−0.191169
14.97	−0.008060	−0.205850	15.27	−0.067933	−0.190374
14.98	−0.010117	−0.205621	15.28	−0.069833	−0.189561
14.99	−0.012172	−0.205373	15.29	−0.071724	−0.188729
15.00	−0.014224	−0.205104	15.30	−0.073608	−0.187879
15.01	−0.016274	−0.204815	15.31	−0.075482	−0.187012
15.02	−0.018321	−0.204506	15.32	−0.077348	−0.186126
15.03	−0.020364	−0.204176	15.33	−0.079204	−0.185222
15.04	−0.022404	−0.203827	15.34	−0.081052	−0.184300
15.05	−0.024441	−0.203457	15.35	−0.082890	−0.183360
15.06	−0.026473	−0.203068	15.36	−0.084719	−0.182403
15.07	−0.028502	−0.202658	15.37	−0.086538	−0.181428
15.08	−0.030526	−0.202229	15.38	−0.088348	−0.180436
15.09	−0.032546	−0.201779	15.39	−0.090147	−0.179427
15.10	−0.034562	−0.201310	15.40	−0.091936	−0.178400
15.11	−0.036573	−0.200821	15.41	−0.093715	−0.177357
15.12	−0.038578	−0.200313	15.42	−0.095483	−0.176296
15.13	−0.040579	−0.199785	15.43	−0.097241	−0.175218
15.14	−0.042574	−0.199237	15.44	−0.098988	−0.174124
15.15	−0.044563	−0.198670	15.45	−0.100723	−0.173013
15.16	−0.046547	−0.198084	15.46	−0.102447	−0.171886
15.17	−0.048525	−0.197478	15.47	−0.104161	−0.170742
15.18	−0.050497	−0.196853	15.48	−0.105863	−0.169582
15.19	−0.052462	−0.196209	15.49	−0.107553	−0.168405
15.20	−0.054421	−0.195545	15.50	−0.109231	−0.167213

c. Table of Bessel functions, $J_p(1)$ to $J_p(29)$:

p	$J_p(1)$	$J_p(2)$	$J_p(3)$	$J_p(4)$	$J_p(5)$
0	$+0.7652$	$+0.2239$	-0.2601	-0.3971	-0.1776
0.5	$+0.6714$	$+0.5130$	$+0.06501$	-0.3019	-0.3422
1.0	$+0.4401$	$+0.5767$	$+0.3391$	-0.06604	-0.3276
1.5	$+0.2403$	$+0.4913$	$+0.4777$	$+0.1853$	-0.3276
2.0	$+0.1149$	$+0.3528$	$+0.4861$	$+0.3641$	$+0.04657$
2.5	$+0.04950$	$+0.2239$	$+0.4127$	$+0.4409$	$+0.2404$
3.0	$+0.01956$	$+0.1289$	$+0.3091$	$+0.4302$	$+0.3648$
3.5	$+0.0^2 7186$	$+0.06852$	$+0.2101$	$+0.3658$	$+0.4100$
4.0	$+0.0^2 2477$	$+0.03400$	$+0.1320$	$+0.2811$	$+0.3912$
4.5	$+0.0^3 807$	$+0.01589$	$+0.07760$	$+0.1993$	$+0.3337$
5.0	$+0.0^3 2498$	$+0.0^2 7040$	$+0.04303$	$+0.1321$	$+0.2611$
5.5	$+0.0^4 74$	$+0.0^2 2973$	$+0.02266$	$+0.08261$	$+0.1906$
6.0	$+0.0^4 2094$	$+0.0^2 1202$	$+0.01139$	$+0.04909$	$+0.1310$
6.5	$+0.0^5 6$	$+0.0^3 467$	$+0.0^2 5493$	$+0.02787$	$+0.08558$
7.0	$+0.0^5 1502$	$+0.0^3 1749$	$+0.0^2 2547$	$+0.01518$	$+0.05338$
8	$+0.0^7 9422$	$+0.0^4 2218$	$+0.0^3 4934$	$+0.0^2 4029$	$+0.01841$
9	$+0.0^8 5249$	$+0.0^5 2492$	$+0.0^4 8440$	$+0.0^3 9386$	$+0.0^2 5520$
10	$+0.0^9 2631$	$+0.0^6 2515$	$+0.0^4 1293$	$+0.0^3 1950$	$+0.0^2 1468$
11	$+0.0^{10} 1198$	$+0.0^7 2304$	$+0.0^5 1794$	$+0.0^4 3660$	$+0.0^3 3509$
12	$+0.0^{12} 5000$	$+0.0^8 1933$	$+0.0^6 2276$	$+0.0^5 6264$	$+0.0^4 7628$
13	$+0.0^{13} 1926$	$+0.0^9 1495$	$+0.0^7 2659$	$+0.0^6 9859$	$+0.0^4 1521$
14	$+0.0^{15} 689$	$+0.0^{10} 1073$	$+0.0^8 2880$	$+0.0^6 1436$	$+0.0^5 2801$
15	$+0.0^{16} 23$	$+0.0^{12} 7183$	$+0.0^9 2908$	$+0.0^7 1948$	$+0.0^6 4797$
16	$+0.0^{17} 1$	$+0.0^{13} 4506$	$+0.0^{10} 2749$	$+0.0^8 2472$	$+0.0^7 7675$
17		$+0.0^{14} 2659$	$+0.0^{11} 2444$	$+0.0^9 2947$	$+0.0^7 1153$
18		$+0.0^{15} 148$	$+0.0^{12} 2050$	$+0.0^{10} 3313$	$+0.0^8 1631$
19		$+0.0^{17} 8$	$+0.0^{13} 1628$	$+0.0^{11} 3525$	$+0.0^9 2183$
20			$+0.0^{14} 1228$	$+0.0^{12} 3560$	$+0.0^{10} 2770$
21			$+0.0^{16} 88$	$+0.0^{13} 3420$	$+0.0^{11} 3344$
22			$+0.0^{17} 6$	$+0.0^{14} 3134$	$+0.0^{12} 3848$
23				$+0.0^{15} 275$	$+0.0^{13} 4231$
24				$+0.0^{16} 23$	$+0.0^{14} 4454$
25				$+0.0^{17} 2$	$+0.0^{15} 450$
26					$+0.0^{16} 44$
27					$+0.0^{17} 4$

p	$J_p(6)$	$J_p(7)$	$J_p(8)$	$J_p(9)$	$J_p(10)$
0	$+0.1506$	$+0.3001$	$+0.1717$	-0.09033	-0.2459
0.5	-0.09102	$+0.1981$	$+0.2791$	$+0.1096$	-0.1373
1.0	-0.2767	$-0.0^{2}4683$	$+0.2346$	$+0.2453$	$+0.04347$
1.5	-0.3279	-0.1991	$+0.07593$	$+0.2545$	$+0.1980$
2.0	-0.2429	-0.3014	-0.1130	$+0.1448$	$+0.2546$
2.5	-0.07295	-0.2834	-0.2506	-0.02477	$+0.1967$
3.0	$+0.1148$	-0.1676	-0.2911	-0.1809	$+0.05838$
3.5	$+0.2671$	$-0.0^{2}3403$	-0.2326	-0.2683	-0.09965
4.0	$+0.3576$	$+0.1578$	-0.1054	-0.2655	-0.2196
4.5	$+0.3846$	$+0.2800$	$+0.04712$	-0.1839	-0.2664
5.0	$+0.3621$	$+0.3479$	$+0.1858$	-0.05504	-0.2341
5.5	$+0.3098$	$+0.3634$	$+0.2856$	$+0.08439$	-0.1401
6.0	$+0.2458$	$+0.3392$	$+0.3376$	$+0.2043$	-0.01446
6.5	$+0.1833$	$+0.2911$	$+0.3456$	$+0.2870$	$+0.1123$
7.0	$+0.1296$	$+0.2236$	$+0.3206$	$+0.3275$	$+0.2167$
7.5	$+0.08741$	$+0.1772$	$+0.2759$	$+0.3302$	$+0.2861$
8.0	$+0.05653$	$+0.1280$	$+0.2235$	$+0.3051$	$+0.3179$
8.5	$+0.03520$	$+0.08854$	$+0.1718$	$+0.2633$	$+0.3169$
9.0	$+0.02117$	$+0.05892$	$+0.1263$	$+0.2149$	$+0.2919$
9.5	$+0.01232$	$+0.03785$	$+0.08921$	$+0.1672$	$+0.2526$
10.0	$+0.0^{2}6964$	$+0.02354$	$+.06077$	$+0.1247$	$+0.2075$
10.5	$+0.0^{2}3827$	$+0.01421$	$+0.04005$	$+0.08959$	$+0.1630$
11.0	$+0.0^{2}2048$	$+0.0^{2}8335$	$+0.02560$	$+0.06222$	$+0.1231$
11.5	$+0.0^{2}1069$	$+0.0^{2}4763$	$+0.01590$	$+0.04188$	$+0.08976$
12.0	$+0.0^{3}5452$	$+0.0^{2}2656$	$+0.0^{2}9624$	$+0.02739$	$+0.06337$
12.5	$+0.0^{3}272$	$+0.0^{2}1446$	$+0.0^{2}5680$	$+0.01744$	$+0.04344$
13.0	$+0.0^{3}1327$	$+0.0^{3}7702$	$+0.0^{2}3275$	$+0.01083$	$+0.02897$
13.5	$+0.0^{4}63$	$+0.0^{3}402$	$+0.0^{2}1846$	$+0.0^{2}6568$	$+0.01884$
14.0	$+0.0^{4}2976$	$+0.0^{3}2052$	$+0.0^{2}1019$	$+0.0^{2}3895$	$+0.01196$
15	$+0.0^{5}6192$	$+0.0^{4}5059$	$+0.0^{3}2926$	$+0.0^{2}1286$	$+0.0^{2}4508$
16	$+0.0^{5}1202$	$+0.0^{4}1161$	$+0.0^{4}7801$	$+0.0^{3}3993$	$+0.0^{2}1567$
17	$+0.0^{6}2187$	$+0.0^{5}2494$	$+0.0^{4}1942$	$+0.0^{3}1120$	$+0.0^{3}5056$
18	$+0.0^{7}3746$	$+0.0^{5}5037$	$+0.0^{5}4538$	$+0.0^{4}2988$	$+0.0^{3}1524$
19	$+0.0^{8}6062$	$+0.0^{7}9598$	$+0.0^{6}9992$	$+0.0^{5}7497$	$+0.0^{4}4315$
20	$+0.0^{9}9296$	$+0.0^{7}1731$	$+0.0^{6}2081$	$+0.0^{5}1777$	$+0.0^{4}1161$
21	$+0.0^{9}1355$	$+0.0^{8}2966$	$+0.0^{7}4110$	$+0.0^{6}3990$	$+0.0^{5}2907$
22	$+0.0^{10}1882$	$+0.0^{9}4839$	$+0.0^{8}7725$	$+0.0^{7}8515$	$+0.0^{6}6969$
23	$+0.0^{11}2497$	$+0.0^{10}7535$	$+0.0^{8}1385$	$+0.0^{7}1732$	$+0.0^{6}1590$
24	$+0.0^{12}3168$	$+0.0^{10}1122$	$+.0^{9}2373$	$+0.0^{8}3364$	$+0.0^{7}3463$

p	$J_p(6)$	$J_p(7)$	$J_p(8)$	$J_p(9)$	$J_p(10)$
25	$+0.0^{13}3855$	$+0.0^{11}1602$	$+0.0^{10}3895$	$+0.0^9 6257$	$+0.0^8 7215$
26	$+0.0^{14}4415$	$+0.0^{12}2195$	$+0.0^{11}6135$	$+0.0^9 1116$	$+0.0^8 1441$
27	$+0.0^{15}507$	$+0.0^{13}2893$	$+0.0^{12}9289$	$+0.0^{10}1913$	$+0.0^9 2762$
28	$+0.0^{16}55$	$+0.0^{14}3673$	$+0.0^{12}1354$	$+0.0^{11}3154$	$+0.0^{10}5094$
29	$+0.0^{17}6$	$+0.0^{15}450$	$+0.0^{13}1903$	$+0.0^{12}5014$	$+0.0^{11}9050$
30	$+0.0^{17}1$	$+0.0^{16}53$	$+0.0^{14}2583$	$+0.0^{13}7692$	$+0.0^{11}1551$
31		$+0.0^{17}6$	$+0.0^{15}339$	$+0.0^{13}1140$	$+0.0^{12}2568$
32		$+0.0^{17}1$	$+0.0^{16}43$	$+0.0^{14}1636$	$+0.0^{18}4112$
33			$+0.0^{17}5$	$+0.0^{15}227$	$+0.0^{14}6376$
34			$+0.0^{17}1$	$+0.0^{16}31$	$+0.0^{15}958$
35				$+0.0^{17}4$	$+0.0^{15}140$
36					$+0.0^{16}20$
37					$+0.0^{17}3$

p	$J_p(11)$	$J_p(12)$	$J_p(13)$	$J_p(14)$	$J_p(15)$
0	-0.1712	$+0.04769$	$+0.2069$	$+0.1711$	-0.01422
0.5	-0.2406	-0.1236	$+0.09298$	$+0.2112$	$+0.1340$
1.0	-0.1768	-0.2234	-0.07032	$+0.1334$	$+0.2051$
1.5	-0.02293	-0.2047	-0.1937	-0.01407	$+0.1654$
2.0	$+0.1390$	-0.08493	-0.2177	-0.1520	$+0.04157$
2.5	$+0.2343$	$+0.07242$	$+0.1377$	-0.2143	-0.1009
3.0	$+0.2273$	$+0.1951$	$+0.0^2 3320$	-0.1768	-0.1940
3.5	$+0.1294$	$+0.2348$	$+0.1407$	-0.06245	-0.1991
4.0	-0.01504	$+0.1825$	$+0.2193$	$+0.07624$	-0.1192
4.5	-0.1519	$+0.06457$	$+0.2134$	$+0.1830$	$+0.0^2 7984$
5.0	-0.2383	-0.07347	$+0.1316$	$+0.2204$	$+0.1305$
5.5	-0.2538	-0.1864	$+0.0^2 7055$	$+0.1801$	$+0.2039$
6.0	-0.2016	-0.2437	-0.1180	$+0.08117$	$+0.2061$
6.5	-0.1018	-0.2354	-0.2075	-0.04151	$+0.1415$
7.0	$+0.01838$	-0.1703	-0.2406	-0.1508	$+0.03446$
7.5	$+0.1334$	-0.06865	-0.2145	-0.2187	-0.08121
8.0	$+0.2250$	$+0.04510$	-0.1410	-0.2320	-0.1740
8.5	$+0.2838$	$+0.1496$	-0.04006	-0.1928	-0.2227
9.0	$+0.3089$	$+0.2304$	$+0.06698$	-0.1143	-0.2200
9.5	$+0.3051$	$+0.2806$	$+0.1621$	-0.01541	-0.1712
10.0	$+0.2804$	$+0.3005$	$+0.2338$	$+0.08501$	$+0.09007$
10.5	$+0.2433$	$+0.2947$	$+0.2770$	$+0.1718$	$+0.0^2 5862$
11.0	$+0.2010$	$+0.2704$	$+0.2927$	$+0.2357$	$+0.09995$
11.5	$+0.1593$	$+0.2351$	$+0.2854$	$+0.2732$	$+0.1794$
12.0	$+0.1216$	$+0.1953$	$+0.2615$	$+0.2855$	$+0.2367$

p	$J_p(11)$	$J_p(12)$	$J_p(13)$	$J_p(14)$	$J_p(15)$
12.5	$+0.08978$	$+0.1559$	$+0.2279$	$+0.2770$	$+0.2692$
13.0	$+0.06429$	$+0.1201$	$+0.1901$	$+0.2536$	$+0.2787$
13.5	$+0.04477$	$+0.08970$	$+0.1528$	$+0.2214$	$+0.2693$
14.0	$+0.03037$	$+0.06504$	$+0.1188$	$+0.1855$	$+0.2464$
14.5	$+0.02011$	$+0.04591$	$+0.08953$	$+0.1500$	$+0.2155$
15.0	$+0.01301$	$+0.03161$	$+0.06564$	$+0.1174$	$+0.1813$
15.5	$+0.0^{2}8237$	$+0.02126$	$+0.04691$	$+0.08931$	$+0.1474$
16.0	$+0.0^{2}5110$	$+0.01399$	$+0.03272$	$+0.06613$	$+0.1162$
16.5	$+0.0^{2}3108$	$+0.0^{2}9017$	$+0.02232$	$+0.04777$	$+0.08905$
17.0	$+0.0^{2}1856$	$+0.0^{2}5698$	$+0.01491$	$+0.03372$	$+0.06653$
17.5	$+0.0^{2}1086$	$+0.0^{2}3532$	$+0.0^{2}9760$	$+0.02330$	$+0.04853$
18.0	$+0.0^{3}6280$	$+0.0^{2}2152$	$+0.0^{2}6269$	$+0.01577$	$+0.03463$
18.5	$+0.0^{3}355$	$+0.0^{2}1288$	$+0.0^{2}3955$	$+0.01047$	$+0.02419$
19.0	$+0.0^{3}1990$	$+0.0^{3}7590$	$+0.0^{2}2452$	$+0.0^{2}6824$	$+0.01657$
20	$+0.0^{4}5931$	$+0.0^{3}2512$	$+0.0^{3}8971$	$+0.0^{2}2753$	$+0.0^{2}7360$
21	$+0.0^{4}1670$	$+0.0^{4}7839$	$+0.0^{3}3087$	$+0.0^{2}1041$	$+0.0^{2}3054$
22	$+0.0^{5}4458$	$+0.0^{4}2315$	$+0.0^{3}1004$	$+0.0^{3}3711$	$+0.0^{2}1190$
23	$+0.0^{5}1132$	$+0.0^{5}6491$	$+0.0^{4}3092$	$+0.0^{3}1251$	$+0.0^{3}4379$
24	$+0.0^{6}2738$	$+0.0^{5}1733$	$+0.0^{5}9060$	$+0.0^{4}4006$	$+0.0^{3}1527$
25	$+0.0^{7}6333$	$+0.0^{6}4418$	$+0.0^{5}2532$	$+0.0^{4}1221$	$+0.0^{4}5060$
26	$+0.0^{7}1403$	$+0.0^{6}1078$	$+0.0^{6}6761$	$+0.0^{5}3555$	$+0.0^{4}1599$
27	$+0.0^{8}2981$	$+0.0^{7}2521$	$+0.0^{6}1730$	$+0.0^{6}9902$	$+0.0^{5}4829$
28	$+0.0^{9}6092$	$+0.0^{8}5665$	$+0.0^{7}4249$	$+0.0^{6}2645$	$+0.0^{5}1398$
29	$+0.0^{9}1198$	$+0.0^{8}1225$	$+0.0^{7}1004$	$+0.0^{7}6790$	$+0.0^{6}3883$
30	$+0.0^{10}2274$	$+0.0^{9}2552$	$+0.0^{8}2283$	$+0.0^{7}1678$	$+0.0^{6}1037$
31	$+0.0^{11}4165$	$+0.0^{10}5133$	$+0.0^{9}5009$	$+0.0^{8}3995$	$+0.0^{7}2670$
32	$+0.0^{12}7375$	$+0.0^{11}9976$	$+0.0^{9}1062$	$+0.0^{9}9187$	$+0.0^{8}6632$
33	$+0.0^{12}1264$	$+0.0^{11}1876$	$+0.0^{10}2176$	$+0.0^{9}2042$	$+0.0^{8}1591$
34	$+0.0^{13}2100$	$+0.0^{12}3417$	$+0.0^{11}4320$	$+0.0^{10}4392$	$+0.0^{9}3693$
35	$+0.0^{14}3383$	$+0.0^{13}6035$	$+0.0^{12}8310$	$+0.0^{11}9155$	$+0.0^{10}8301$
36	$+0.0^{15}529$	$+0.0^{13}1035$	$+0.0^{12}1551$	$+0.0^{11}1851$	$+0.0^{10}1809$
37	$+0.0^{16}80$	$+0.0^{14}1723$	$+0.0^{13}2812$	$+0.0^{12}3632$	$+0.0^{11}3827$
38	$+0.0^{16}12$	$+0.0^{15}279$	$+0.0^{14}4956$	$+0.0^{13}6928$	$+0.0^{12}7863$
39	$+0.0^{17}2$	$+0.0^{16}44$	$+0.0^{15}850$	$+0.0^{13}1285$	$+0.0^{12}1571$
40		$+0.0^{17}7$	$+0.0^{15}142$	$+0.0^{14}2320$	$+0.0^{13}3054$
41		$+0.0^{17}1$	$+0.0^{16}23$	$+0.0^{15}408$	$+0.0^{14}5781$
42			$+0.0^{17}4$	$+0.0^{16}70$	$+0.0^{14}1067$
43			$+0.0^{17}1$	$+0.0^{16}12$	$+0.0^{15}192$
44				$+0.0^{17}2$	$+0.0^{16}34$
45					$+0.0^{17}6$
46					$+0.0^{17}1$

p	$J_p\,(16)$	$J_p\,(17)$	$J_p\,(18)$	$J_p\,(19)$	$J_p\,(20)$
0	−0.1749	−0.1699	−0.01336	+0.1466	+0.1670
0.5	−0.05743	−0.1860	−0.1412	+0.02744	+0.1629
1.0	+0.09040	−0.09767	−0.1880	−0.1057	+0.06683
1.5	+0.1874	+0.04231	−0.1320	−0.1795	−0.06466
2.0	+0.1862	+0.1584	−0.0²7533	−0.1578	−0.1603
2.5	+0.09257	+0.1935	+0.1192	−0.05578	−0.1726
3.0	−0.04385	+0.1349	+0.1863	+0.07249	−0.09890
3.5	−0.1585	+0.01461	+0.1651	+0.1649	+0.02152
4.0	−0.2026	−0.1107	+0.06964	+0.1806	+0.1307
4.5	−0.1619	−0.1875	−0.05501	+0.1165	+0.1801
5.0	−0.05747	−0.1870	−0.1554	+0.0²3572	+0.1512
5.5	+0.06743	−0.1139	−0.1926	−0.1097	+0.05953
6.0	+0.1667	+0.0³7153	−0.1560	−0.1788	−0.05509
6.5	+0.2083	+0.1138	−0.06273	−0.1800	−0.1474
7.0	+0.1825	+0.1875	+0.05140	−0.1165	−0.1842
7.5	+0.1018	+0.2009	+0.1473	−0.01350	−0.1553
8.0	−0.0²7021	+0.1537	+0.1959	+0.09294	−0.07387
8.5	−0.1128	+0.06346	+0.1855	+0.1694	+0.03088
9.0	−0.1895	−0.04286	+0.1228	+0.1947	+0.1251
9.5	−0.2217	−0.1374	+0.02786	+0.1650	+0.1816
10.0	−0.2062	−0.1991	−0.07317	+0.09155	+0.1865
10.5	−0.1504	−0.2171	−0.1561	−0.0²4326	+0.1416
11.0	−0.06822	−0.1914	−0.2041	−0.09837	+0.06136
11.5	+0.02427	−0.1307	−0.2100	−0.1698	−0.03288
12.0	+0.1124	−0.04857	−0.1762	−0.2055	−0.1190
12.5	+0.1853	+0.04024	−0.1122	−0.2012	−0.1794
13.0	+0.2368	+0.1228	−0.03092	−0.1612	−0.2041
13.5	+0.2653	+0.1899	+0.05414	−0.09497	−0.1914
14.0	+0.2724	+0.2364	+0.1316	−0.01507	−0.1464
14.5	+0.2623	+0.2613	+0.1934	+0.06627	−0.07897
15.0	+0.2399	+0.2666	+0.2356	+0.1389	−0.0³8121
15.5	+0.2102	+0.2559	+0.2575	+0.1961	+0.07689
16.0	+0.1775	+0.2340	+0.2611	+0.2345	+0.1452
16.5	+0.1450	+0.2054	+0.2500	+0.2537	+0.1982
17.0	+0.1150	+0.1739	+0.2286	+0.2559	+0.2331
17.5	+0.08876	+0.1427	+0.2009	+0.2445	+0.2501
18.0	+0.06685	+0.1138	+0.1706	+0.2235	+0.2511
18.5	+0.04920	+0.08844	+0.1406	+0.1968	+0.2395
19.0	+0.03544	+0.06710	+0.1127	+0.1676	+0.2189

p	$J_p(16)$	$J_p(17)$	$J_p(18)$	$J_p(19)$	$J_p(20)$
20	$+0.01733$	$+0.03619$	$+0.06731$	$+0.1116$	$+0.1647$
21	$+0.0^2 7879$	$+0.01804$	$+0.03686$	$+0.06746$	$+0.1106$
22	$+0.0^2 3354$	$+0.0^2 8380$	$+0.01871$	$+0.03748$	$+0.06758$
23	$+0.0^2 1343$	$+0.0^2 3651$	$+0.0^2 8864$	$+0.01934$	$+0.03805$
24	$+0.0^3 5087$	$+0.0^2 1500$	$+0.0^2 3946$	$+0.0^2 9331$	$+0.01993$
25	$+0.0^3 1828$	$+0.0^3 5831$	$+0.0^2 1658$	$+0.0^2 4237$	$+0.0^2 9781$
26	$+0.0^4 6253$	$+0.0^3 2154$	$+0.0^3 6607$	$+0.0^3 1819$	$+0.0^2 4524$
27	$+0.0^4 2042$	$+0.0^4 7586$	$+0.0^3 2504$	$+0.0^3 7412$	$+0.0^2 1981$
28	$+0.0^5 6380$	$+0.0^4 2553$	$+0.0^4 9057$	$+0.0^3 2877$	$+0.0^3 8242$
29	$+0.0^5 1912$	$+0.0^5 8228$	$+0.0^4 3133$	$+0.0^3 1066$	$+0.0^3 3270$
30	$+0.0^6 5505$	$+0.0^5 2546$	$+0.0^4 1039$	$+0.0^4 3785$	$+0.0^3 1240$
31	$+0.0^6 1525$	$+0.0^6 7577$	$+0.0^5 3313$	$+0.0^4 1289$	$+0.0^4 4508$
32	$+0.0^7 4078$	$+0.0^6 2172$	$+0.0^5 1016$	$+0.0^5 4223$	$+0.0^4 1574$
33	$+0.0^7 1052$	$+0.0^7 6009$	$+0.0^6 3005$	$+0.0^5 1333$	$+0.0^5 5289$
34	$+0.0^8 2625$	$+0.0^7 1606$	$+0.0^7 8583$	$+0.0^6 4057$	$+0.0^5 1713$
35	$+0.0^9 6339$	$+0.0^8 4153$	$+0.0^7 2370$	$+0.0^6 1193$	$+0.0^6 5358$
36	$+0.0^9 1484$	$+0.0^8 1040$	$+0.0^8 6335$	$+0.0^7 3396$	$+0.0^6 1620$
37	$+0.0^{10} 3368$	$+0.0^9 2526$	$+0.0^8 1641$	$+0.0^8 9362$	$+0.0^7 4742$
38	$+0.0^{11} 7426$	$+0.0^{10} 5956$	$+0.0^9 4126$	$+0.0^8 2503$	$+0.0^7 1345$
39	$+0.0^{11} 1591$	$+0.0^{10} 1364$	$+0.0^9 1007$	$+0.0^9 6496$	$+0.0^8 3704$
40	$+0.0^{12} 3317$	$+0.0^{11} 3039$	$+0.0^{10} 2391$	$+0.0^9 1638$	$+0.0^9 9902$
41	$+0.0^{13} 6733$	$+0.0^{12} 6590$	$+0.0^{11} 5520$	$+0.0^{10} 4018$	$+0.0^9 2574$
42	$+0.0^{13} 1331$	$+0.0^{12} 1392$	$+0.0^{11} 1241$	$+0.0^{11} 9594$	$+0.0^{10} 6510$
43	$+0.0^{14} 2567$	$+0.0^{13} 2865$	$+0.0^{12} 2719$	$+0.0^{11} 2231$	$+0.0^{10} 1604$
44	$+0.0^{15} 483$	$+0.0^{14} 5752$	$+0.0^{13} 5810$	$+0.0^{12} 5059$	$+0.0^{11} 3849$
45	$+0.0^{16} 89$	$+0.0^{14} 1127$	$+0.0^{13} 1211$	$+0.0^{12} 1119$	$+0.0^{12} 9011$
46	$+0.0^{16} 16$	$+0.0^{15} 216$	$+0.0^{14} 2466$	$+0.0^{13} 2416$	$+0.0^{12} 2059$
47	$+0.0^{17} 3$	$+0.0^{16} 40$	$+0.0^{15} 490$	$+0.0^{14} 5096$	$+0.0^{13} 4594$
48		$+0.0^{17} 7$	$+0.0^{16} 95$	$+0.0^{14} 1051$	$+0.0^{13} 1002$
49		$+0.0^{17} 1$	$+0.0^{16} 18$	$+0.0^{15} 212$	$+0.0^{14} 2135$
50			$+0.0^{17} 3$	$+0.0^{16} 42$	$+0.0^{15} 445$
51				$+0.0^{17} 8$	$+0.0^{16} 91$
52				$+0.0^{17} 2$	$+0.0^{16} 18$
53					$+0.0^{17} 4$
54					$+0.0^{17} 1$

p	$J_p(21)$	$J_p(22)$	$J_p(23)$	$J_p(24)$
0	$+0.03658$	-0.1207	-0.1624	-0.05623
0.5	$+0.1457$	-0.0^21506	-0.1408	-0.1475
1.0	$+0.1711$	$+0.1172$	-0.03952	-0.1540
1.5	$+0.1023$	$+0.1700$	$+0.08253$	-0.07523
2.0	-0.02028	$+0.1313$	$+0.1590$	$+0.04339$
2.5	-0.1311	$+0.02469$	$+0.1516$	$+0.1381$
3.0	-0.1750	-0.09330	$+0.06717$	$+0.1613$
3.5	-0.1335	-0.1644	-0.04958	$+0.1040$
4.0	-0.02971	-0.1568	-0.1415	-0.0^23076
4.5	$+0.08656$	-0.07701	-0.1666	-0.1078
5.0	$+0.1637$	$+0.03630$	-0.1164	-0.1623
5.5	$+0.1706$	$+0.1329$	-0.01563	-0.1444
6.0	$+0.1076$	$+0.1733$	$+0.09086$	-0.06455
6.5	$+0.0^22808$	$+0.1435$	$+0.1592$	$+0.04157$
7.0	-0.1022	$+0.05820$	$+0.1638$	$+0.1300$
8	-0.1757	-0.1362	$+0.0^28829$	$+0.1404$
9	-0.3175	-0.1573	-0.1576	-0.03643
10	$+0.1485$	$+0.0^27547$	-0.1322	-0.1677
11	$+0.1732$	$+0.1641$	$+0.04268$	-0.1033
12	$+0.03293$	$+0.1566$	$+0.1730$	$+0.07299$
13	-0.1356	$+0.0^26688$	$+0.1379$	$+0.1763$
14	-0.2008	-0.1487	-0.01718	$+0.1180$
15	-0.1321	-0.1959	-0.1588	-0.03863
16	$+0.01202$	-0.1185	-0.1899	-0.1663
17	$+0.1505$	$+0.02358$	-0.1055	-0.1831
18	$+0.2316$	$+0.1549$	$+0.03402$	-0.09311
19	$+0.2465$	$+0.2299$	$+0.1587$	$+0.04345$
20	$+0.2145$	$+0.2422$	$+0.2282$	$+0.1619$
21	$+0.1621$	$+0.2105$	$+0.2381$	$+0.2264$
22	$+0.1097$	$+0.1596$	$+0.2067$	$+0.2343$
23	$+0.06767$	$+0.1087$	$+0.1573$	$+0.2031$
24	$+0.03857$	$+0.06773$	$+0.1078$	$+0.1550$
25	$+0.02049$	$+0.03905$	$+0.06777$	$+0.1070$
26	$+0.01022$	$+0.02102$	$+0.03949$	$+0.06778$
27	$+0.0^24806$	$+0.01064$	$+0.02152$	$+0.03990$
28	$+0.0^22143$	$+0.0^25084$	$+0.01104$	$+0.02200$
29	$+0.0^39094$	$+0.0^22307$	$+0.0^25357$	$+0.01143$
30	$+0.0^33682$	$+0.0^39965$	$+0.0^22470$	$+0.0^25626$
31	$+0.0^31427$	$+0.0^34113$	$+0.0^21085$	$+0.0^22633$
32	$+0.0^45304$	$+0.0^31626$	$+0.0^34561$	$+0.0^21176$
33	$+0.0^41895$	$+0.0^46171$	$+0.0^31837$	$+0.0^35024$
34	$+0.0^56521$	$+0.0^42253$	$+0.0^47110$	$+0.0^32060$

p	$J_p(21)$	$J_p(22)$	$J_p(23)$	$J_p(24)$
35	$+0.0^52164$	$+0.0^57927$	$+0.0^42649$	$+0.0^48119$
36	$+0.0^66941$	$+0.0^52692$	$+0.0^59516$	$+0.0^43083$
37	$+0.0^62153$	$+0.0^68839$	$+0.0^53302$	$+0.0^41130$
38	$+0.0^76471$	$+0.0^62890$	$+0.0^51108$	$+0.0^54000$
39	$+0.0^71886$	$+0.0^78652$	$+0.0^63603$	$+0.0^51371$
40	$+0.0^85336$	$+0.0^72586$	$+0.0^61136$	$+0.0^64553$
41	$+0.0^81467$	$+0.0^87506$	$+0.0^73476$	$+0.0^61467$
42	$+0.0^93922$	$+0.0^82118$	$+0.0^71034$	$+0.0^74590$
43	$+0.0^91021$	$+0.0^95816$	$+0.0^82989$	$+0.0^71396$
44	$+0.0^{10}2589$	$+0.0^91555$	$+0.0^98417$	$+0.0^84133$
45	$+0.0^{11}6402$	$+0.0^{10}4054$	$+0.0^92309$	$+0.0^81191$
46	$+0.0^{11}1544$	$+0.0^{10}1031$	$+0.0^{10}6175$	$+0.0^93347$
47	$+0.0^{12}3637$	$+0.0^{11}2557$	$+0.0^{10}1611$	$+0.0^{10}9172$
48	$+0.0^{13}8368$	$+0.0^{12}6196$	$+0.0^{11}4105$	$+0.0^{10}2453$
49	$+0.0^{13}1882$	$+0.0^{12}1467$	$+0.0^{11}1022$	$+0.0^{11}6409$
50	$+0.0^{14}4139$	$+0.0^{13}3397$	$+0.0^{12}2486$	$+0.0^{11}1636$
51	$+0.0^{15}891$	$+0.0^{14}7696$	$+0.0^{13}5917$	$+0.0^{12}4085$
52	$+0.0^{15}188$	$+0.0^{14}1706$	$+0.0^{13}1378$	$+0.0^{13}9976$
53	$+0.0^{16}39$	$+0.0^{15}370$	$+0.0^{14}3142$	$+0.0^{13}2385$
54	$+0.0^{17}8$	$+0.0^{16}79$	$+0.0^{15}702$	$+0.0^{14}5585$
55	$+0.0^{17}2$	$+0.0^{16}16$	$+0.0^{15}154$	$+0.0^{14}1281$
56		$+0.0^{17}3$	$+0.0^{16}34$	$+0.0^{15}288$
57		$+0.0^{17}1$	$+0.0^{17}7$	$+0.0^{16}64$
58			$+0.0^{17}1$	$+0.0^{16}14$
59				$+0.0^{17}3$
60				$+0.0^{17}1$

p	$J_p(25)$	$J_p(26)$	$J_p(27)$	$J_p(28)$	$J_p(29)$
0	$+0.0963$	$+0.1560$	$+0.0727$	-0.0732	-0.1478
1	-0.1254	$+0.0150$	$+0.1366$	$+0.1306$	$+0.0069$
2	-0.1063	-0.1548	-0.0626	$+0.0825$	$+0.1483$
3	$+0.1083$	-0.0389	-0.1459	-0.1188	$+0.0135$
4	$+0.1323$	$+0.1459$	$+0.0302$	-0.1079	-0.1455
5	-0.0660	$+0.0838$	$+0.1548$	$+0.0879$	-0.0537
6	-0.1587	-0.1137	$+0.0271$	$+0.1393$	$+0.1270$
7	-0.0102	-0.1362	-0.1428	-0.0282	$+0.1062$
8	$+0.1530$	$+0.0403$	-0.1012	-0.1534	-0.0757
9	$+0.1081$	$+0.1610$	$+0.0828$	-0.0595	-0.1480

p	$J_p(25)$	$J_p(26)$	$J_p(27)$	$J_p(28)$	$J_p(29)$
10	-0.0752	$+0.0712$	$+0.1564$	$+0.1152$	-0.0161
11	-0.1682	-0.1063	$+0.0330$	$+0.1418$	$+0.1369$
12	-0.0729	-0.1611	-0.1295	-0.0038	$+0.1200$
13	$+0.0983$	-0.0424	-0.1481	-0.1450	-0.0376
14	$+0.1751$	$+0.1187$	-0.0131	-0.1309	-0.1537
15	$+0.0978$	$+0.1702$	$+0.1345$	$+0.0142$	-0.1108
16	-0.0577	$+0.0777$	$+0.1625$	$+0.1461$	$+0.0391$
17	-0.1717	-0.0745	$+0.0582$	$+0.1527$	$+0.1539$
18	-0.1758	-0.1752	-0.0893	$+0.0394$	$+0.1414$
19	-0.0814	-0.1681	-0.1772	-0.1021	$+0.0216$
20	$+0.0520$	-0.0704	-0.1601	-0.1779	-0.1131
21	$+0.1646$	$+0.0597$	-0.0600	-0.1521	-0.1776
22	$+0.2246$	$+0.1669$	$+0.0668$	-0.0502	-0.1441
23	$+0.2306$	$+0.2227$	$+0.1688$	$+0.0732$	-0.0410
24	$+0.1998$	$+0.2271$	$+0.2209$	$+0.1704$	$+0.0790$
25	$+0.1529$	$+0.1966$	$+0.2238$	$+0.2190$	$+0.1718$
26	$+0.1061$	$+0.1510$	$+0.1936$	$+0.2207$	$+0.2172$
27	$+0.06778$	$+0.1053$	$+0.1491$	$+0.1908$	$+0.2176$
28	$+0.04028$	$+0.06776$	$+0.1045$	$+0.1473$	$+0.1881$
29	$+0.02245$	$+0.04063$	$+0.06773$	$+0.1038$	$+0.1456$
30	$+0.01181$	$+0.02288$	$+0.04096$	$+0.06769$	$+0.1030$
31	$+0.0^{2}5889$	$+0.01217$	$+0.02329$	$+0.04126$	$+0.06763$
32	$+0.0^{2}2795$	$+0.0^{2}6147$	$+0.01253$	$+0.02368$	$+0.04155$
33	$+0.0^{2}1267$	$+0.0^{2}2957$	$+0.0^{2}6400$	$+0.01287$	$+0.02405$
34	$+0.0^{3}550$	$+0.0^{2}1360$	$+0.0^{2}3118$	$+0.0^{2}6648$	$+0.01320$
35	$+0.0^{3}229$	$+0.0^{3}599$	$+0.0^{2}1453$	$+0.0^{2}3278$	$+0.0^{2}6891$
36	$+0.0^{4}92$	$+0.0^{3}254$	$+0.0^{3}650$	$+0.0^{2}1548$	$+0.0^{2}3437$
37	$+0.0^{4}36$	$+0.0^{3}103$	$+0.0^{3}279$	$+0.0^{3}701$	$+0.0^{2}1642$
38	$+0.0^{4}13$	$+0.0^{4}41$	$+0.0^{3}116$	$+0.0^{3}306$	$+0.0^{3}754$
39	$+0.0^{5}5$	$+0.0^{4}15$	$+0.0^{3}46$	$+0.0^{3}128$	$+0.0^{3}333$
40	$+0.0^{5}2$	$+0.0^{5}6$	$+0.0^{4}18$	$+0.0^{4}52$	$+0.0^{3}142$
41	$+0.0^{5}1$	$+0.0^{5}2$	$+0.0^{5}7$	$+0.0^{4}20$	$+0.0^{4}58$
42		$+0.0^{5}1$	$+0.0^{5}2$	$+0.0^{5}8$	$+0.0^{4}23$
43			$+0.0^{5}1$	$+0.0^{5}3$	$+0.0^{5}9$
44				$+0.0^{5}1$	$+0.0^{5}3$

11. CURVES AND TABLES OF SINE AND COSINE INTEGRALS
a. Sine and cosine integral curves:

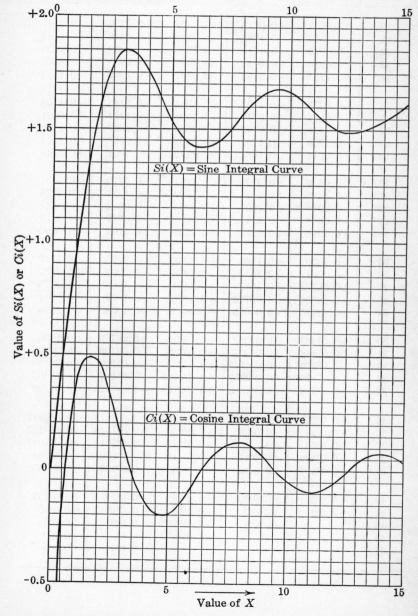

b. Sine and cosine integral tables:

x	$Si(x)$	$Ci(x)$	$\overline{Ei}(x)$	$Ei(-x)$
0.00	+0.000000	$-\infty$	$-\infty$	$-\infty$
0.01	+0.010000	−4.0280	−4.0179	−4.0379
0.02	+0.019999	−3.3349	−3.3147	−3.3547
0.03	+0.029998	−2.9296	−2.8991	−2.9591
0.04	+0.039996	−2.6421	−2.6013	−2.6813
0.05	+0.04999	−2.4191	−2.3679	−2.4679
0.06	+0.05999	−2.2371	−2.1753	−2.2953
0.07	+0.06998	−2.0833	−2.0108	−2.1508
0.08	+0.07997	−1.9501	−1.8669	−2.0269
0.09	+0.08996	−1.8328	−1.7387	−1.9187
0.10	+0.09994	−1.7279	−1.6228	−1.8229
0.11	+0.10993	−1.6331	−1.5170	−1.7371
0.12	+0.11990	−1.5466	−1.4193	−1.6595
0.13	+0.12988	−1.4672	−1.3287	−1.5889
0.14	+0.13985	−1.3938	−1.2438	−1.5241
0.15	+0.14981	−1.3255	−1.1641	−1.4645
0.16	+0.15977	−1.2618	−1.0887	−1.4092
0.17	+0.16973	−1.2020	−1.0172	−1.3578
0.18	+0.1797	−1.1457	−0.9491	−1.3098
0.19	+0.1896	−1.0925	−0.8841	−1.2649
0.20	+0.1996	−1.0422	−0.8218	−1.2227
0.21	+0.2095	−0.9944	−0.7619	−1.1829
0.22	+0.2194	−0.9490	−0.7042	−1.1454
0.23	+0.2293	−0.9057	−0.6485	−1.1099
0.24	+0.2392	−0.8643	−0.5947	−1.0762
0.25	+0.2491	−0.8247	−0.5425	−1.0443
0.26	+0.2590	−0.7867	−0.4919	−1.0139
0.27	+0.2689	−0.7503	−0.4427	−0.9849
0.28	+0.2788	−0.7153	−0.3949	−0.9573
0.29	+0.2886	−0.6816	−0.3482	−0.9309
0.30	+0.2985	−0.6492	−0.3027	−0.9057
0.31	+0.3083	−0.6179	−0.2582	−0.8815
0.32	+0.3182	−0.5877	−0.2147	−0.8583
0.33	+0.3280	−0.5585	−0.17210	−0.8361
0.34	+0.3378	−0.5304	−0.13036	−0.8147
0.35	+0.3476	−0.5031	−0.08943	−0.7942
0.36	+0.3574	−0.4767	−0.04926	−0.7745
0.37	+0.3672	−0.4511	−0.00979	−0.7554
0.38	+0.3770	−0.4263	+0.02901	−0.7371
0.39	+0.3867	−0.4022	+0.06718	−0.7194
0.40	+0.3965	−0.3788	+0.10477	−0.7024
0.41	+0.4062	−0.3561	+0.14179	−0.6859
0.42	+0.4159	−0.3341	+0.17828	−0.6700
0.43	+0.4256	−0.3126	+0.2143	−0.6546
0.44	+0.4353	−0.2918	+0.2498	−0.6397
0.45	+0.4450	−0.2715	+0.2849	−0.6253
0.46	+0.4546	−0.2517	+0.3195	−0.6114
0.47	+0.4643	−0.2325	+0.3537	−0.5979
0.48	+0.4739	−0.2138	+0.3876	−0.5848
0.49	+0.4835	−0.1956	+0.4211	−0.5721

x	$Si(x)$	$Ci(x)$	$\overline{Ei}(x)$	$Ei(-x)$
0.50	+0.4931	−0.17778	+0.4542	−0.5598
0.51	+0.5027	−0.16045	+0.4870	−0.5478
0.52	+0.5123	−0.14355	+0.5195	−0.5362
0.53	+0.5218	−0.12707	+0.5517	−0.5250
0.54	+0.5313	−0.11099	+0.5836	−0.5140
0.55	+0.5408	−0.09530	+0.6153	−0.5034
0.56	+0.5503	−0.07999	+0.6467	−0.4930
0.57	+0.5598	−0.06504	+0.6778	−0.4830
0.58	+0.5693	−0.05044	+0.7087	−0.4732
0.59	+0.5787	−0.03619	+0.7394	−0.4636
0.60	+0.5881	−0.02227	+0.7699	−0.4544
0.61	+0.5975	−$0.0^{2}8675$	+0.8002	−0.4454
0.62	+0.6069	+$0.0^{2}4606$	+0.8302	−0.4366
0.63	+0.6163	+0.01758	+0.8601	−0.4280
0.64	+0.6256	+$0.0^{3}026$	+0.8898	−0.4197
0.65	+0.6349	+0.04265	+0.9194	−0.4115
0.66	+0.6442	+0.05476	+0.9488	−0.4036
0.67	+0.6535	+0.06659	+0.9780	−0.3959
0.68	+0.6628	+0.07816	+1.0071	−0.3883
0.69	+0.6720	+0.08946	+1.0361	−0.3810
0.70	+0.6812	+0.10051	+1.0649	−0.3738
0.71	+0.6904	+0.11132	+1.0936	−0.3668
0.72	+0.6996	+0.12188	+1.1222	−0.3599
0.73	+0.7087	+0.13220	+1.1507	−0.3532
0.74	+0.7179	+0.14230	+1.1791	−0.3467
0.75	+0.7270	+0.15216	+1.2073	−0.3403
0.76	+0.7360	+0.16181	+1.2355	−0.3341
0.77	+0.7451	+0.17124	+1.2636	−0.3280
0.78	+0.7541	+0.1805	+1.2916	−0.3221
0.79	+0.7631	+0.1895	+1.3195	−0.3163
0.80	+0.7721	+0.1983	+1.3474	−0.3106
0.81	+0.7811	+0.2069	+1.3752	−0.3050
0.82	+0.7900	+0.2153	+1.4029	−0.2996
0.83	+0.7989	+0.2235	+1.4306	−0.2943
0.84	+0.8078	+0.2316	+1.4582	−0.2891
0.85	+0.8166	+0.2394	+1.4857	−0.2840
0.86	+0.8254	+0.2471	+1.5132	−0.2790
0.87	+0.8342	+0.2546	+1.5407	−0.2742
0.88	+0.8430	+0.2619	+1.5681	−0.2694
0.89	+0.8518	+0.2691	+1.5955	−0.2647
0.90	+0.8605	+0.2761	+1.6228	−0.2602
0.91	+0.8692	+0.2829	+1.6501	−0.2557
0.92	+0.8778	+0.2896	+1.6774	−0.2513
0.93	+0.8865	+0.2961	+1.7047	−0.2470
0.94	+0.8951	+0.3024	+1.7319	−0.2429
0.95	+0.9036	+0.3086	+1.7591	−0.2387
0.96	+0.9122	+0.3147	+1.7864	−0.2347
0.97	+0.9207	+0.3206	+1.8136	−0.2308
0.98	+0.9292	+0.3263	+1.8407	−0.2269
0.99	+0.9377	+0.3319	+1.8679	−0.2231
1.00	+0.9461	+0.3374	+1.8951	−0.2194

x	Si(x)	Ci(x)	$\overline{\text{Ei}}(x)$	Ei$(-x)$
1.0	+0.9461	+0.3374	+1.8951	−0.2194
1.1	+1.0287	+0.3849	+2.1674	−0.1860
1.2	+1.1080	+0.4205	+2.4421	−0.1584
1.3	+1.1840	+0.4457	+2.7214	−0.1355
1.4	+1.2562	+0.4620	+3.0072	−0.1162
1.5	+1.3247	+0.4704	+3.3013	−0.1000
1.6	+1.3892	+0.4717	+3.6053	−0.08631
1.7	+1.4496	+0.4670	+3.9210	−0.07465
1.8	+1.5058	+0.4568	+4.2499	−0.06471
1.9	+1.5578	+0.4419	+4.5937	−0.05620
2.0	+1.6054	+0.4230	+4.9542	−0.04890
2.1	+1.6487	+0.4005	+5.3332	−0.04261
2.2	+1.6876	+0.3751	+5.7326	−0.03719
2.3	+1.7222	+0.3472	+6.1544	−0.03250
2.4	+1.7525	+0.3173	+6.6007	−0.02844
2.5	+1.7785	+0.2859	+7.0738	−0.02491
2.6	+1.8004	+0.2533	+7.5761	−0.02185
2.7	+1.8182	+0.2201	+8.1103	−0.01918
2.8	+1.8321	+0.1865	+8.6793	−0.01686
2.9	+1.8422	+0.1529	+9.2860	−0.01482
3.0	+1.8487	+0.1196	+9.9338	−0.01304
3.1	+1.8517	+0.08699	+10.6263	−0.01149
3.2	+1.8514	+0.05526	+11.3673	−0.01013
3.3	+1.8481	+0.02468	+12.1610	$-0.0^{2}8939$
3.4	+1.8419	−0.004518	+13.0121	$-0.0^{2}7890$
3.5	+1.8331	−0.03213	+13.9254	$-0.0^{2}6970$
3.6	+1.8219	−0.05797	+14.9063	$-0.0^{2}6160$
3.7	+1.8086	−0.08190	+15.9606	$-0.0^{2}5448$
3.8	+1.7934	−0.1038	+17.0948	$-0.0^{2}4820$
3.9	+1.7765	−0.1235	+18.3157	$-0.0^{2}4267$
4.0	+1.7582	−0.1410	+19.6309	$-0.0^{2}3779$
4.1	+1.7387	−0.1562	+21.0485	$-0.0^{2}3349$
4.2	+1.7184	−0.1690	+22.5774	$-0.0^{2}2969$
4.3	+1.6973	−0.1795	+24.2274	$-0.0^{2}2633$
4.4	+1.6758	−0.1877	+26.0090	$-0.0^{2}2336$
4.5	+1.6541	−0.1935	+27.9337	$-0.0^{2}2073$
4.6	+1.6325	−0.1970	+30.0141	$-0.0^{2}1841$
4.7	+1.6110	−0.1984	+32.2639	$-0.0^{2}1635$
4.8	+1.5900	−0.1976	+34.6979	$-0.0^{2}1453$
4.9	+1.5696	−0.1948	+37.3325	$-0.0^{2}1291$
5.0	+1.5499	−0.1900	+40.1853	$-0.0^{2}1148$
6	+1.4247	−0.06806	+85.9898	$-0.0^{3}3601$
7	+1.4546	+0.07670	+191.505	$-0.0^{3}1155$
8	+1.5742	+0.1224	+440.380	$-0.0^{4}3767$
9	+1.6650	+0.05535	+1037.88	$-0.0^{4}1245$
10	+1.6583	−0.04546	+2492.23	$-0.0^{5}4157$
11	+1.5783	−0.08956	+6071.41	$-0.0^{5}1400$
12	+1.5050	−0.04978	+14959.5	$-0.0^{6}4751$
13	+1.4994	+0.02676	+37197.7	$-0.0^{6}1622$
14	+1.5562	+0.06940	+93192.5	$-0.0^{7}5566$
15	+1.6182	+0.04628	+23495.6	$-0.0^{7}1918$

x	Si(x)	Ci(x)	x	Si(x)	Ci(x)
20	+1.5482	+0.04442	140	+1.5722	+0.007011
25	+1.5315	−0.00685	150	+1.5662	−0.004800
30	+1.5668	−0.03303	160	+1.5769	+0.001409
35	+1.5969	−0.01148	170	+1.5653	+0.002010
40	+1.5870	+0.01902	180	+1.5741	−0.004432
45	+1.5587	+0.01863	190	+1.5704	+0.005250
50	+1.5516	−0.00563	200	+1.5684	−0.004378
55	+1.5707	−0.01817	300	+1.5709	−0.003332
60	+1.5867	−0.00481	400	+1.5721	−0.002124
65	+1.5775	+0.01285	500	+1.5726	−0.0009320
70	+1.5616	+0.01092	600	+1.5725	+0.0000764
75	+1.5586	−0.00533	700	+1.5720	+0.0007788
80	+1.5723	−0.01240	800	+1.5714	+0.001118
85	+1.5824	−0.001935	900	+1.5707	+0.001109
90	+1.5757	+0.009986	10^3	+1.5702	+0.000826
95	+1.5630	+0.007110	10^4	+1.5709	−0.0000306
100	+1.5622	−0.005149	10^5	+1.5708	+0.0000004
110	+1.5799	−0.000320	10^6	+1.5708	−0.0000004
120	+1.5640	+0.004781	10^7	+1.5708	+0.0
130	+1.5737	−0.007132	∞	½ π	0.0

$\dfrac{x}{\pi}$	Max. Min. (Ci x)	$\dfrac{x}{\pi}$	Max. Min. (Si x)
0.5	+0.472 00	1	+0.281 14
1.5	−0.198 41	2	−0.152 64
2.5	+0.123 77	3	+0.103 96
3.5	−0.089 564	4	−0.078 635
4.5	+0.070 065	5	+0.063 168
5.5	−0.057 501	6	−0.052 762
6.5	+0.048 742	7	+0.045 289
7.5	−0.042 292	8	−0.039 665
8.5	+0.037 345	9	+0.035 280
9.5	−0.033 433	10	−0.031 767
10.5	+0.030 260	11	+0.028 889
11.5	−0.027 637	12	−0.026 489
12.5	+0.025 432	13	+0.024 456
13.5	−0.023 552	14	−0.022 713
14.5	+0.021 931	15	+0.021 201
15.5	−0.020 519		

12. FACTORIALS OF NUMBERS FROM 1 TO 20 AND THEIR RECIPROCALS

n	$n!$ or $\lfloor n$			$\dfrac{1}{n!}$ or $\dfrac{1}{\lfloor n}$		
1	1			1.		
2	2			5.		10^{-1}
3	6			1.6666	6667	10^{-1}
4	2.4		10	4.1666	6667	10^{-2}
5	1.2		10^{2}	8.3333	3333	10^{-3}
6	7.2		10^{2}	1.3888	8889	10^{-4}
7	5.04		10^{3}	1.9841	2698	10^{-4}
8	4.032		10^{4}	2.4857	0718	10^{-5}
9	3.6288		10^{5}	2.7557	3192	10^{-6}
10	3.6288		10^{6}	2.7557	3192	10^{-7}
11	3.9916	8	10^{7}	2.5052	1084	10^{-8}
12	4.7900	16	10^{8}	2.0876	7570	10^{-9}
13	6.2270	208	10^{9}	1.6059	0438	10^{-10}
14	8.7178	2912	10^{10}	1.1470	7456	10^{-11}
15	1.3076	7437	10^{12}	7.6471	6373	10^{-13}
16	2.0922	7899	10^{13}	4.7794	7733	10^{-14}
17	3.5568	7428	10^{14}	2.8114	5725	10^{-15}
18	6.4023	7371	10^{15}	1.5619	2069	10^{-16}
19	1.2164	5100	10^{17}	8.2206	3525	10^{-18}
20	2.4329	0201	10^{18}	4.1103	1761	10^{-19}

13. USEFUL CONSTANTS

(1) $\epsilon = 2.71828183$

(2) $\dfrac{1}{\epsilon} = 0.36787944$

(3) $\log \epsilon = 0.43429448$

(4) $\log \log \epsilon = 9.63778431 - 10$

(5) $\pi = 3.14159265$

(6) $\dfrac{1}{\pi} = 0.31830989$

(7) $\pi^2 = 9.86960440$

(8) $\sqrt{\pi} = 1.77245385$

(9) $\log \pi = 0.49714987$

(10) $\ln \pi = 1.14472989$

(11) $\log 2 = 0.30103032$

(12) $\log 3 = 0.47712125$

(13) $\ln 2 = 0.69314718$

(14) $\ln 3 = 1.09861229$

(15) $\ln 10 = 2.30258509$

(16) $\gamma = 0.57721566$

         $= $ Euler's constant

(17) $\dfrac{N_{db}}{\alpha} = \dfrac{\text{decibels}}{\text{nepers}} = 8.68588964$

(18) $\dfrac{\alpha}{N_{db}} = \dfrac{\text{nepers}}{\text{decibels}} = 0.11512925$

(19) $1 \text{ radian} = \dfrac{180}{\pi} = 57°17'44.8''$

         $= 57°.29577951$

(20) $1° = \dfrac{\pi}{180} = 0.01745329 \text{ radians}$

(21) $\sqrt{2} = 1.41421356$

(22) $\sqrt{3} = 1.73205081$

14. ALGEBRAIC FORMULAS

a. **Miscellaneous Formulas:**

(1) $a + b = b + a$

(2) $(a + b) + c = a + (b + c)$

(3) $a + c = b + d$, if $a = b$ and $c = d$

(4) $ab = ba$

(5) $(ab)c = a(bc)$

(6) $a(b + c) = ab + ac$

(7) $ac = bd$, if $a = b$ and $c = d$

(8) $a + (-b) = a - b$

(9) $a - (-b) = a + b$

(10) $0 \cdot a = 0$

(11) $\dfrac{0}{a} = 0$

(12) $\infty \cdot a = \infty$

(13) $\dfrac{\infty}{a} = \infty$

(14) $0 \cdot \infty = $ indeterminate

(15) $\dfrac{0}{0} = $ indeterminate

(16) $\dfrac{\infty}{\infty} = $ indeterminate

(17) $a(-b) = -ab$

(18) $(-a)(-b) = ab$

(19) $-(a - b + c) = -a + b - c$

(20) $\dfrac{a}{b} = \dfrac{cc}{bc}$

(21) $\dfrac{-a}{b} = \dfrac{a}{-b} = -\dfrac{a}{b}$

(22) $\dfrac{a}{c} + \dfrac{b}{c} = \dfrac{a + b}{c}$

(23) $\dfrac{a}{c} - \dfrac{b}{c} = \dfrac{a - b}{c}$

(24) $\dfrac{a}{b} + \dfrac{c}{d} = \dfrac{ad + bc}{bd}$

(25) $\left(\dfrac{a}{b}\right)\left(\dfrac{c}{d}\right) = \dfrac{ac}{bd}$

(26) $\dfrac{\dfrac{a}{b}}{\dfrac{c}{d}} = \left(\dfrac{a}{b}\right)\left(\dfrac{d}{c}\right) = \dfrac{ad}{bc}$

(27) $(a^m)(a^n) = a^{m+n}$

(28) $(a^m)^n = a^{mn}$

(29) $(abc)^m = a^m b^m c^m$

(30) $\left(\dfrac{a}{b}\right)^m = \dfrac{a^m}{b^m}$

(31) $\dfrac{a^m}{a^n} = a^{m-n} = \dfrac{1}{a^{n-m}}$

(32) $a^o = 1$

(33) $a^{\frac{m}{n}} = \sqrt[n]{a^m}$

(34) $a^{-m} = \dfrac{1}{a^m}$

(35) $(a + b)(a + b) = a^2 + 2ab + b^2$

(36) $(a + b)(a - b) = a^2 - b^2$

(37) $(a - b)(a - b) = a^2 - 2ab + b^2$

(38) $(a + b)(c - d) = ac + bc - ad - bd$

(39) Factorial number $n! = \lfloor n = 1 \cdot 2 \cdot 3 \cdots (n - 1)n$

b. Simultaneous equations:

1. The solution of the two simultaneous equations

$$a_1 x + b_1 y = c_1$$
$$a_2 x + b_2 y = c_2$$

by determinants is

$$x = \frac{\begin{vmatrix} c_1 & b_1 \\ c_2 & b_2 \end{vmatrix}}{\begin{vmatrix} a_1 & b_1 \\ a_2 & b_2 \end{vmatrix}}$$

$$y = \frac{\begin{vmatrix} a_1 & c_1 \\ a_2 & c_2 \end{vmatrix}}{\begin{vmatrix} a_1 & b_1 \\ a_2 & b_2 \end{vmatrix}}$$

2. The solution of three simultaneous equations

$$a_1 x + b_1 y + c_1 z = d_1$$
$$a_2 x + b_2 y + c_2 z = d_2$$
$$a_3 x + b_3 y + c_3 z = d_3$$

by determinants is

$$x = \frac{\begin{vmatrix} d_1 & b_1 & c_1 \\ d_2 & b_2 & c_2 \\ d_3 & b_3 & c_3 \end{vmatrix}}{\begin{vmatrix} a_1 & b_1 & c_1 \\ a_2 & b_2 & c_2 \\ a_3 & b_3 & c_3 \end{vmatrix}}$$

$$y = \frac{\begin{vmatrix} a_1 & d_1 & c_1 \\ a_2 & d_2 & c_2 \\ a_3 & d_3 & c_3 \end{vmatrix}}{\begin{vmatrix} a_1 & b_1 & c_1 \\ a_2 & b_2 & c_2 \\ a_3 & b_3 & c_3 \end{vmatrix}}$$

$$z = \frac{\begin{vmatrix} a_1 & b_1 & d_1 \\ a_2 & b_2 & d_2 \\ a_3 & b_3 & d_3 \end{vmatrix}}{\begin{vmatrix} a_1 & b_1 & c_1 \\ a_2 & b_2 & c_2 \\ a_3 & b_3 & c_3 \end{vmatrix}}$$

c. **Quadratic equations:**

For the quadratic equation

$$ax^2 + bx + c = 0$$

the solution by the quadratic formula is

$$x = \frac{-b \pm \sqrt{b^2 - 4ac}}{2a}$$

If the discriminant $b^2 - 4ac$ is positive, zero, or negative, the roots are accordingly real and unequal, real and equal, or unequal and complex numbers.

d. **Binomial theorem** (n being a positive integer):

$$(a \pm b)^n = a^n \pm na^{n-1}b$$
$$+ \frac{n(n-1)}{\lfloor 2} a^{n-2}b^2 \pm \frac{n(n-1)(n-2)}{\lfloor 3} a^{n-3}b^3 + \cdots$$

e. **Trapezoidal rule:**

$$A = \Delta x \left[\tfrac{1}{2}(y_o + y_n) + \sum_{k=1}^{k=n-1} y_k \right]$$

where A = area

Δx = width of strips

y_k = height of kth strip

n = number of strips

f. **Simpson's rule:**

$$A = \frac{\Delta x}{3} \left[(y_o + y_n) + 4 \sum_{k=1}^{k=\frac{n}{2}} y_{(2k-1)} + 2 \sum_{k=1}^{k=\frac{n}{2}-1} y_{2k} \right]$$

where the letters have the same meaning as given above in the trapezoidal rule.

15. LOGARITHMIC FORMULAS

(1) $\ln$ = natural logarithm to base ϵ

(2) $\log$ = common logarithm to base 10

(3) $\log 1 = 0$ $\qquad$ $\ln 1 = 0$

(4) $\log 10 = 1$ $\qquad$ $\ln \epsilon = 1$

(5) $\log ab = \log a + \log b$ $\qquad$ $\ln ab = \ln a + \ln b$

(6) $\log a^n = n \log a$ $\qquad$ $\ln a^n = n \ln a$

(7) $\log a^{\frac{1}{n}} = \frac{1}{n} \log a$ $\qquad$ $\ln a^{\frac{1}{n}} = \frac{1}{n} \ln a$

(8) If $y = \log x$ $\qquad$ If $y = \ln x$
$10^y = x$ $\qquad$ $\epsilon^y = x$

(9) $\log x = \log \epsilon \ln x = 0.4343 \ln x$

(10) $\ln x = \ln 10 \log x = 2.3026 \log x$

(11) The characteristic of a number is the whole number part of the common logarithm and is the exponent of 10 when the number is written in scientific notation.

(12) The mantissa of a number is the decimal part of the common logarithm found in the tables.

(13) Example of characteristic and mantissa

$$\log (3.1623)10^2 = 2.500$$

where 2 = the characteristic, from exponent of 10

0.5 = the mantissa, from logarithm tables

Thus $\qquad$ $316.23 = 10^{2.5}$

16. COMPLEX QUANTITIES

(1) $j = \sqrt{-1}$ $\qquad$ or $\qquad$ $j^2 = -1$

(2) $a + jb = \sqrt{a^2 + b^2} \, (\cos \alpha + j \sin \alpha)$
$\qquad = C\epsilon^{j\alpha} = C\underline{/\alpha}$

where $C = \sqrt{a^2 + b^2}$

$\qquad \tan \alpha = \dfrac{b}{a} = \dfrac{\sin \alpha}{\cos \alpha}$

(3) $(a + jb) + (c + jd) = (a + c) + j(b + d)$

(4) $(a + jb) - (c + jd) = (a - c) + j(b - d)$

(5) $(a + jb)(c + jd) = (ac - bd) + j(bc + ad)$

(6) $(a + jb)(c - jd) = (ac + bd) + j(bc - ad)$

(7) $\dfrac{a + jb}{c + jd} = \dfrac{a + jb}{c + jd} \cdot \dfrac{c - jd}{c - jd} = \dfrac{ac + bd}{c^2 + d^2} + j\dfrac{bc - ad}{c^2 + d^2}$

(8) $\dfrac{a + jb}{c + jd} = \dfrac{C\epsilon^{j\alpha}}{E\epsilon^{j\beta}} = \dfrac{C}{E} \epsilon^{j(\alpha-\beta)} = \dfrac{C}{E} \cos (\alpha - \beta) + j\dfrac{C}{E} \sin (\alpha - \beta)$

where $C = \sqrt{a^2 + b^2}$; $\tan \alpha = \dfrac{b}{a}$

$\qquad E = \sqrt{c^2 + d^2}$; $\tan \beta = \dfrac{d}{c}$

(9) If $a + jb = c + jd$

then $\qquad a = c$

and $\qquad b = d$

17. TRIGONOMETRIC CHARTS AND FORMULAS

a. Chart of fraction values for trigonometric functions:

Degrees	Sine	Cosine	Tangent	Cotangent
0	0	1	0	∞
30	½	½ $\sqrt{3}$	$\dfrac{1}{\sqrt{3}}$	$\sqrt{3}$
45	½ $\sqrt{2}$	½ $\sqrt{2}$	1	1
60	½ $\sqrt{3}$	½	$\sqrt{3}$	$\dfrac{1}{\sqrt{3}}$
90	1	0	∞	0
120	½ $\sqrt{3}$	−½	−$\sqrt{3}$	−$\dfrac{1}{\sqrt{3}}$
135	½ $\sqrt{2}$	−½ $\sqrt{2}$	−1	−1
150	½	−½ $\sqrt{3}$	−$\dfrac{1}{\sqrt{3}}$	−$\sqrt{3}$
180	0	−1	0	∞

b. Chart for reducing angles:

Angle	Sine	Cosine	Tangent	Cotangent
± α	± sin α	+ cos α	± tan α	± cot α
90° ± α	+ cos α	∓ sin α	∓ ctn α	∓ tan α
180° ± α	∓ sin α	− cos α	± tan α	± cot α
270° ± α	− cos α	± sin α	∓ ctn α	∓ tan α
360° ± α	± sin α	+ cos α	± tan α	± cot α

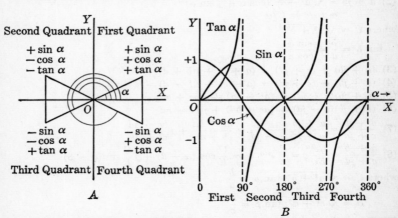

FIG. 98.—Algebraic signs and graphs of trigonometric functions in the various quadrants.

c. Trigonometric functions in terms of each other:

Sine	Cosine	Tangent	Cotangent	Secant	Cosecant
$\sin \alpha$	$\sqrt{1 - \cos^2 \alpha}$	$\dfrac{\tan \alpha}{\sqrt{1 + \tan^2 \alpha}}$	$\dfrac{1}{\sqrt{1 + \cot^2 \alpha}}$	$\dfrac{\sqrt{\sec^2 \alpha - 1}}{\sec \alpha}$	$\dfrac{1}{\csc \alpha}$
$\sqrt{1 - \sin^2 \alpha}$	$\cos \alpha$	$\dfrac{1}{\sqrt{1 + \tan^2 \alpha}}$	$\dfrac{\cot \alpha}{\sqrt{1 + \cot^2 \alpha}}$	$\dfrac{1}{\sec \alpha}$	$\dfrac{\sqrt{\csc^2 \alpha - 1}}{\csc \alpha}$
$\dfrac{\sin \alpha}{\sqrt{1 - \sin^2 \alpha}}$	$\dfrac{\sqrt{1 - \cos^2 \alpha}}{\cos \alpha}$	$\tan \alpha$	$\dfrac{1}{\cot \alpha}$	$\sqrt{\sec^2 \alpha - 1}$	$\dfrac{1}{\sqrt{\csc^2 \alpha - 1}}$
$\dfrac{\sqrt{1 - \sin^2 \alpha}}{\sin \alpha}$	$\dfrac{\cos \alpha}{\sqrt{1 - \cos^2 \alpha}}$	$\dfrac{1}{\tan \alpha}$	$\cot \alpha$	$\dfrac{1}{\sqrt{\sec^2 \alpha - 1}}$	$\sqrt{\csc^2 \alpha - 1}$
$\dfrac{1}{\sqrt{1 - \sin^2 \alpha}}$	$\dfrac{1}{\cos \alpha}$	$\sqrt{1 + \tan^2 \alpha}$	$\dfrac{\sqrt{1 + \cot^2 \alpha}}{\cot \alpha}$	$\sec \alpha$	$\dfrac{\csc \alpha}{\sqrt{\csc^2 \alpha - 1}}$
$\dfrac{1}{\sin \alpha}$	$\dfrac{1}{\sqrt{1 - \cos^2 \alpha}}$	$\dfrac{\sqrt{1 + \tan^2 \alpha}}{\tan \alpha}$	$\sqrt{1 + \cot^2 \alpha}$	$\dfrac{\sec \alpha}{\sqrt{\sec^2 \alpha - 1}}$	$\csc \alpha$

d. Trigonometric formulas:

(1) $\sin \alpha = \dfrac{b}{c} = \cos \beta$

(2) $\cos \alpha = \dfrac{a}{c} = \sin \beta$

(3) $\tan \alpha = \dfrac{b}{a} = \cot \beta$

(4) $\tan \alpha = \dfrac{\sin \alpha}{\cos \alpha} = \dfrac{\cos \beta}{\sin \beta}$

(5) $\sin \alpha = \dfrac{\epsilon^{j\alpha} - \epsilon^{-j\alpha}}{2j}$

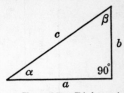

Fig. 99.—Right triangle for use with trigonometric formulas.

(6) $\cos \alpha = \dfrac{\epsilon^{j\alpha} + \epsilon^{-j\alpha}}{2}$

(7) $\tan \alpha = -j \dfrac{\epsilon^{j\alpha} - \epsilon^{-j\alpha}}{\epsilon^{j\alpha} + \epsilon^{-j\alpha}}$

(8) $\sin (-\alpha) = -\sin \alpha$

(9) $\cos (-\alpha) = \cos \alpha$

(10) $\tan (-\alpha) = -\tan \alpha$

(11) $\sin \left(\dfrac{\pi}{2} \pm \alpha \right) = \cos \alpha$

(12) $\cos \left(\dfrac{\pi}{2} \pm \alpha \right) = \mp \sin \alpha$

(13) $\tan \left(\dfrac{\pi}{2} + \alpha \right) = \mp \cot \alpha$

(14) $\sin (\pi \pm \alpha) = \mp \sin \alpha$

(15) $\cos (\pi \pm \alpha) = -\cos \alpha$

(16) $\tan (\pi \pm \alpha) = \pm \tan \alpha$

(17) $\sin \dfrac{\alpha}{2} = \sqrt{\dfrac{1}{2} (1 - \cos \alpha)}$

(18) $\cos \dfrac{\alpha}{2} = \sqrt{\dfrac{1}{2} (1 + \cos \alpha)}$

(19) $\tan \dfrac{\alpha}{2} = \dfrac{1 - \cos \alpha}{\sin \alpha} = \dfrac{\sin \alpha}{1 + \cos \alpha}$

(20) $\sin 2\alpha = 2 \sin \alpha \cos \alpha$

(21) $\cos 2\alpha = 1 - 2 \sin^2 \alpha = 2 \cos^2 \alpha - 1$

(22) $\tan 2\alpha = \dfrac{2 \tan \alpha}{1 - \tan^2 \alpha}$

(23) $\sin 3\alpha = 3 \sin \alpha - 4 \sin^3 \alpha$

(24) $\cos 3\alpha = 4 \cos^3 \alpha - 3 \cos \alpha$

(25) $\sin^2 \alpha = \dfrac{1 - \cos 2\alpha}{2}$

(26) $\cos^2 \alpha = \dfrac{1 + \cos 2\alpha}{2}$

(27) $\sin^2 \alpha + \cos^2 \alpha = 1$

(28) $\sin^3 \alpha = \dfrac{3 \sin \alpha - \sin 3\alpha}{4}$

(29) $\cos^3 \alpha = \dfrac{3 \cos \alpha + \cos 3\alpha}{4}$

(30) $\sin (\alpha + \beta) = \sin \alpha \cos \beta + \cos \alpha \sin \beta$

(31) $\sin (\alpha - \beta) = \sin \alpha \cos \beta - \cos \alpha \sin \beta$

(32) $\cos (\alpha + \beta) = \cos \alpha \cos \beta - \sin \alpha \sin \beta$

(33) $\cos (\alpha - \beta) = \cos \alpha \cos \beta + \sin \alpha \sin \beta$

(34) $\tan (\alpha + \beta) = \dfrac{\tan \alpha + \tan \beta}{1 - \tan \alpha \tan \beta}$

(35) $\tan (\alpha - \beta) = \dfrac{\tan \alpha - \tan \beta}{1 + \tan \alpha \tan \beta}$

(36) $\sin (\alpha + \beta) + \sin (\alpha - \beta) = 2 \sin \alpha \cos \beta$

(37) $\sin (\alpha + \beta) - \sin (\alpha - \beta) = 2 \cos \alpha \sin \beta$

(38) $\cos (\alpha + \beta) + \cos (\alpha - \beta) = 2 \cos \alpha \cos \beta$

(39) $\cos (\alpha - \beta) - \cos (\alpha + \beta) = 2 \sin \alpha \cos \beta$

18. EXPONENTIAL AND HYPERBOLIC FORMULAS

a. **Exponential formulas:**

(1) $\epsilon^{j\beta} = \cos \beta + j \sin \beta$

(2) $\epsilon^{-j\beta} = \cos \beta - j \sin \beta$

(3) $\epsilon^{\alpha} = \cosh \alpha + \sinh \alpha$

(4) $\epsilon^{-\alpha} = \cosh \alpha - \sinh \alpha$

(5) $\epsilon^{\alpha+j\beta} = \epsilon^{\alpha} \cos \beta + j\epsilon^{\alpha} \sin \beta$
$$= (\cosh \alpha \cos \beta + \sinh \alpha \cos \beta)$$
$$+ j(\cosh \alpha \sin \beta) + \sinh \alpha \sin \beta)$$

b. **Relation between hyperbolic and circular functions:**

(1) $\sinh j\beta = j \sin \beta$

(2) $\cosh j\beta = \cos \beta$

(3) $\sin j\beta = j \sinh \beta$

(4) $\cos j\beta = \cosh \beta$

c. **Hyperbolic functions:**

(1) $\sinh \beta = \dfrac{\epsilon^{\beta} - \epsilon^{-\beta}}{2}$

(2) $\cosh \beta = \dfrac{\epsilon^{\beta} + \epsilon^{-\beta}}{2}$

(3) $\tanh \beta = \dfrac{\epsilon^{\beta} - \epsilon^{-\beta}}{\epsilon^{\beta} + \epsilon^{-\beta}}$

(4) $\sinh (-\beta) = - \sinh \beta$

(5) $\cosh (-\beta) = \cosh \beta$

(6) $\cosh^2 \beta - \sinh^2 \beta = 1$

(7) $\sinh (\alpha + \beta) = \sinh \alpha \cosh \beta + \cosh \alpha \sinh \beta$

(8) $\sinh (\alpha - \beta) = \sinh \alpha \cosh \beta - \cosh \alpha \sinh \beta$

(9) $\cosh (\alpha + \beta) = \cosh \alpha \cosh \beta + \sinh \alpha \sinh \beta$

d. **Circular and hyperbolic functions of complex quantities:**

(1) $\sinh (\alpha \pm j\beta) = \sinh \alpha \cosh j\beta \pm \cosh \alpha \sinh j\beta$
$$= \sinh \alpha \cos \beta \pm j \cosh \alpha \sin \beta$$
$$= \sqrt{\sinh^2 \alpha + \sin^2 \beta} \Big/ \pm \tan^{-1} \frac{\tan \beta}{\tanh \alpha}$$

(2) $\cosh (\alpha \pm j\beta) = \cosh \alpha \cosh j\beta \pm \sinh \alpha \sinh j\beta$
$$= \cosh \alpha \cos \beta \pm j \sinh \alpha \sin \beta$$
$$= \sqrt{\sinh^2 \alpha + \cos^2 \beta} / \pm \tan^{-1} (\tan \beta \tanh \alpha)$$

(3) $\sin (\alpha \pm j\beta) = \sin \alpha \cos j\beta \pm \cos \alpha \sin j\beta$
$$= \sin \alpha \cosh \beta \pm j \cos \alpha \sinh \beta$$
$$= \sqrt{\sin^2 \alpha + \sinh^2 \beta} \Big/ \pm \tan^{-1} \frac{\tan \beta}{\tan \alpha}$$

(4) $\cos (\alpha \pm j\beta) = \cos \alpha \cos j\beta \mp \sin \alpha \sin j\beta$
$$= \cos \alpha \cosh \beta \mp j \sin \alpha \sinh \beta$$
$$= \sqrt{\cos^2 \alpha + \sinh^2 \beta} / \mp \tan^{-1} (\tanh \beta \tan \alpha)$$

19. STANDARD ELEMENTARY CALCULUS FORMULAS

Derivative $\dfrac{dy}{dx}$	Function y	Integral $\int y\,dx$
	Algebraic	
0	0	C
0	1	$x + C$
0	a	$ax + C$
1	x	$\frac{1}{2}\,x^2 + C$
a	ax	$\frac{1}{2}\,ax^2 + C$
$2x$	x^2	$\frac{1}{3}\,x^3 + C$
nx	x^n	$\dfrac{1}{n+1}\,x^{n+1} + C$
$-x^{-2}$	x^{-1}	$\ln x + C$
$\dfrac{du}{dx} + \dfrac{dv}{dx}$	$u + v$	$\int u\,dx + \int v\,dx$
$u\,\dfrac{dv}{dx} + v\,\dfrac{du}{dx}$	$u\,v$	No general form
$\dfrac{v\,\dfrac{du}{dx} - u\,\dfrac{dv}{dx}}{v^2}$	$\dfrac{u}{v}$	No general form
$\dfrac{du}{dv}$	u	$\int u\,dv = uv - \int v\,du + C$
$-\dfrac{1}{(x+a)^2}$	$\dfrac{1}{x+a}$	$\ln(x+a) + C$
$-\dfrac{x}{(a^2+x^2)^{3/2}}$	$\dfrac{1}{\sqrt{a^2+x^2}}$	$\ln(x+\sqrt{a^2+x^2}) + C$
$\mp\dfrac{b}{(a \pm bx)^2}$	$\dfrac{1}{a \pm bx}$	$\pm\dfrac{1}{b}\ln(a+bx) + C$
$\dfrac{-3a^2x}{(a^2+x^2)^{5/2}}$	$\dfrac{a^2}{(a^2+x^2)^{3/2}}$	$\dfrac{x}{\sqrt{a^2+x^2}} + C$
	Transcendental	
ϵ^x	ϵ^x	$\epsilon^x + C$
$a\epsilon^{ax}$	ϵ^{ax}	$\dfrac{1}{a}\,\epsilon^{ax} + C$
$a^x \ln a$	a^x	$\dfrac{a^x}{\ln a} + C$
$ba^{bx} \ln a$	a^{bx}	$\dfrac{a^{bx}}{b \ln a} + C$
x^{-1}	$\ln x$	$x(\ln x - 1) + C$
$0.4343x^{-1}$	$\log x$	$0.4343(\ln x - 1) + C$
$\cos x$	$\sin x$	$-\cos x + C$

19. STANDARD ELEMENTARY CALCULUS FORMULAS.—*(Continued)*

Derivative $\dfrac{dy}{dx}$	Function y	Integral $\int y\,dx$
$a \cos ax$	$\sin ax$	$-\dfrac{1}{a}\cos ax + C$
$-\sin x$	$\cos x$	$\sin x + C$
$-a \sin ax$	$\cos ax$	$\dfrac{1}{a}\sin ax + C$
$\sec^2 x$	$\tan x$	$-\ln \cos x + C$
$a \sec^2 ax$	$\tan ax$	$-\dfrac{1}{a}\ln \cos ax + C$
$\cosh x$	$\sinh x$	$\cosh x + C$
$a \cosh ax$	$\sinh ax$	$\dfrac{1}{a}\cosh ax + C$
$\sinh x$	$\cosh x$	$\sinh x + C$
$a \sinh x$	$\cosh ax$	$\dfrac{1}{a}\sinh ax + C$
$\operatorname{sech}^2 x$	$\tanh x$	$\ln \cosh x + C$
$a \operatorname{sech}^2 ax$	$\tanh ax$	$-\dfrac{1}{a}\ln \cosh ax + C$

20. OTHER USEFUL INTEGRALS

$$\int x\epsilon^{\alpha x}\,dx = \frac{1}{\alpha^2}\,\epsilon^{\alpha x}(\alpha x - 1)$$

$$\int \epsilon^{\alpha t}\sin(\omega t + \psi)\,dt = \frac{\epsilon^{\alpha t}}{\alpha^2 + \omega^2}\left[\alpha \sin(\omega t + \psi) - \omega \cos(\omega t + \psi)\right]$$

$$\int \epsilon^{\alpha t}\cos(\omega t + \psi)\,dt = \frac{\epsilon^{\alpha t}}{\alpha^2 + \omega^2}\left[\alpha \cos(\omega t + \psi) + \omega \sin(\omega t + \psi)\right]$$

$$\mathrm{Si}(x) = \int_0^x \frac{\sin x}{x}\,dx$$

$$\mathrm{Ci}(x) = \int_\infty^x \frac{\cos x}{x}\,dx$$

$$J_0(x) = \frac{1}{2\pi}\int_0^{2\pi}\cos(x \sin\theta)\,d\theta = \frac{1}{2\pi}\int_0^{2\pi}\cos(x \cos\theta)\,d\theta$$

$$= \frac{1}{\pi}\int_0^\pi \cos(x \cos\theta)\,d\theta$$

$$= \frac{j}{2\pi}\int_0^{2\pi}\sin(x \sin\theta)\,d\theta$$

$$= \frac{1}{2\pi}\int_0^{2\pi}\epsilon^{jx\sin\theta}\,d\theta = \frac{1}{2\pi}\int_0^{2\pi}\epsilon^{jx\cos\theta}\,d\theta = \frac{1}{\pi}\int_0^\pi \epsilon^{jx\cos\theta}\,d\theta$$

$$J_n(x) = \frac{1}{\pi}\int_0^\pi \cos(n\theta - x \sin\theta)\,d\theta$$

$$= \frac{j}{\pi}\int_0^\pi \sin(n\theta - x \sin\theta)\,d\theta$$

$$= \frac{1}{\pi}\int_0^\pi \epsilon^{j(n\theta - x \sin\theta)}\,d\theta$$

21. SERIES

a. Exponential:

(1) $\epsilon^x = 1 + x + \dfrac{x^2}{\underline{2}} + \dfrac{x^3}{\underline{3}} + \cdots$

(2) $a^x = 1 + x \log a + \dfrac{(x \log a)^2}{\underline{2}} + \dfrac{(x \log a)^3}{\underline{3}} + \cdots$

b. Trigonometric:

(1) $\sin x = x - \dfrac{x^3}{\underline{3}} + \dfrac{x^5}{\underline{5}} - \dfrac{x^7}{\underline{7}} + \cdots$

(2) $\cos x = 1 - \dfrac{x^2}{\underline{2}} + \dfrac{x^4}{\underline{4}} - \dfrac{x^6}{\underline{6}} + \cdots$

(3) $\tan x = x + \dfrac{x^3}{3} + \dfrac{2x^5}{15} + \dfrac{17x^7}{315} + \cdots$

c. Hyperbolic:

(1) $\sinh x = x + \dfrac{x^3}{\underline{3}} + \dfrac{x^5}{\underline{5}} + \dfrac{x^7}{\underline{7}} + \cdots$

(2) $\cosh x = 1 + \dfrac{x^2}{\underline{2}} + \dfrac{x^4}{\underline{4}} + \dfrac{x^6}{\underline{6}} + \cdots$

(3) $\tanh x = x - \dfrac{x^3}{3} + \dfrac{2x^5}{15} - \dfrac{17x^7}{315} + \cdots$

d. Logarithmic:

$$\ln (1 + x) = x - \tfrac{1}{2} x^2 + \tfrac{1}{3} x^3 - \tfrac{1}{4} x^4 + \cdots$$

e. Sine and cosine integral:

$$\mathrm{Si}(x) = \int_0^x \frac{\sin x}{x}\, dx = x - \frac{x^3}{3\underline{3}} + \frac{x^5}{5\underline{5}} - \cdots$$

$$\mathrm{Ci}(x) = \int_\infty^x \frac{\cos x}{x}\, dx = \gamma + \ln x - \frac{x^2}{2\underline{2}} + \frac{x^4}{4\underline{4}} - \frac{x^6}{6\underline{6}} + \cdots$$

f. Bessel's:

(1) $J_0(x) = 1 - \dfrac{x^2}{2} + \dfrac{x^4}{2^2 \cdot 4^2} - \dfrac{x^6}{2^2 \cdot 4^2 \cdot 6^2} + \cdots$

(2) $J_n(x) = \dfrac{x^n}{2^n \underline{n}} \left[1 - \dfrac{x^2}{2(2n + 2)} + \dfrac{x^4}{2 \cdot 4(2n + 2)(2n + 4)} \right.$

$$\left. - \frac{x^6}{2 \cdot 4 \cdot 6(2n + 2)(2n + 4)(2n + 6)} + \cdots \right]$$

$$= \sum_{k=0}^{k=\infty} \frac{(-1)^k}{\underline{k}\,\underline{n+k}} \left(\frac{x}{2}\right)^{n+2k} \qquad (n \text{ an integer})$$

g. Binomial:

$$(1 \pm x)^n = 1 \pm nx + \frac{n(n - 1)}{\underline{2}} x^2 \pm \frac{n(n - 1)(n - 2)}{\underline{3}} x^3 + \cdots$$

h. Power:

$$f(x) = a_o + a_1 x + a_2 x^2 + a_3 x^3 + \cdots$$

i. **Maclaurin's:**

$$f(x) = f(o) + xf'(o) + \frac{x^2}{\lfloor 2} f''(o) + \frac{x^3}{\lfloor 3} f'''(o) + \cdots$$

j. **Taylor's:**

(1) $f(x) = f(a) + (x - a)f'(a) + \frac{(x - a)^2}{\lfloor 2} f''(a) + \frac{(x - a)^3}{\lfloor 3} f'''(a) + \cdots$

(2) $f(x + h) = f(x) + hf'(x) + \frac{h^2}{\lfloor 2} f''(x) + \frac{h^3}{\lfloor 3} f'''(x) + \cdots$

k. **Fourier's:**

(1) $f(x) = \dfrac{A_0}{2} + A_1 \sin x + A_2 \cos 2x + A_3 \cos 3x + \cdots$

$$\qquad\qquad + B_1 \cos x + B_2 \cos 2x + B_3 \cos 3x + \cdots$$

$$= \frac{A_0}{2} + \sum_{n=1}^{n=\infty} (A_n \cos nx + B_n \sin nx)$$

where $A_0 = \dfrac{1}{\pi} \displaystyle\int_0^{2\pi} f(x)\, dx$

$A_n = \dfrac{1}{\pi} \displaystyle\int_0^{2\pi} f(x) \cos nx\, dx$

$B_n = \dfrac{1}{\pi} \displaystyle\int_0^{2\pi} f(x) \sin nx\, dx$

(2) $f(x) = M_0 + M_1 \sin (\omega t + \psi_1) + M_2 \sin (\omega t + \psi_2) + \cdots$

$$= \sum_{n=o}^{n=\infty} M_n \sin (\omega t + \psi_n)$$

where $n = 0$

$M_o = \dfrac{1}{2\pi} \displaystyle\int_0^{2\pi} f(x)\, dx$

and for $n = 1, 2, 3, \cdots$

$$M_n \underline{/\psi_n} = \frac{j}{\pi} \int_0^{2\pi} f(x) \epsilon^{-jnx}\, dx$$

22. WAVEFORMS

a. **Square sine wave:**

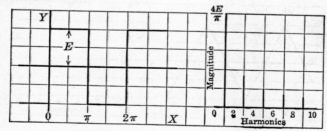

$$y = \frac{4E}{\pi} \sum_{n=1}^{n=\infty} \frac{1}{2n - 1} \sin (2n - 1)x$$

$$= \frac{4E}{\pi} \left[\sin x + \frac{1}{3} \sin 3x + \frac{1}{5} \sin 5x + \cdots \right]$$

b. **Square cosine wave:**

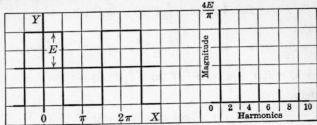

$$y = \frac{4E}{\pi} \sum_{n=1}^{n=\infty} \frac{1}{2n-1} \sin (2n-1)x$$

$$= \frac{4E}{\pi} \left[\cos x - \frac{1}{3} \cos 3x + \frac{1}{5} \cos 5x - \cdots \right]$$

c. **Sawtooth sine wave:**

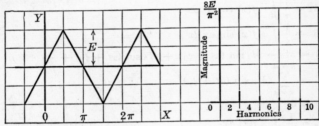

$$y = \frac{8E}{\pi^2} \sum_{n=1}^{n=\infty} \frac{(-1)^{n+1}}{(2n-1)^2} \sin (2n-1)x$$

$$= \frac{8E}{\pi^2} \left[\sin x - \frac{1}{9} \sin 3x + \frac{1}{25} \sin 5x - \cdots \right]$$

d. **Sawtooth cosine wave:**

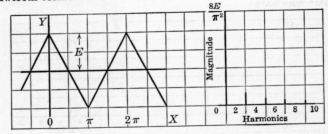

$$y = \frac{8E}{\pi^2} \sum_{n=1}^{n=\infty} \frac{1}{(2n-1)^2} \cos (2n-1)x$$

$$= \frac{8E}{\pi^2} \left[\cos x + \frac{1}{9} \cos 3x + \frac{1}{25} \cos 5x + \cdots \right]$$

e. **Positive scanning wave:**

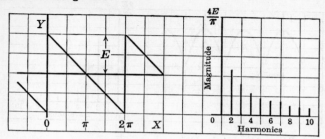

$$y = \frac{2E}{\pi} \sum_{n=1}^{n=\infty} \frac{\sin nx}{n} = \frac{2E}{\pi} \left[\sin x + \frac{1}{2} \sin 2x + \frac{1}{3} \sin 3x + \cdots \right]$$

f **Negative scanning wave:**

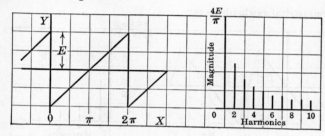

$$y = -\frac{2E}{\pi} \sum_{n=1}^{n=\infty} \frac{\sin nx}{n} = \frac{2E}{\pi} \left[-\sin x - \frac{1}{2} \sin 2x - \frac{1}{3} \sin 3x - \cdots \right]$$

g. **Half-wave rectifier pulse wave:**

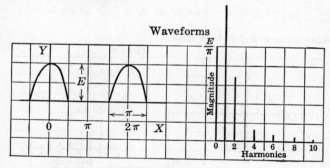

$$y = \frac{E}{\pi} + \frac{E}{2} \cos x + \frac{2E}{\pi} \sum_{n=1}^{n=\infty} \frac{(-1)^{n+1}}{4n^2 - 1} \cos 2nx$$

$$= \frac{E}{\pi} \left[1 + \frac{\pi}{2} \cos x + \frac{2}{3} \cos 2x - \frac{2}{15} \cos 4x + \cdots \right]$$

h. Full-wave rectifier pulse wave:

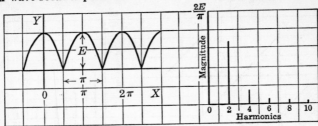

$$y = \frac{2E}{\pi} + \frac{4E}{\pi} \sum_{n=1}^{n=\infty} \frac{(-1)^{n+1}}{4n^2 - 1} \cos 2nx$$

$$= \frac{2E}{\pi} \left[1 + \frac{2}{3} \cos 2x - \frac{2}{15} \cos 4x + \frac{2}{35} \cos 6x - \cdots \right]$$

i. Unsymmetrical sawtooth wave:

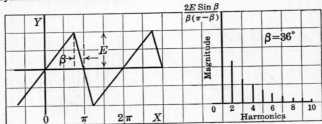

$$y = \frac{2E}{\beta(\pi - \beta)} \sum_{n=1}^{n=\infty} \frac{(-1)^{n+1}}{n^2} \sin n\beta \sin nx$$

$$= \frac{2E}{\beta(\pi - \beta)} \left[\sin \beta \sin x - \frac{1}{4} \sin 2\beta \sin 2x + \frac{1}{9} \sin 3\beta \sin 3x - \cdots \right]$$

Scanning wave with β flyback time:

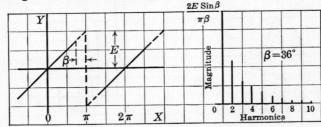

$$y = \frac{2E}{\pi\beta} \sum_{n=1}^{n=\infty} \frac{(-1)^{n+1}}{n^2} \sin n\beta \sin nx$$

$$= \frac{2E}{\pi\beta} \left[\sin \beta \sin x - \frac{1}{4} \sin 2\beta \sin 2x + \frac{1}{9} \sin 3\beta \sin 3x - \cdots \right]$$

k. Rectangular pulse wave:

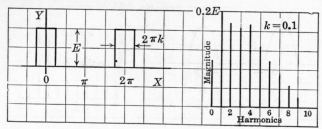

$$y = kE + \frac{2E}{\pi} \sum_{n=1}^{n=\infty} \frac{1}{n} \sin nk\pi \cos n(x)$$

$$= kE + \frac{2E}{\pi} \left[\sin k\pi \cos (x) + \frac{1}{2} \sin 2k\pi \cos 2(x) + \cdots \right]$$

l. Symmetrical trapezoidal pulse wave:

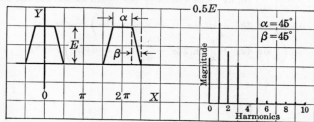

$$y = \frac{E}{2\pi} (\alpha + \beta) + \frac{8}{\beta} \sum_{n=1}^{n=\infty} \frac{1}{n^2} \sin \frac{n\beta}{2} \sin \frac{n}{2} (\alpha + \beta) \cos nx$$

$$= \frac{E(\alpha + \beta)}{2\pi} + \frac{4E}{\pi\beta} \left[\sin \frac{\beta}{2} \sin \left(\frac{\alpha + \beta}{2} \right) \cos x \right.$$

$$\left. + \frac{1}{4} \sin \beta \sin (\alpha + \beta) \cos 2x + \cdots \right.$$

m. Symmetrical triangular pulse wave:

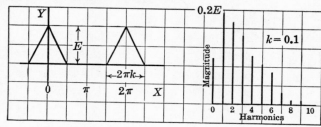

$$y = kE + \frac{2E}{k\pi^2} \sum_{n=1}^{n=\infty} \frac{1}{n^2} (\sin nk\pi)^2 \cos nx$$

$$= kE + \frac{2E}{k\pi^2} \left[\sin^2 k\pi \cos x + \frac{1}{4} \sin^2 2k\pi \cos 2x + \cdots \right]$$

n. **Fractional cosine pulse wave:**

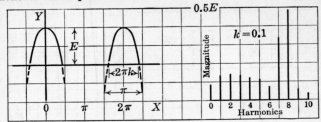

$$y = \frac{E}{\pi(1 - \cos k\pi)} \left[\sin k\pi - k\pi \cos k\pi + (k\pi - \sin k\pi \cos k\pi) \cos x \right.$$

$$+ \sum_{n=2}^{n=\infty} \left\{ \frac{\sin (n+1)k\pi}{n+1} + \frac{\sin (n-1)k\pi}{n-1} - \frac{2 \sin nk\pi \cos k\pi}{n} \right\} \cos nx \left. \right]$$

$$= \frac{E}{\pi(1 - \cos k\pi)} \left[\sin k\pi - k\pi \cos \pi k + (k\pi - \sin k\pi \cos k\pi) \cos x \right.$$

$$+ \left(\frac{1}{3} \sin 3k\pi + \sin k\pi - \sin 2k\pi \cos k\pi \right) \cos 2x$$

$$+ \left(\frac{1}{4} \sin 4k\pi + \frac{1}{2} \sin 2k\pi - \frac{2}{3} \sin 3k\pi \cos k\pi \right) \cos 3x + \cdots \left. \right]$$

INDEX

ANSWERS TO EXERCISES

Chapter 1

1. +31

2. −24

3. −67

4. +755

5. −64

6. −75

7. +26

8. +7020

9. 30

10. 1.333×10^{-31}

11. 6^{-26}

12. 9.87×10^5; 7.6456×10; 7×10^{-4};
9×10^3; 8.97650001×10^6; 1.2×10^{19}.

13. 3.125×10^{12}

14.
9×10^{-7} farad
0.9 μf
9×10^5 $\mu\mu$f

104×10^6 $\mu\mu$h
104 μh
104×10^{-6} henrys

1 henry or 1000 mh
1×10^6 μh
1×10^{12} $\mu\mu$h

300 $\mu\mu$f
0.0003 μf
3×10^{-10} farad

6×10^6 $\mu\mu$f
6 μf
6×10^{-6} farad

100,000 $\mu\mu$f
0.1 μf
1×10^{-7} farad

67 $\mu\mu$f
67×10^{-6} μf
67×10^{-12} farad

8×10^9 $\mu\mu$f
8000 μf
0.008 farad

15. 943 with a remainder of 386
99 with a remainder of 175
99.7
2.427 with a remainder of 0.000002
3×10^{-5}
0.021679+
0.070 with a remainder of 0.000078

Chapter 2

SLIDE-RULE EXERCISES

	Multiply	Divide	Square Root	Square
1.	78,440	1.117	16.28	87,620
2.	65,800	0.5898	18.28	38,810
3.	175,446	1.346	19.0	236,200
4.	623.7	12.3	2.668	7,674
5.	1.201	3.037	0.7931	3.648

6. 3.29×10^{-4}	8.655	0.07855	0.002852
7. 0.3056	3.06×10^6	0.01778	935,100
8. 1.106×10^{10}	0.1587	513.8	1.756×10^9
9. 0.4204	507,700	0.03017	213,400
10. 4.726×10^9	0.0678	513.8	3.204×10^8
11. 8.33×10^{-5}	2,882	0.01304	0.2401
12. 3.528×10^{-9}	50	0.002898	1.764×10^{-7}
13. 56.51	1.424×10^{10}	0.007937	8.04×10^{11}
14. 1.109×10^6	111.1	9.995	1.232×10^8
15. 1.755×10^8	2.078×10^{-4}	958.6	36,480
16. 1.037×10^4	1.629×10^{-10}	28.25	1.69×10^{-14}

CHAPTER EXERCISES

1. 363,250

2. 116.38

3. 3.6314

4. 7,907.96

5. 4.5113

6. 6.7678×10^9

7. 2.5628×10^{-7}

8. 24,992.6

9. 0.026794

10. 310.54

11. 0.35475

12. 7.82520

13. 0.0117985

14. 0.140887

15. 1.22147

16. 5.7974266×10^{19}

17. 1.18894×10^{14}

18. 7.5333×10^{-12}

19. 5.280829×10^{-8}

20. 8.5306×10^{28}

Chapter 3

1. $y = a - b - x$
$b = a - x - y$

2. $b = \dfrac{R - ax + cz}{y}$

$z = \dfrac{-R + ax + by}{c}$

3. $S = \dfrac{XY - JQ}{RT}$

$Q = \dfrac{XY - RST}{J}$

4. $z = \dfrac{xy}{ab}$

$y = \dfrac{abz}{x}$

5. $x = z(a + bz) - y$

$b = \dfrac{x + y - az}{z^2}$

6. $y = \dfrac{axz + cx - z}{az + c}$

$a = \dfrac{cx - cy - z}{yz - xz}$

7. $M = \dfrac{NPQ + X + Y}{PQ}$

$Y = PQ(M - N) - X$

8. $T = \dfrac{X(R - S)}{O + P}$

$S = \dfrac{RX - T(O + P)}{X}$

9. $T = \sqrt[3]{(X + Y)(R - SP)}$

$P = \dfrac{R(X + Y) - T^3}{S(X + Y)}$

10. $a = -b + x^2y^4 + 2xy^2z + z^2$

$y = \sqrt{\dfrac{\sqrt{a + b} - z}{x}}$

11. $R = \dfrac{E - IJX}{I}$

12. $C = \dfrac{C_1 C_2}{C_1 + C_2}$

$C_1 = \dfrac{CC_2}{C_2 - C}$

13. $a = \dfrac{a^2 n^2 - 10bL}{9L}$

$n = \sqrt{\dfrac{L(9a + 10b)}{a^2}}$

14. $t = \dfrac{N}{e \times 10^8}$

15. $I = \sqrt{\dfrac{4.187W}{Rt}}$

18. $L_1 = \dfrac{M^2}{K^2L_2}$

16. $r = \dfrac{2\pi m}{F}$

19. $t = \dfrac{R_t - R_o}{aR_o}$

17. $H = \dfrac{4\pi^2 I}{T^2 m}$

20. $C = \dfrac{\lambda^2}{(1,884)^2 L}$

Chapter 4

1. (a) 50
(b) 10
(c) 5

(d) 24
(e) 1.0955
(f) 500

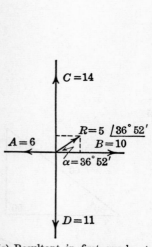

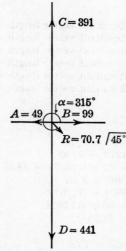

2. (a) Resultant in first quadrant
$(\alpha = 36°52' = 36°.87)$

2. (b) Resultant in fourth quadrant

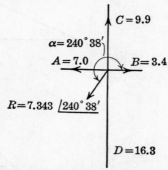

2. (c) Resultant in third quadrant $(\alpha = 240°38' = 240°.64)$

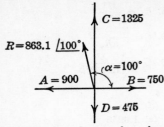

2. (*d*) Resultant in second quadrant

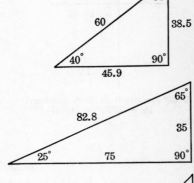

2. (*e*) Resultant in fourth quadrant
($\alpha = 318°48' = 318°.81$)

3. *a.* Resultant vector length = 198.3
   b. Resultant vector length = 139.3
   c. Resultant vector length = 4.28
   d. Resultant vector length = 5
   e. Resultant vector length = 252.8
   f. Resultant vector length = 368.0

Chapter 5

1. $\sin 40° = Y/R$
$0.64279 = Y/60$
$Y = 60 \times 0.64279 = 38.57$
$\cos 40° = X/R$
$0.76604 = X_x/60$
$X = 60 \times 0.76604$
$X = 45.96$

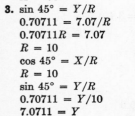

2. $\sin 25° = Y/R$
$0.42262 = 35/R$
$R = 35/0.42262 = 82.8$
$\cos 25° = X/R$
$0.90631 = X/82.8$
$X = (82.8)(0.90631)$
$X = 75$

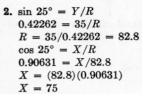

3. $\sin 45° = Y/R$
$0.70711 = 7.07/R$
$0.70711R = 7.07$
$R = 10$
$\cos 45° = X/R$
$R = 10$
$\sin 45° = Y/R$
$0.70711 = Y/10$
$7.0711 = Y$

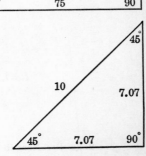

4. $\tan \theta = Y/X$
$\tan \theta = {}^{20}\!/_{10} = 2$
$\theta = 63°26' = 63°43$
$\sin 63°26' = Y/R$
$0.89441 = 20/R$
$0.89441R = 20$
$R = 22.3$
$26°34' = 26°57$

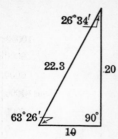

5. $\cos \theta = X/R$
$\cos \theta = {}^{5}\!/_{15}$
$\cos \theta = 0.33333$
$\theta = 70°32' = 70°53 = Y/R$
$0.94284 = Y/15$
$Y = 14.1$
$19°34' = 19°47$

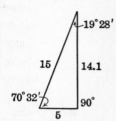

6. $\sin \theta = Y/R$
$\sin \theta = {}^{50}\!/_{90}$
$\theta = 33°45' = 33°75$
$\cos 33°45' = X/R$
$0.83147 = X/90$
$X = 74.8$
$56°15' = 56°25$

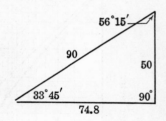

Chapter 6

The student should draw the vector diagrams, which have been omitted here.

1. $V_R = 178.4\underline{/38°47}$

2. $Z_R = 134.9\underline{/22°35}$

3. $I_R = 5.205 \underline{/264°95}$

4. $V_R = 86.6\underline{/90°}$

5. $F_R = 6.229\underline{/132°40}$

6. $c = 5$

7. $c = 7.07$

8. $c = 17.8$

9. $c = 78.8$

10. $c = 1.57$

Chapter 7

1. $c = 43.3015 + j25.000$

2. $c = 5.0000 - j8.6603$

3. $c = 36.05\underline{/123°68}$

4. $A \times B = -130.74 + j1494.285$

5. $A/B = 0.1758 - j0.3770$

Chapter **8**

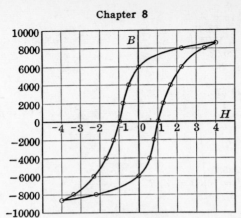

1. Plot of *B-H* curve

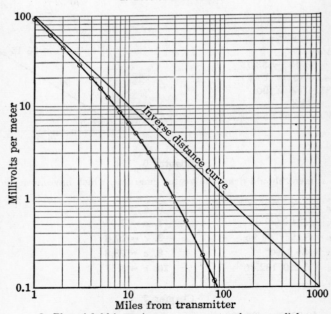

2. Plot of field intensity measurements, along a radial

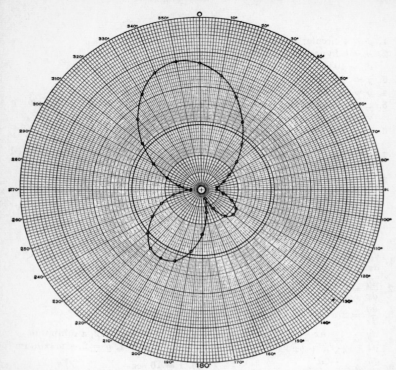

3. Plot of field intensity polar pattern for a three-tower directional antenna

Chapter 9

1. Dependent
2. $x = 3 \qquad y = 5$
3. Inconsistent
4. Dependent
5. Inconsistent
6. $x = 1 \qquad y = 2 \qquad z = 10$
7. $x = 2 \qquad y = \frac{2}{5}$
8. $x = b \qquad y = a$
9. $x = 8.65 \qquad y = 1.4$
10. $R_1 = 10 \qquad R_2 = 20$

Chapter 10

1. $x = 7$ or -1
2. $x = -14$ or 2
3. $x = 3 \pm \sqrt{13}$
4. $x = \dfrac{3 \pm \sqrt{89}}{10}$
5. $x = \frac{2}{3}$ or $\frac{3}{2}$
6. $x = \sqrt{r/2}$ or $\sqrt{s/2}$
7. $x = r/s$ or s/r
8. $k = 4$ or 0
9. $k = 2$ or -6
10. $f = 6$ or 8

Chapter 11

1. $\beta = 4$ circular radians.
2. $\alpha = 6$ hyperbolic radians.
   $\epsilon^\alpha = 403.4$
3. $y = \pm 0.707$
4. $y = \pm 1.732$
5. $\cosh \alpha$ varies from 1 to ∞ as α is increased from 0 to ∞ while $\sinh \alpha$ varies from 0 to ∞ as α is increased from 0 to ∞.
6. $\sin \beta$ and $\cos \beta$ vary between the limits of ± 1. The limits of $\tan \beta$ are $\pm \infty$.
7. $\epsilon^{j\beta}$ multiplied by a vector will rotate the vector β radians. ϵ^α multiplied by a vector will change only its magnitude.
8. $\tanh \alpha = 0.76159$
   $\sinh \alpha = 1.17520$
   $\cosh \alpha = 1.54308$
   $\coth \alpha = 1.313$
   $\alpha = 1$ radian.

Chapter 12

1. $\dfrac{dy}{dx} = 2ax + b$

2. $\dfrac{dy}{dx} = 3\sqrt{\dfrac{x}{2}}$

3. $\dfrac{dy}{dx} = 2(a + x)$

4. $\dfrac{dy}{dx} = \dfrac{bx}{2\sqrt{a + bx}} + \sqrt{a + bx}$

5. $\dfrac{dy}{dx} = \dfrac{-2a}{(a + x)^2}$

6. $\dfrac{d^2y}{dx^2} = -\dfrac{1}{4}\,x^{-3/2}$

7. $\dfrac{dI}{dt} = b + 2ct$

8. $v = 16; a = 8$

9. For $x = 1$, $y = 2$, a minimum
   $x = -1$, $y = 6$, a maximum

10. $t = 16$ sec

Chapter 13

1. $\epsilon^2 = 7.38905$
2. $dy/dx = (\alpha + \beta)\epsilon^{(\alpha+\beta)x}$
3. $dy/dx = 2/x$
4. $d(\sin x)/dx = \cos x$
5. $\log 8 = 0.9031$
6. $E = LI\omega \cos \omega t$
7. $dy/d\theta = -2 \cos \theta \sin \theta$
8. $dy/d\theta = -\csc^2 \theta$
9. $d^2y/dx^2 = \alpha^2 \cosh \alpha x$
10. $F = -\frac{1}{2}$, a minimum

Chapter 14

1. $I_{av} = \dfrac{A}{\text{total } x} = \dfrac{10°(5.7149)}{90°} = 0.6349$

2. $I_{av} = \dfrac{A}{\text{total } x} = \dfrac{\dfrac{15°}{3}\,(11.4592)}{90°} = 0.6366$

3. $I_{av} = \dfrac{A}{\text{total } x} = \dfrac{1}{\pi/2} = \dfrac{2}{\pi} = 0.6366$

The trapezoidal rule using nine strips gives an accuracy to two decimal places. Simpson's rule using only six strips gives an accuracy to four decimal places. The integral gives the exact answer $\dfrac{2}{\pi}$.

4. $S_n = 0.6345$

5. $\int \dfrac{dx}{x^5} = \dfrac{x^{-4}}{-4} + C$

$\int ax^9\, dx = \dfrac{a}{10}\, x^{10} + C$

6. $\int 2(x + 1)\, dx = x^2 + 2x + C$

$\int 4(x^2 + 2)(x - 1)\, dx = x^4 - \tfrac{4}{3}\, x^3 + 4x^2 - 8x + C$

7. $\int a^2 \dfrac{dx}{x} = a^2 \ln x + C$

8. $\int x^2 \epsilon^x\, dx = x^2 \epsilon^x - 2x\epsilon^x + 2\epsilon^x + C$

9. $\int \cos 6\ \omega t\, d(\omega t) = \tfrac{1}{6} \sin 6\omega t + C$

$\int 16^{2x}\, dx = \dfrac{16^{2x}}{2 \ln 16} + C$

10. $\int a \ln 10x\, dx = ax(\ln 10x - x) + C$

Chapter 15

1. The nth term is $\dfrac{nx^n}{\lfloor n}$ or $\dfrac{x^n}{\lfloor n - 1}$

The given series is

$$S_n = 0 + x + \frac{x^2}{1} + \frac{x^3}{\lfloor 2} + \cdots + \frac{x^n}{\lfloor n - 1}$$

while the convergent test series is

$$S_n = 1 + x + x^2 + x^3 + \cdots + n^n$$

Comparing term by term, the given series is equal or less than corresponding terms of the test series; hence the series is convergent.

2. Given series $S_n = 1 + \dfrac{1}{2\frac{2}{3}} + \dfrac{1}{3\frac{2}{3}} + \cdots + \dfrac{1}{n\frac{2}{3}}$

Test series $S_n = 1 + \dfrac{1}{2^p} + \dfrac{1}{3^p} + \cdots + \dfrac{1}{n^p}$

Comparing terms, the exponent p is less than 1; hence the series is convergent and the nth term is given by the first equation.

3. Ratio test $\dfrac{\dfrac{1}{\lfloor n}}{\dfrac{1}{\lfloor n - 1}} = \dfrac{1}{n} < 1$; hence the series is convergent.

4. $\sqrt{37} = (1 + 6^2)^{\frac{1}{2}} = 6\left(1 + \dfrac{1}{6^2}\right)^{\frac{1}{2}} = 6 + \dfrac{1}{12} - \dfrac{1}{1728} + \cdots$

$= 6.082754$ accurate to four decimal places

$= 6.082763.$ *Check by extracting the square root.*

5.
$$\begin{aligned}
f(x) &= \sin x & f(0) &= 0 \\
f'(x) &= \cos x & f'(0) &= 1 \\
f''(x) &= -\sin x & f''(0) &= 0 \\
f'''(x) &= -\cos x & f'''(0) &= -1
\end{aligned}$$

From these values

$$\sin x = 0 + x + 0 - \frac{x^3}{\underline{3}} + 0 + \frac{x^5}{\underline{5}} + \cdots$$

$$= x - \frac{x^3}{\underline{3}} + \frac{x^5}{\underline{5}} - \cdots$$

6. Dividing the series of $\sin x$ by $1 - x$ gives

$$\frac{\sin x}{1 - x} = x + x^2 + \frac{5}{6} x^3 + \cdots$$

7. $\epsilon^{2.1} = \epsilon^2 + (2.1 - 2)\epsilon^2 + \frac{(2.1 - 2)^2}{\underline{2}} \epsilon^2$

$$= 7.3891(1 + \frac{1}{10} + \frac{1}{200}) = 7.3891(1.105) = 8.1670$$

The tables give $\epsilon^{2.1} = 8.1660$, or an error of 0.0008.

8. $M_3/\underline{\psi_3} = \frac{j}{\pi} \int_0^\pi \epsilon^{-i3x} dx + \frac{j}{\pi} \int_\pi^{2\pi} - E\epsilon^{-i3x} dx = \frac{4E}{3\pi} \underline{/0°}$

$M_3 \sin (3\omega t + \psi_3) = \frac{4E}{\pi} \left(\frac{1}{3} \sin 3\omega t \right)$

9. $M_2/\underline{\psi_2} = \frac{j}{\pi} \int_{-\pi}^{+\pi} \frac{E}{\pi} x\epsilon^{-i2x} dx = \frac{-E}{2\pi} \underline{/0°}$

$M_2 \sin (2\omega t + \psi_2) = \frac{-E}{\pi} \sin 2\omega t$

10. $M_1/\underline{\psi_1} = \frac{j}{\pi} \int_{-\frac{\pi}{2}}^{+\frac{\pi}{2}} \frac{2E}{\pi} x\epsilon^{-ix} dx + \frac{j}{\pi} \int_{\frac{\pi}{2}}^{\frac{3\pi}{2}} \left(2E - \frac{2E}{\pi} x \right) \epsilon^{-ix} dx$

$$= \frac{8E}{\pi^2}$$

$$m_1 \sin (\omega t + \psi_1) = \frac{8E}{\pi^2} \sin \omega t$$

MICROWAVE TRANSMISSION DATA
by Theodore Moreno

Radio engineers, microwave systems designers, applied physicists, power and communications engineers will find this book both an excellent introduction to general transmission-line theory and a detailed study of microwave transmission lines and associated components. Originally produced as a classified government publication, it was completely rewritten and enlarged (4 entirely new chapters) under the auspices of the Sperry Corporation for declassified publication following the war.

Ordinary transmission-line theory, attenuation, power carrying capacity, parameters of coaxial lines, breakdown in a coaxial line, higher modes; flexible cables, coaxial line structures and transformers; field distribution and power-carrying capacity of wave guides, wave guides without metal walls; attenuation in wave guides through conductor losses, dialectric losses, or both; obstacles, discontinuities and junctions; resonant structures; coupling between coaxial lines and wave guides, tunable wave guide impedance transformers; wave guides partially and completely filled with dialectric material; cavity resonators, calculation of resonator parameters, effects of temperature and humidity; and many other important topics are carefully analyzed. Of particular importance, even the most theoretical discussions are related·to practical questions of design — there is nothing which is not of immediate value or reference use to the engineer.

Complete, revised and enlarged edition. 324 circuit diagrams, figures, etc. Tables of dialectric, flexible cable, etc., data. Index. ix + 248pp. 5-3/8 x 8.   S459 Paperbound **$1.50**

MICROWAVE TRANSMISSION
by J. C. Slater

This was the first text dealing exclusively with microwaves. It brings together points of view of field and circuit theory, both for the graduate student in physics or electrical engineering, and the microwave technician. This volume continues to be a most valuable text for students, since it contains a point of view not represented in most later studies. It is also unusual and helpful in its emphasis on detailed experiments and practical problems as supplements to mathematical analysis.

The study is concerned with generators which produce microwaves, receivers which detect them, and the intermediate stage of radiation between antennas. Maxwell's equations are used to study the electromagnetic field, which demands much more attention in this area than in ordinary circuits. Much of the work is devoted to finding out how far the simple circuit methods are really justified by the more correct methods of Maxwell's equations, and how far these simple methods must be supplemented.

The author discusses such aspects of transmission lines as the infiinte line with distributed parameters, the terminated line and reflection, impedance of the terminated line, and other problems. Maxwell's equations, plane waves, and reflection are examined, as well as rectangular wave guides, undamped waves in rectangular pipes, and Poynting's vectors and plane waves. Other chapters cover the general transmission line problem, the principa wave in the parallel-wire transmission line, in the coaxial line, composite transmission lines and impedance matching, Maxwell's equations in spherical coordinates, the field of an electric dipole, absorption and scattering by a dipole, coupling of coaxial lines and wave guides, and much more.

Corrected, unabridged reprinting of 1st edition. Introduction. Index. 76 illustrations. x + 309pp. 5⅜ x 8.   S564 Paperbound **$1.50**

CALCULUS REFRESHER FOR TECHNICAL MEN
by A. A. Klaf

This book is unique in English as a refresher for engineers, technicians and students who either wish to brush up their calculus or who find parts of calculus unclear. Not an ordinary textbook, it is instead an examination of the most important aspects of integral and differential calculus in terms of the 756 questions most likely to occur to the technical reader. It provides an easily followed presentation, and may be used as either an introductory or a supplementary textbook.

The first part of this volume deals with simple differential calculus, covering constants, variables, functions, increments, derivatives, differentiation, logarithms, curvature of curves, and similar topics. The second part treats fundamental ideas of integration (inspection, substitution, transformation, reduction), areas and volumes, mean value, successive and partial integration, double and triple intergration. In all cases, the author stresses practical rather than theoretical aspects, and builds upon situations such as might occur under normal working conditions.

A 50-page section illustrates the application of calculus to specific problems of civil and nautical engineering, electricity, stress and strain, elasticity, industrial engineering, and similar fields.

Index. 756 questions answered. 566 problems for measuring knowledge and improvement, with answers included. 36 pages of constants and formulae for easy reference. v + 431pp. 5⅜ x 8.

S370 Paperbound **$2.00**

TRIGONOMETRY REFRESHER FOR TECHNICAL MEN
by A. Albert Klaf

This modern question and answer text covers most important aspects of plane and spherical trigonometry. 913 specially selected questions and detailed answers will help you to brush up your trigonometry or clear up difficulties on special areas.

The first portion of this book discusses plane trigonometry, covering angles, quadrants, trigonometrical functions, graphical representation, interpolation, equations, logarithms, solution of triangles, and the use of the slide rule, and similar topics. 188 pages then discuss the application of plane trigonometry to special problems in navigation, surveying, elasticity, architecture, and various fields of engineering. Small angles, periodic functions, vectors, polar coordinates, De Moivre's theorem are fully examined. The third section of the book then discusses spherical trigonometry and the solution of spherical triangles, with their application in terrestrial and astronomical problems.

Methods of saving time in numerical calculations, a simplification of the principal functions of an angle by use of a "shadow and perpendicular" concept, and much practical information on calculation aids make this an especially valuable book.

913 questions answered for you. 1738 problems to test your progress; answers to odd numbers. 494 figures. 24 pages of useful formulaes, functions. Index. x + 629pp. 5⅜ x 8.

Paperbound $2.00

Catalogue of Dover
SCIENCE BOOKS

BOOKS THAT EXPLAIN SCIENCE

THE NATURE OF LIGHT AND COLOUR IN THE OPEN AIR, M. Minnaert. Why is falling snow sometimes black? What causes mirages, the fata morgana, multiple suns and moons in the sky; how are shadows formed? Prof. Minnaert of U. of Utrecht answers these and similar questions in optics, light, colour, for non-specialists. Particularly valuable to nature, science students, painters, photographers. "Can best be described in one word—fascinating!" Physics Today. Translated by H. M. Kremer-Priest, K. Jay. 202 illustrations, including 42 photos. xvi + 362pp. 5⅜ x 8.   T196 Paperbound **$1.95**

THE RESTLESS UNIVERSE, Max Born. New enlarged version of this remarkably readable account by a Nobel laureate. Moving from sub-atomic particles to universe, the author explains in very simple terms the latest theories of wave mechanics. Partial contents: air and its relatives, electrons and ions, waves and particles, electronic structure of the atom, nuclear physics. Nearly 1000 illustrations, including 7 animated sequences. 325pp. 6 x 9.   T412 Paperbound **$2.00**

MATTER AND LIGHT, THE NEW PHYSICS, L. de Broglie. Non-technical papers by a Nobel laureate explain electromagnetic theory, relativity, matter, light, radiation, wave mechanics, quantum physics, philosophy of science. Einstein, Planck, Bohr, others explained so easily that no mathematical training is needed for all but 2 of the 21 chapters. "Easy simplicity and lucidity . . . should make this source-book of modern physcis available to a wide public," Saturday Review. Unabridged. 300pp. 5⅜ x 8.   T35 Paperbound **$1.60**

THE COMMON SENSE OF THE EXACT SCIENCES, W. K. Clifford. Introduction by James Newman, edited by Karl Pearson. For 70 years this has been a guide to classical scientific, mathematical thought. Explains with unusual clarity basic concepts such as extension of meaning of symbols, characteristics of surface boundaries, properties of plane figures, vectors, Cartesian method of determining position, etc. Long preface by Bertrand Russell. Bibliography of Clifford. Corrected. 130 diagrams redrawn. 249pp. 5⅜ x 8.
                                                                    T61 Paperbound **$1.60**

THE EVOLUTION OF SCIENTIFIC THOUGHT FROM NEWTON TO EINSTEIN, A. d'Abro. Einstein's special, general theories of relativity, with historical implications, analyzed in non-technical terms. Excellent accounts of contributions of Newton, Riemann, Weyl, Planck, Eddington, Maxwell, Lorentz, etc., are treated in terms of space, time, equations of electromagnetics, finiteness of universe, methodology of science. "Has become a standard work," Nature. 21 diagrams. 482pp. 5⅜ x 8.   T2 Paperbound **$2.00**

BRIDGES AND THEIR BUILDERS, D. Steinman, S. R. Watson. Engineers, historians, everyone ever fascinated by great spans will find this an endless source of information and interest. Dr. Steinman, recent recipient of Louis Levy Medal, is one of the great bridge architects, engineers of all time. His analysis of great bridges of history is both authoritative and easily followed. Greek, Roman, medieval, oriental bridges; modern works such as Brooklyn Bridge, Golden Gate Bridge, etc. described in terms of history, constructional principles, artistry, function. Most comprehensive, accurate semi-popular history of bridges in print in English. New, greatly revised, enlarged edition. 23 photographs, 26 line drawings. xvii + 401pp. 5⅜ x 8.   T431 Paperbound **$1.95**

CONCERNING THE NATURE OF THINGS, Sir William Bragg. Christmas lectures at Royal Society by Nobel laureate, dealing with atoms, gases, liquids, and various types of crystals. No scientific background is needed to understand this remarkably clear introduction to basic processes and aspects of modern science. "More interesting than any bestseller," London Morning Post. 32pp. of photos. 57 figures. xii + 232pp. 5⅜ x 8.　　T31 Paperbound **$1.35**

THE RISE OF THE NEW PHYSICS, A. d'Abro. Half million word exposition, formerly titled "The Decline of Mechanism," for readers not versed in higher mathematics. Only thorough explanation in everyday language of core of modern mathematical physical theory, treating both classical, modern views. Scientifically impeccable coverage of thought from Newtonian system through theories of Dirac, Heisenberg, Fermi's statistics. Combines history, exposition; broad but unified, detailed view, with constant comparison of classical, modern views. "A must for anyone doing serious study in the physical sciences," J. of the Franklin Inst. "Extraordinary faculty . . . to explain ideas and theories . . . in language of everyday life," Isis. Part I of set: philosophy of science, from practice of Newton, Maxwell, Poincaré, Einstein, etc. Modes of thought, experiment, causality, etc. Part II: 100 pp. on grammar, vocabulary of mathematics, discussions of functions, groups, series, Fourier series, etc. Remainder treats concrete, detailed coverage of both classical, quantum physics: analytic mechanics, Hamilton's principle, electromagnetic waves, thermodynamics, Brownian movement, special relativity, Bohr's atom, de Broglie's wave mechanics, Heisenberg's uncertainty, scores of other important topics. Covers discoveries, theories of d'Alembert, Born, Cantor, Debye, Euler, Foucault, Galois, Gauss, Hadamard, Kelvin, Kepler Laplace, Maxwell, Pauli, Rayleigh Volterra, Weyl, more than 180 others. 97 illustrations. ix + 982pp. 5⅜ x 8.
　　T3 Vol. 1 Paperbound **$2.00**
　　T4 Vol. II Paperbound **$2.00**

SPINNING TOPS AND GYROSCOPIC MOTION, John Perry. Well-known classic of science still unsurpassed for lucid, accurate, delightful exposition. How quasi-rigidity is induced in flexible, fluid bodies by rapid motions; why gyrostat falls, top rises; nature, effect of internal fluidity on rotating bodies; etc. Appendixes describe practical use of gyroscopes in ships, compasses, monorail transportation. 62 figures. 128pp. 5⅜ x 8.
　　T416 Paperbound **$1.00**

FOUNDATIONS OF PHYSICS, R. B. Lindsay, H. Margenau. Excellent bridge between semipopular and technical writings. Discussion of methods of physical description, construction of theory; valuable to physicist with elementary calculus. Gives meaning to data, tools of modern physics. Contents: symbolism, mathematical equations; space and time; foundations of mechanics; probability; physics, continua; electron theory; relativity; quantum mechanics; causality; etc. "Thorough and yet not overdetailed. Unreservedly recommended," Nature. Unabridged corrected edition. 35 illustrations. xi + 537pp. 5⅜ x 8.　　S377 Paperbound **$2.45**

FADS AND FALLACIES IN THE NAME OF SCIENCE, Martin Gardner. Formerly entitled "In the Name of Science," the standard account of various cults, quack systems, delusions which have masqueraded as science: hollow earth fanatics, orgone sex energy, dianetics, Atlantis, Forteanism, flying saucers, medical fallacies like zone therapy, etc. New chapter on Bridey Murphy, psionics, other recent manifestations. A fair reasoned appraisal of eccentric theory which provides excellent innoculation. "Should be read by everyone, scientist or non-scientist alike," R. T. Birge, Prof. Emeritus of Physics, Univ. of Calif; Former Pres., Amer. Physical Soc. x + 365pp. 5⅜ x 8.　　T394 Paperbound **$1.50**

ON MATHEMATICS AND MATHEMATICIANS, R. E. Moritz. A 10 year labor of love by discerning, discriminating Prof. Moritz, this collection conveys the full sense of mathematics and personalities of great mathematicians. Anecdotes, aphorisms, reminiscences, philosophies, definitions, speculations, biographical insights, etc. by great mathematicians, writers: Descartes, Mill, Locke, Kant, Coleridge, Whitehead, etc. Glimpses into lives of great mathematicians, from Archimedes to Euler, Gauss, Weierstrass. To mathematicians, a superb browsing-book. To laymen, exciting revelation of fullness of mathematics. Extensive cross index. 410pp. 5⅜ x 8.　　T489 Paperbound **$1.95**

GUIDE TO THE LITERATURE OF MATHEMATICS AND PHYSICS, N. G. Parke III. Over 5000 entries under approximately 120 major subject headings, of selected most important books, monographs, periodicals, articles in English, plus important works in German, French, Italian, Spanish, Russian (many recently available works). Covers every branch of physics, math, related engineering. Includes author, title, edition, publisher, place, date, number of volumes, number of pages. 40 page introduction on basic problems of research, study provides useful information on organization, use of libraries, psychology of learning, etc. Will save you hours of time. 2nd revised edition. Indices of authors, subjects. 464pp. 5⅜ x 8.　　S447 Paperbound **$2.49**

THE STRANGE STORY OF THE QUANTUM, An Account for the General Reader for the Growth of Ideas Underlying Our Present Atomic Knowledge, B. Hoffmann. Presents lucidly, expertly, with barest amount of mathematics, problems and theories which led to modern quantum physics. Begins with late 1800's when discrepancies were noticed; with illuminating analogies, examples, goes through concepts of Planck, Einstein, Pauli, Schroedinger, Dirac, Sommerfield, Feynman, etc. New postscript through 1958. "Of the books attempting an account of the history and contents of modern atomic physics which have come to my attention, this is the best," H. Margenau, Yale U., in Amer. J. of Physics. 2nd edition. 32 tables, illustrations. 275pp. 5⅜ x 8.　　T518 Paperbound **$1.45**

HISTORY OF SCIENCE
AND PHILOSOPHY OF SCIENCE

THE VALUE OF SCIENCE, Henri Poincaré. Many of most mature ideas of "last scientific universalist" for both beginning, advanced workers. Nature of scientific truth, whether order is innate in universe or imposed by man, logical thought vs. intuition (relating to Weierstrass, Lie, Riemann, etc), time and space (relativity, psychological time, simultaneity), Herz's concept of force, values within disciplines of Maxwell, Carnot, Mayer, Newton, Lorentz, etc. iii + 147pp. 5⅜ x 8.   S469 Paperbound **$1.35**

PHILOSOPHY AND THE PHYSICISTS, L. S. Stebbing. Philosophical aspects of modern science examined in terms of lively critical attack on ideas of Jeans, Eddington. Tasks of science, causality, determinism, probability, relation of world physics to that of everyday experience, philosophical significance of Planck-Bohr concept of discontinuous energy levels, inferences to be drawn from Uncertainty Principle, implications of "becoming" involved in 2nd law of thermodynamics, other problems posed by discarding of Laplacean determinism. 285pp. 5⅜ x 8.   T480 Paperbound **$1.65**

THE PRINCIPLES OF SCIENCE, A TREATISE ON LOGIC AND THE SCIENTIFIC METHOD, W. S. Jevons. Milestone in development of symbolic logic remains stimulating contribution to investigation of inferential validity in sciences. Treats inductive, deductive logic, theory of number, probability, limits of scientific method; significantly advances Boole's logic, contains detailed introduction to nature and methods of probability in physics, astronomy, everyday affairs, etc. In introduction, Ernest Nagel of Columbia U. says, "[Jevons] continues to be of interest as an attempt to articulate the logic of scientific inquiry." liii + 786pp. 5⅜ x 8.   S446 Paperbound **$2.98**

A HISTORY OF ASTRONOMY FROM THALES TO KEPLER, J. L. E. Dreyer. Only work in English to give complete history of cosmological views from prehistoric times to Kepler. Partial contents: Near Eastern astronomical systems, Early Greeks, Homocentric spheres of Euxodus, Epicycles, Ptolemaic system, Medieval cosmology, Copernicus, Kepler, much more. "Especially useful to teachers and students of the history of science . . . unsurpassed in its field," Isis. Formerly "A History of Planetary Systems from Thales to Kepler." Revised foreword by W. H. Stahl. xvii + 430pp. 5⅜ x 8.   S79 Paperbound **$1.98**

A CONCISE HISTORY OF MATHEMATICS, D. Struik. Lucid study of development of ideas, techniques, from Ancient Near East, Greece, Islamic science, Middle Ages, Renaissance, modern times. Important mathematicians described in detail. Treatment not anecdotal, but analytical development of ideas. Non-technical—no math training needed. "Rich in content, thoughtful in interpretations," U.S. Quarterly Booklist. 60 illustrations including Greek, Egyptian manuscripts, portraits of 31 mathematicians. 2nd edition. xix + 299pp. 5⅜ x 8.   S255 Paperbound **$1.75**

THE PHILOSOPHICAL WRITINGS OF PEIRCE, edited by Justus Buchler. A carefully balanced expositon of Peirce's complete system, written by Peirce himself. It covers such matters as scientific method, pure chance vs. law, symbolic logic, theory of signs, pragmatism, experiment, and other topics. "Excellent selection . . . gives more than adequate evidence of the range and greatness," Personalist. Formerly entitled "The Philosophy of Peirce." xvi + 368pp.   T217 Paperbound **$1.95**

SCIENCE AND METHOD, Henri Poincaré. Procedure of scientific discovery, methodology, experiment, idea-germination—processes by which discoveries come into being. Most significant and interesting aspects of development, application of ideas. Chapters cover selection of facts, chance, mathematical reasoning, mathematics and logic; Whitehead, Russell, Cantor, the new mechanics, etc. 288pp. 5⅜ x 8.   S222 Paperbound **$1.35**

SCIENCE AND HYPOTHESIS, Henri Poincaré. Creative psychology in science. How such concepts as number, magnitude, space, force, classical mechanics developed, how modern scientist uses them in his thought. Hypothesis in physics, theories of modern physics. Introduction by Sir James Larmor. "Few mathematicians have had the breadth of vision of Poincaré, and none is his superior in the gift of clear exposition," E. T. Bell. 272pp. 5⅜ x 8.   S221 Paperbound **$1.35**

ESSAYS IN EXPERIMENTAL LOGIC, John Dewey. Stimulating series of essays by one of most influential minds in American philosophy presents some of his most mature thoughts on wide range of subjects. Partial contents: Relationship between inquiry and experience; dependence of knowledge upon thought; character logic; judgments of practice, data, and meanings; stimuli of thought, etc. viii + 444pp. 5⅜ x 8.   T73 Paperbound **$1.95**

WHAT IS SCIENCE, Norman Campbell. Excellent introduction explains scientific method, role of mathematics, types of scientific laws. Contents: 2 aspects of science, science and nature, laws of chance, discovery of laws, explanation of laws, measurement and numerical laws, applications of science. 192pp. 5⅜ x 8.   S43 Paperbound **$1.25**

FROM EUCLID TO EDDINGTON: A STUDY OF THE CONCEPTIONS OF THE EXTERNAL WORLD, Sir Edmund Whittaker. Foremost British scientist traces development of theories of natural philosophy from western rediscovery of Euclid to Eddington, Einstein, Dirac, etc. 5 major divisions: Space, Time and Movement; Concepts of Classical Physics; Concepts of Quantum Mechanics; Eddington Universe. Contrasts inadequacy of classical physics to understand physical world with present day attempts of relativity, non-Euclidean geometry, space curvature, etc. 212pp. 5⅜ x 8. T491 Paperbound **$1.35**

THE ANALYSIS OF MATTER, Bertrand Russell. How do our senses accord with the new physics? This volume covers such topics as logical analysis of physics, prerelativity physics, causality, scientific inference, physics and perception, special and general relativity, Weyl's theory, tensors, invariants and their physical interpretation, periodicity and qualitative series. "The most thorough treatment of the subject that has yet been published," The Nation. Introduction by L. E. Denonn. 422pp. 5⅜ x 8. T231 Paperbound **$1.95**

LANGUAGE, TRUTH, AND LOGIC, A. Ayer. A clear introduction to the Vienna and Cambridge schools of Logical Positivism. Specific tests to evaluate validity of ideas, etc. Contents: function of philosophy, elimination of metaphysics, nature of analysis, a priori, truth and probability, etc. 10th printing. "I should like to have written it myself," Bertrand Russell. 160pp. 5⅜ x 8. T10 Paperbound **$1.25**

THE PSYCHOLOGY OF INVENTION IN THE MATHEMATICAL FIELD, J. Hadamard. Where do ideas come from? What role does the unconscious play? Are ideas best developed by mathematical reasoning, word reasoning, visualization? What are the methods used by Einstein, Poincaré, Galton, Riemann? How can these techniques be applied by others? One of the world's leading mathematicians discusses these and other questions. xiii + 145pp. 5⅜ x 8. T107 Paperbound **$1.25**

GUIDE TO PHILOSOPHY, C. E. M. Joad. By one of the ablest expositors of all time, this is not simply a history or a typological survey, but an examination of central problems in terms of answers afforded by the greatest thinkers: Plato, Aristotle, Scholastics, Leibniz, Kant, Whitehead, Russell, and many others. Especially valuable to persons in the physical sciences; over 100 pages devoted to Jeans, Eddington, and others, the philosophy of modern physics, scientific materialism, pragmatism, etc. Classified bibliography. 592pp. 5⅜ x 8. T50 Paperbound **$2.00**

SUBSTANCE AND FUNCTION, and EINSTEIN'S THEORY OF RELATIVITY, Ernst Cassirer. Two books bound as one. Cassirer establishes a philosophy of the exact sciences that takes into consideration new developments in mathematics, shows historical connections. Partial contents: Aristotelian logic, Mill's analysis, Helmholtz and Kronecker, Russell and cardinal numbers, Euclidean vs. non-Euclidean geometry, Einstein's relativity. Bibliography. Index. xxi + 464pp. 5⅜ x 8. T50 Paperbound **$2.00**

FOUNDATIONS OF GEOMETRY, Bertrand Russell. Nobel laureate analyzes basic problems in the overlap area between mathematics and philosophy: the nature of geometrical knowledge, the nature of geometry, and the applications of geometry to space. Covers history of non-Euclidean geometry, philosophic interpretations of geometry, especially Kant, projective and metrical geometry. Most interesting as the solution offered in 1897 by a great mind to a problem still current. New introduction by Prof. Morris Kline, N.Y. University. "Admirably clear, precise, and elegantly reasoned analysis," International Math. News. xii + 201pp. 5⅜ x 8. S233 Paperbound **$1.60**

THE NATURE OF PHYSICAL THEORY, P. W. Bridgman. How modern physics looks to a highly unorthodox physicist—a Nobel laureate. Pointing out many absurdities of science, demonstrating inadequacies of various physical theories, weighs and analyzes contributions of Einstein, Bohr, Heisenberg, many others. A non-technical consideration of correlation of science and reality. xi + 138pp. 5⅜ x 8. S33 Paperbound **$1.25**

EXPERIMENT AND THEORY IN PHYSICS, Max Born. A Nobel laureate examines the nature and value of the counterclaims of experiment and theory in physics. Synthetic versus analytical scientific advances are analyzed in works of Einstein, Bohr, Heisenberg, Planck, Eddington, Milne, others, by a fellow scientist. 44pp. 5⅜ x 8. S308 Paperbound **60¢**

A SHORT HISTORY OF ANATOMY AND PHYSIOLOGY FROM THE GREEKS TO HARVEY, Charles Singer. Corrected edition of "The Evolution of Anatomy." Classic traces anatomy, physiology from prescientific times through Greek, Roman periods, dark ages, Renaissance, to beginning of modern concepts. Centers on individuals, movements, that definitely advanced anatomical knowledge. Plato, Diocles, Erasistratus, Galen, da Vinci, etc. Special section on Vesalius. 20 plates. 270 extremely interesting illustrations of ancient, Medieval, enaissance, Oriental origin. xii + 209pp. 5⅜ x 8. T389 Paperbound **$1.75**

SPACE - TIME - MATTER, Hermann Weyl. "The standard treatise on the general theory of relativity," (Nature), by world renowned scientist. Deep, clear discussion of logical coherence of general theory, introducing all needed tools: Maxwell, analytical geometry, non-Euclidean geometry, tensor calculus, etc. Basis is classical space-time, before absorption of relativity. Contents: Euclidean space, mathematical form, metrical continuum, general theory, etc. 15 diagrams. xviii + 330pp. 5⅜ x 8. S267 Paperbound **$1.75**

MATTER AND MOTION, James Clerk Maxwell. Excellent exposition begins with simple particles, proceeds gradually to physical systems beyond complete analysis; motion, force, properties of centre of mass of material system; work, energy, gravitation, etc. Written with all Maxwell's original insights and clarity. Notes by E. Larmor. 17 diagrams. 178pp. 5⅜ x 8.
S188 Paperbound **$1.25**

PRINCIPLES OF MECHANICS, Heinrich Hertz. Last work by the great 19th century physicist is not only a classic, but of great interest in the logic of science. Creating a new system of mechanics based upon space, time, and mass, it returns to axiomatic analysis, understanding of the formal or structural aspects of science, taking into account logic, observation, a priori elements. Of great historical importance to Poincaré, Carnap, Einstein, Milne. A 20 page introduction by R. S. Cohen, Wesleyan University, analyzes the implications of Hertz's thought and the logic of science. 13 page introduction by Helmholtz. xlii + 274pp. 5⅜ x 8.
S316 Clothbound **$3.50**
S317 Paperbound **$1.75**

FROM MAGIC TO SCIENCE, Charles Singer. A great historian examines aspects of science from Roman Empire through Renaissance. Includes perhaps best discussion of early herbals, penetrating physiological interpretation of "The Visions of Hildegarde of Bingen." Also examines Arabian, Galenic influences; Pythagoras' sphere, Paracelsus; reawakening of science under Leonardo da Vinci, Vesalius; Lorica of Gildas the Briton; etc. Frequent quotations with translations from contemporary manuscripts. Unabridged, corrected edition. 158 unusual illustrations from Classical, Medieval sources. xxvii + 365pp. 5⅜ x 8.
T390 Paperbound **$2.00**

A HISTORY OF THE CALCULUS, AND ITS CONCEPTUAL DEVELOPMENT, Carl B. Boyer. Provides laymen, mathematicians a detailed history of the development of the calculus, from beginnings in antiquity to final elaboration as mathematical abstraction. Gives a sense of mathematics not as technique, but as habit of mind, in progression of ideas of Zeno, Plato, Pythagoras, Eudoxus, Arabic and Scholastic mathematicians, Newton, Leibniz, Taylor, Descartes, Euler, Lagrange, Cantor, Weierstrass, and others. This first comprehensive, critical history of the calculus was originally entitled "The Concepts of the Calculus." Foreword by R. Courant. 22 figures. 25 page bibliography. v + 364pp. 5⅜ x 8.
S509 Paperbound **$2.00**

A DIDEROT PICTORIAL ENCYCLOPEDIA OF TRADES AND INDUSTRY, Manufacturing and the Technical Arts in Plates Selected from "L'Encyclopédie ou Dictionnaire Raisonné des Sciences, des Arts, et des Métiers" of Denis Diderot. Edited with text by C. Gillispie. First modern selection of plates from high-point of 18th century French engraving. Storehouse of technological information to historian of arts and science. Over 2,000 illustrations on 485 full page plates, most of them original size, show trades, industries of fascinating era in such great detail that modern reconstructions might be made of them. Plates teem with men, women, children performing thousands of operations; show sequence, general operations, closeups, details of machinery. Illustrates such important, interesting trades, industries as sowing, harvesting, beekeeping, tobacco processing, fishing, arts of war, mining, smelting, casting iron, extracting mercury, making gunpowder, cannons, bells, shoeing horses, tanning, papermaking, printing, dying, over 45 more categories. Professor Gillispie of Princeton supplies full commentary on all plates, identifies operations, tools, processes, etc. Material is presented in lively, lucid fashion. Of great interest to all studying history of science, technology. Heavy library cloth. 920pp. 9 x 12.
T421 2 volume set **$18.50**

DE MAGNETE, William Gilbert. Classic work on magnetism, founded new science. Gilbert was first to use word "electricity," to recognize mass as distinct from weight, to discover effect of heat on magnetic bodies; invented an electroscope, differentiated between static electricity and magnetism, conceived of earth as magnet. This lively work, by first great experimental scientist, is not only a valuable historical landmark, but a delightfully easy to follow record of a searching, ingenious mind. Translated by P. F. Mottelay. 25 page biographical memoir. 90 figures. lix + 368pp. 5⅜ x 8.
S470 Paperbound **$2.00**

HISTORY OF MATHEMATICS, D. E. Smith. Most comprehensive, non-technical history of math in English. Discusses lives and works of over a thousand major, minor figures, with footnotes giving technical information outside book's scheme, and indicating disputed matters. Vol. I: A chronological examination, from primitive concepts through Egypt, Babylonia, Greece, the Orient, Rome, the Middle Ages, The Renaissance, and to 1900. Vol. II: The development of ideas in specific fields and problems, up through elementary calculus. "Marks an epoch . . . will modify the entire teaching of the history of science," George Sarton. 2 volumes, total of 510 illustrations, 1355pp. 5⅜ x 8. Set boxed in attractive container.
T429, 430 Paperbound, the set **$5.00**

THE PHILOSOPHY OF SPACE AND TIME, H. Reichenbach. An important landmark in development of empiricist conception of geometry, covering foundations of geometry, time theory, consequences of Einstein's relativity, including: relations between theory and observations; coordinate definitions; relations between topological and metrical properties of space; psychological problem of visual intuition of non-Euclidean structures; many more topics important to modern science and philosophy. Majority of ideas require only knowledge of intermediate math. "Still the best book in the field," Rudolf Carnap. Introduction by R. Carnap. 49 figures. xviii + 296pp. 5⅜ x 8.
S443 Paperbound **$2.00**

FOUNDATIONS OF SCIENCE: THE PHILOSOPHY OF THEORY AND EXPERIMENT, N. Campbell.
A critique of the most fundamental concepts of science, particularly physics. Examines why certain propositions are accepted without question, demarcates science from philosophy, etc. Part I analyzes presuppositions of scientific thought: existence of material world, nature of laws, probability, etc; part 2 covers nature of experiment and applications of mathematics: conditions for measurement, relations between numerical laws and theories, error, etc. An appendix covers problems arising from relativity, force, motion, space, time. A classic in its field. "A real grasp of what science is," Higher Educational Journal. xiii + 565pp. 5⅝ x 8⅜. S372 Paperbound **$2.95**

THE STUDY OF THE HISTORY OF MATHEMATICS and THE STUDY OF THE HISTORY OF SCIENCE, G. Sarton. Excellent introductions, orientation, for beginning or mature worker. Describes duty of mathematical historian, incessant efforts and genius of previous generations. Explains how today's discipline differs from previous methods. 200 item bibliography with critical evaluations, best available biographies of modern mathematicians, best treatises on historical methods is especially valuable. 10 illustrations. 2 volumes bound as one. 113pp. + 75pp. 5⅜ x 8. T240 Paperbound **$1.25**

MATHEMATICAL PUZZLES

MATHEMATICAL PUZZLES OF SAM LOYD, selected and edited by **Martin Gardner.** 117 choice puzzles by greatest American puzzle creator and innovator, from his famous "Cyclopedia of Puzzles." All unique style, historical flavor of originals. Based on arithmetic, algebra, probability, game theory, route tracing, topology, sliding block, operations research, geometrical dissection. Includes famous "14-15" puzzle which was national craze, "Horse of a Different Color" which sold millions of copies. 120 line drawings, diagrams. Solutions. xx + 167pp. 5⅜ x 8. T498 Paperbound **$1.00**

SYMBOLIC LOGIC and THE GAME OF LOGIC, Lewis Carroll. "Symbolic Logic" is not concerned with modern symbolic logic, but is instead a collection of over 380 problems posed with charm and imagination, using the syllogism, and a fascinating diagrammatic method of drawing conclusions. In "The Game of Logic" Carroll's whimsical imagination devises a logical game played with 2 diagrams and counters (included) to manipulate hundreds of tricky syllogisms. The final section, "Hit or Miss" is a lagniappe of 101 additional puzzles in the delightful Carroll manner. Until this reprint edition, both of these books were rarities costing up to $15 each. Symbolic Logic: Index. xxxi + 199pp. The Game of Logic: 96pp. 2 vols. bound as one. 5⅜ x 8. T492 Paperbound **$1.50**

PILLOW PROBLEMS and A TANGLED TALE, Lewis Carroll. One of the rarest of all Carroll's works, "Pillow Problems" contains 72 original math puzzles, all typically ingenious. Particularly fascinating are Carroll's answers which remain exactly as he thought them out, reflecting his actual mental process. The problems in "A Tangled Tale" are in story form, originally appearing as a monthly magazine serial. Carroll not only gives the solutions, but uses answers sent in by readers to discuss wrong approaches and misleading paths, and grades them for insight. Both of these books were rarities until this edition, "Pillow Problems" costing up to $25, and "A Tangled Tale" $15. Pillow Problems: Preface and Introduction by Lewis Carroll. xx + 109pp. A Tangled Tale: 6 illustrations. 152pp. Two vols. bound as one. 5⅜ x 8. T493 Paperbound **$1.50**

NEW WORD PUZZLES, G. L. Kaufman. 100 brand new challenging puzzles on words, combinations, never before published. Most are new types invented by author, for beginners and experts both. Squares of letters follow chess moves to build words; symmetrical designs made of synonyms; rhymed crostics; double word squares; syllable puzzles where you fill in missing syllables instead of missing letter; many other types, all new. Solutions. "Excellent," Recreation. 100 puzzles. 196 figures. vi + 122pp. 5⅜ x 8. T344 Paperbound **$1.00**

MATHEMATICAL EXCURSIONS, H. A. Merrill. Fun, recreation, insights into elementary problem solving. Math expert guides you on by-paths not generally travelled in elementary math courses—divide by inspection, Russian peasant multiplication; memory systems for pi; odd, even magic squares; dyadic systems; square roots by geometry; Tchebichev's machine; dozens more. Solutions to more difficult ones. "Brain stirring stuff . . . a classic," Genie. 50 illustrations. 145pp. 5⅜ x 8. T350 Paperbound **$1.00**

THE BOOK OF MODERN PUZZLES, G. L. Kaufman. Over 150 puzzles, absolutely all new material based on same appeal as crosswords, deduction puzzles, but with different principles, techniques. 2-minute teasers, word labyrinths, design, pattern, logic, observation puzzles, puzzles testing ability to apply general knowledge to peculiar situations, many others. Solutions. 116 illustrations. 192pp. 5⅜ x 8. T143 Paperbound **$1.00**

MATHEMAGIC, MAGIC PUZZLES, AND GAMES WITH NUMBERS, R. V. Heath. Over 60 puzzles, stunts, on properties of numbers. Easy techniques for multiplying large numbers mentally, identifying unknown numbers, finding date of any day in any year. Includes The Lost Digit, 3 Acrobats, Psychic Bridge, magic squares, triangles, cubes, others not easily found elsewhere. Edited by J. S. Meyer. 76 illustrations. 128pp. 5⅜ x 8. T110 Paperbound **$1.00**

PUZZLE QUIZ AND STUNT FUN, J. Meyer. 238 high-priority puzzles, stunts, tricks—math puzzles like The Clever Carpenter, Atom Bomb, Please Help Alice; mysteries, deductions like The Bridge of Sighs, Secret Code; observation puzzlers like The American Flag, Playing Cards, Telephone Dial; over 200 others with magic squares, tongue twisters, puns, anagrams. Solutions. Revised, enlarged edition of "Fun-To-Do." Over 100 illustrations. 238 puzzles, stunts, tricks. 256pp. 5⅜ x 8. **T337 Paperbound $1.00**

101 PUZZLES IN THOUGHT AND LOGIC, C. R. Wylie, Jr. For readers who enjoy challenge, stimulation of logical puzzles without specialized math or scientific knowledge. Problems entirely new, range from relatively easy to brainteasers for hours of subtle entertainment. Detective puzzles, find the lying fisherman, how a blind man identifies color by logic, many more. Easy-to-understand introduction to logic of puzzle solving and general scientific method. 128pp. 5⅜ x 8. **T367 Paperbound $1.00**

CRYPTANALYSIS, H. F. Gaines. Standard elementary, intermediate text for serious students. Not just old material, but much not generally known, except to experts. Concealment, Transposition, Substitution ciphers; Vigenere, Kasiski, Playfair, multafid, dozens of other techniques. Formerly "Elementary Cryptanalysis." Appendix with sequence charts, letter frequencies in English, 5 other languages, English word frequencies. Bibliography. 167 codes. New to this edition: solutions to codes. vi + 230pp. 5⅜ x 8⅜. **T97 Paperbound $1.95**

CRYPTOGRAPHY, L. D. Smith. Excellent elementary introduction to enciphering, deciphering secret writing. Explains transposition, substitution ciphers; codes; solutions; geometrical patterns, route transcription, columnar transposition, other methods. Mixed cipher systems; single, polyalphabetical substitutions; mechanical devices; Vigenere; etc. Enciphering Japanese; explanation of Baconian biliteral cipher; frequency tables. Over 150 problems. Bibliography. Index. 164pp. 5⅜ x 8. **T247 Paperbound $1.00**

MATHEMATICS, MAGIC AND MYSTERY, M. Gardner. Card tricks, metal mathematics, stage mind-reading, other "magic" explained as applications of probability, sets, number theory, etc. Creative examination of laws, applications. Scores of new tricks, insights. 115 sections on cards, dice, coins; vanishing tricks, many others. No sleight of hand—math guarantees success. "Could hardly get more entertainment . . . easy to follow," Mathematics Teacher. 115 illustrations. xii + 174pp. 5⅜ x 8. **T335 Paperbound $1.00**

AMUSEMENTS IN MATHEMATICS, H. E. Dudeney. Foremost British originator of math puzzles, always witty, intriguing, paradoxical in this classic. One of largest collections. More than 430 puzzles, problems, paradoxes. Mazes, games, problems on number manipulations, unicursal, other route problems, puzzles on measuring, weighing, packing, age, kinship, chessboards, joiners', crossing river, plane figure dissection, many others. Solutions. More than 450 illustrations. viii + 258pp. 5⅜ x 8. **T473 Paperbound $1.25**

THE CANTERBURY PUZZLES H. E. Dudeney. Chaucer's pilgrims set one another problems in story form. Also Adventures of the Puzzle Club, the Strange Escape of the King's Jester, the Monks of Riddlewell, the Squire's Christmas Puzzle Party, others. All puzzles are original, based on dissecting plane figures, arithmetic, algebra, elementary calculus, other branches of mathematics, and purely logical ingenuity. "The limit of ingenuity and intricacy," The Observer. Over 110 puzzles, full solutions. 150 illustrations. viii + 225 pp. 5⅜ x 8. **T474 Paperbound $1.25**

MATHEMATICAL PUZZLES FOR BEGINNERS AND ENTHUSIASTS, G. Mott-Smith. 188 puzzles to test mental agility. Inference, interpretation, algebra, dissection of plane figures, geometry, properties of numbers, decimation, permutations, probability, all are in these delightful problems. Includes the Odic Force, How to Draw an Ellipse, Spider's Cousin, more than 180 others. Detailed solutions. Appendix with square roots, triangular numbers, primes, etc. 135 illustrations. 2nd revised edition. 248pp. 5⅜ x 8. **T198 Paperbound $1.00**

MATHEMATICAL RECREATIONS, M. Kraitchik. Some 250 puzzles, problems, demonstrations of recreation mathematics on relatively advanced level. Unusual historical problems trom Greek, Medieval, Arabic, Hindu sources; modern problems on "mathematics without numbers," geometry, topology, arithmetic, etc. Pastimes derived from figurative, Mersenne, Fermat numbers: fairy chess; latruncles: reversi; etc. Full solutions. Excellent insights into special fields of math. "Strongly recommended to all who are interested in the lighter side of mathematics," Mathematical Gaz. 181 illustrations. 330pp. 5⅜ x 8. **T163 Paperbound $1.75**

FICTION

FLATLAND, E. A. Abbott. A perennially popular science-fiction classic about life in a 2-dimensional world, and the impingement of higher dimensions. Political, satiric, humorous, moral overtones. This land where women are straight lines and the lowest and most dangerous classes are isosceles triangles with 3° vertices conveys brilliantly a feeling for many concepts of modern science. 7th edition. New introduction by Banesh Hoffmann. 128pp. 5⅜ x 8. **T1 Paperbound $1.00**

SEVEN SCIENCE FICTION NOVELS OF H. G. WELLS. Complete texts, unabridged, of seven of Wells' greatest novels: The War of the Worlds, The Invisible Man, The Island of Dr. Moreau, The Food of the Gods, First Men in the Moon, In the Days of the Comet, The Time Machine. Still considered by many experts to be the best science-fiction ever written, they will offer amusements and instruction to the scientific minded reader. "The great master," Sky and Telescope. 1051pp. 5⅜ x 8.   T264 Clothbound **$3.95**

28 SCIENCE FICTION STORIES OF H. G. WELLS. Unabridged! This enormous omnibus contains 2 full length novels—Men Like Gods, Star Begotten—plus 26 short stories of space, time, invention, biology, etc. The Crystal Egg, The Country of the Blind, Empire of the Ants, The Man Who Could Work Miracles, Aepyornis Island, A Story of the Days to Come, and 20 others "A master . . . not surpassed by . . . writers of today," The English Journal. 915pp. 5⅜ x 8.   T265 Clothbound **$3.95**

FIVE ADVENTURE NOVELS OF H. RIDER HAGGARD. All the mystery and adventure of darkest Africa captured accurately by a man who lived among Zulus for years, who knew African ethnology, folkways as did few of his contemporaries. They have been regarded as examples of the very best high adventure by such critics as Orwell, Andrew Lang, Kipling. Contents: She, King Solomon's Mines, Allan Quatermain, Allan's Wife, Maiwa's Revenge. "Could spin a yarn so full of suspense and color that you couldn't put the story down," Sat. Review. 821pp. 5⅜ x 8.   T108 Clothbound **$3.95**

CHESS AND CHECKERS

LEARN CHESS FROM THE MASTERS, Fred Reinfeld. Easiest, most instructive way to improve your game—play 10 games against such masters as Marshall, Znosko-Borovsky, Bronstein, Najdorf, etc., with each move graded by easy system. Includes ratings for alternate moves possible. Games selected for interest, clarity, easily isolated principles. Covers Ruy Lopez, Dutch Defense, Vienna Game openings; subtle, intricate middle game variations; all-important end game. Full annotations. Formerly "Chess by Yourself." 91 diagrams. viii + 144pp. 5⅜ x 8.   T362 Paperbound **$1.00**

REINFELD ON THE END GAME IN CHESS, Fred Reinfeld. Analyzes 62 end games by Alekhine, Flohr, Tarrasch, Morphy, Capablanca, Rubinstein, Lasker, Reshevsky, other masters. Only 1st rate book with extensive coverage of error—tell exactly what is wrong with each move you might have made. Centers around transitions from middle play to end play. King and pawn, minor pieces, queen endings; blockage, weak, passed pawns, etc. "Excellent . . . a boon," Chess Life. Formerly "Practical End Play." 62 figures. vi + 177pp. 5⅜ x 8.
T417 Paperbound **$1.25**

HYPERMODERN CHESS as developed in the games of its greatest exponent, ARON NIMZO-VICH, edited by Fred Reinfeld. An intensely original player, analyst, Nimzovich's approaches startled, often angered the chess world. This volume, designed for the average player, shows how his iconoclastic methods won him victories over Alekhine, Lasker, Marshall, Rubinstein, Spielmann, others, and infused new life into the game. Use his methods to startle opponents, invigorate play. "Annotations and introductions to each game . . . are excellent," Times (London). 180 diagrams. viii + 220pp. 5⅜ x 8.   T448 Paperbound **$1.35**

THE ADVENTURE OF CHESS, Edward Lasker. Lively reader, by one of America's finest chess masters, including: history of chess, from ancient Indian 4-handed game of Chaturanga to great players of today; such delights and oddities as Maelzel's chess-playing automaton that beat Napoleon 3 times; etc. One of most valuable features is author's personal recollections of men he has played against—Nimzovich, Emanuel Lasker, Capablanca, Alekhine, etc. Discussion of chess-playing machines (newly revised). 5 page chess primer. 11 illustrations. 53 diagrams. 296pp. 5⅜ x 8.   S510 Paperbound **$1.45**

THE ART OF CHESS, James Mason. Unabridged reprinting of latest revised edition of most famous general study ever written. Mason, early 20th century master, teaches beginning, intermediate player over 90 openings; middle game, end game, to see more moves ahead, to plan purposefully, attack, sacrifice, defend, exchange, govern general strategy. "Classic . . . one of the clearest and best developed studies," Publishers Weekly. Also included, a complete supplement by F. Reinfeld, "How Do You Play Chess?", invaluable to beginners for its lively question-and-answer method. 448 diagrams. 1947 Reinfeld-Bernstein text. Bibliography. xvi + 340pp. 5⅜ x 8.   T463 Paperbound **$1.85**

MORPHY'S GAMES OF CHESS, edited by P. W. Sergeant. Put boldness into your game by flowing brilliant, forceful moves of the greatest chess player of all time. 300 of Morphy's best games, carefully annotated to reveal principles. 54 classics against masters like Anderssen, Harrwitz, Bird, Paulsen, and others. 52 games at odds; 54 blindfold games; plus over 100 others. Follow his interpretation of Dutch Defense, Evans Gambit, Giuoco Piano, Ruy Lopez, many more. Unabridged reissue of latest revised edition. New introduction by F. Reinfeld. Annotations, introduction by Sergeant. 235 diagrams. x + 352pp. 5⅜ x 8.
T386 Paperbound **$1.75**

WIN AT CHECKERS, M. Hopper. (Formerly "Checkers.") Former World's Unrestricted Checker Champion discusses principles of game, expert's shots, traps, problems for beginner, standard openings, locating best move, end game, opening "blitzkrieg" moves to draw when behind, etc. Over 100 detailed questions, answers anticipate problems. Appendix. 75 problems with solutions, diagrams. 79 figures. xi + 107pp. 5⅜ x 8. T363 Paperbound $1.00

HOW TO FORCE CHECKMATE, Fred Reinfeld. If you have trouble finishing off your opponent, here is a collection of lightning strokes and combinations from actual tournament play. Starts with 1-move checkmates, works up to 3-move mates. Develops ability to lock ahead, gain new insights into combinations, complex or deceptive positions; ways to estimate weaknesses, strengths of you and your opponent. "A good deal of amusement and instruction," Times, (London). 300 diagrams. Solutions to all positions. Formerly "Challenge to Chess Players." 111pp. 5⅜ x 8. T417 Paperbound $1.25

A TREASURY OF CHESS LORE, edited by Fred Reinfeld. Delightful collection of anecdotes, short stories, aphorisms by, about masters; poems, accounts of games, tournaments, photographs; hundreds of humorous, pithy, satirical, wise, historical episodes, comments, word portraits. Fascinating "must" for chess players; revealing and perhaps seductive to those who wonder what their friends see in game. 49 photographs (14 full page plates). 12 diagrams. xi + 306pp. 5⅜ x 8. T458 Paperbound $1.75

WIN AT CHESS, Fred Reinfeld. 300 practical chess situations, to sharpen your eye, test skill against masters. Start with simple examples, progress at own pace to complexities. This selected series of crucial moments in chess will stimulate imagination, develop stronger, more versatile game. Simple grading system enables you to judge progress. "Extensive use of diagrams is a great attraction," Chess. 300 diagrams. Notes, solutions to every situation. Formerly "Chess Quiz." vi + 120pp. 5⅜ x 8. T433 Paperbound $1.00

MATHEMATICS:
ELEMENTARY TO INTERMEDIATE

HOW TO CALCULATE QUICKLY, H. Sticker. Tried and true method to help mathematics of everyday life. Awakens "number sense"—ability to see relationships between numbers as whole quantities. A serious course of over 9000 problems and their solutions through techniques not taught in schools: left-to-right multiplications, new fast division, etc. 10 minutes a day will double or triple calculation speed. Excellent for scientist at home in higher math, but dissatisfied with speed and accuracy in lower math. 256pp. 5 x 7¼. Paperbound $1.00

FAMOUS PROBLEMS OF ELEMENTARY GEOMETRY, Felix Klein. Expanded version of 1894 Easter lectures at Göttingen. 3 problems of classical geometry: squaring the circle, trisecting angle, doubling cube, considered with full modern implications: transcendental numbers, pi, etc. "A modern classic . . . no knowledge of higher mathematics is required," Scientia. Notes by R. Archibald. 16 figures. xi + 92pp. 5⅜ x 8. T298 Paperbound $1.00

HIGHER MATHEMATICS FOR STUDENTS OF CHEMISTRY AND PHYSICS, J. W. Mellor. Practical, not abstract, building problems out of familiar laboratory material. Covers differential calculus, coordinate, analytical geometry, functions, integral calculus, infinite series, numerical equations, differential equations, Fourier's theorem probability, theory of errors, calculus of variations, determinants. "If the reader is not familiar with this book, it will repay him to examine it," Chem. and Engineering News. 800 problems. 189 figures. xxi + 641pp. 5⅜ x 8. S193 Paperbound $2.25

TRIGONOMETRY REFRESHER FOR TECHNICAL MEN, A. A. Klaf. 913 detailed questions, answers cover most important aspects of plane, spherical trigonometry—particularly useful in clearing up difficulties in special areas. Part I: plane trig, angles, quadrants, functions, graphical representation, interpolation, equations, logs, solution of triangle, use of slide rule, etc. Next 188 pages discuss applications to navigation, surveying, elasticity, architecture, other special fields. Part 3: spherical trig, applications to terrestrial, astronomical problems. Methods of time-saving, simplification of principal angles, make book most useful. 913 questions answered. 1738 problems, answers to odd numbers. 494 figures. 24 pages of formulas, functions. x + 629pp. 5⅜ x 8. T371 Paperbound $2.00

CALCULUS REFRESHER FOR TECHNICAL MEN, A. A. Klaf. 756 questions examine most important aspects of integral, differential calculus. Part I: simple differential calculus, constants, variables, functions, increments, logs, curves, etc. Part 2: fundamental ideas of integrations, inspection, substitution, areas, volumes, mean value, double, triple integration, etc. Practical aspects stressed. 50 pages illustrate applications to specific problems of civil, nautical engineering, electricity, stress, strain, elasticity, similar fields. 756 questions answered. 566 problems, mostly answered. 36pp. of useful constants, formulas. v + 431pp. 5⅜ x 8. T370 Paperbound $2.00

MONOGRAPHS ON TOPICS OF MODERN MATHEMATICS, edited by J. W. A. Young. Advanced mathematics for persons who have forgotten, or not gone beyond, high school algebra. 9 monographs on foundation of geometry, modern pure geometry, non-Euclidean geometry, fundamental propositions of algebra, algebraic equations, functions, calculus, theory of numbers, etc. Each monograph gives proofs of important results, and descriptions of leading methods, to provide wide coverage. "Of high merit," Scientific American. New introduction by Prof. M. Kline, N.Y. Univ. 100 diagrams. xvi + 416pp. 6⅛ x 9¼.
S289 Paperbound **$2.00**

MATHEMATICS IN ACTION, O. G. Sutton. Excellent middle level application of mathematics to study of universe, demonstrates how math is applied to ballistics, theory of computing machines, waves, wave-like phenomena, theory of fluid flow, meteorological problems, statistics, flight, similar phenomena. No knowledge of advanced math required. Differential equations, Fourier series, group concepts, Eigenfunctions, Planck's constant, airfoil theory, and similar topics explained so clearly in everyday language that almost anyone can derive benefit from reading this even if much of high-school math is forgotten. 2nd edition. 88 figures. viii + 236pp. 5⅜ x 8.
T450 Clothbound **$3.50**

ELEMENTARY MATHEMATICS FROM AN ADVANCED STANDPOINT, Felix Klein. Classic text, an outgrowth of Klein's famous integration and survey course at Göttingen. Using one field to interpret, adjust another, it covers basic topics in each area, with extensive analysis. Especially valuable in areas of modern mathematics. "A great mathematician, inspiring teacher, . . . deep insight," Bul., Amer. Math Soc.

Vol. I. ARITHMETIC, ALGEBRA, ANALYSIS. Introduces concept of function immediately, enlivens discussion with graphical, geometric methods. Partial contents: natural numbers, special properties, complex numbers. Real equations with real unknowns, complex quantities. Logarithmic, exponential functions, infinitesimal calculus. Transcendence of e and pi, theory of assemblages. Index. 125 figures. ix + 274pp. 5⅜ x 8.
S151 Paperbound **$1.75**

Vol. II. GEOMETRY. Comprehensive view, accompanies space perception inherent in geometry with analytic formulas which facilitate precise formulation. Partial contents: Simplest geometric manifold; line segments, Grassman determinant principles, classification of configurations of space. Geometric transformations: affine, projective, higher point transformations, theory of the imaginary. Systematic discussion of geometry and its foundations. 141 illustrations. ix + 214pp. 5⅜ x 8.
S151 Paperbound **$1.75**

A TREATISE ON PLANE AND ADVANCED TRIGONOMETRY, E. W. Hobson. Extraordinarily wide coverage, going beyond usual college level, one of few works covering advanced trig in full detail. By a great expositor with unerring anticipation of potentially difficult points. Includes circular functions; expansion of functions of multiple angle; trig tables; relations between sides, angles of triangles; complex numbers; etc. Many problems fully solved. "The best work on the subject," Nature. Formerly entitled "A Treatise on Plane Trigonometry." 689 examples. 66 figures. xvi + 383pp. 5⅜ x 8.
S353 Paperbound **$1.95**

NON-EUCLIDEAN GEOMETRY, Roberto Bonola. The standard coverage of non-Euclidean geometry. Examines from both a historical and mathematical point of view geometries which have arisen from a study of Euclid's 5th postulate on parallel lines. Also included are complete texts, translated, of Bolyai's "Theory of Absolute Space," Lobachevsky's "Theory of Parallels." 180 diagrams. 431pp. 5⅜ x 8.
S27 Paperbound **$1.95**

GEOMETRY OF FOUR DIMENSIONS, H. P. Manning. Unique in English as a clear, concise introduction. Treatment is synthetic, mostly Euclidean, though in hyperplanes and hyperspheres at infinity, non-Euclidean geometry is used. Historical introduction. Foundations of 4-dimensional geometry. Perpendicularity, simple angles. Angles of planes, higher order. Symmetry, order, motion; hyperpyramids, hypercones, hyperspheres; figures with parallel elements; volume, hypervolume in space; regular polyhedroids. Glossary. 78 figures. ix + 348pp. 5⅜ x 8.
S182 Paperbound **$1.95**

MATHEMATICS: INTERMEDIATE TO ADVANCED

GEOMETRY (EUCLIDEAN AND NON-EUCLIDEAN)

THE GEOMETRY OF RENÉ DESCARTES. With this book, Descartes founded analytical geometry. Original French text, with Descartes's own diagrams, and excellent Smith-Latham translation. Contains: Problems the Construction of Which Requires only Straight Lines and Circles; On the Nature of Curved Lines; On the Construction of Solid or Supersolid Problems. Diagrams. 258pp. 5⅜ x 8.
S68 Paperbound **$1.50**

THE WORKS OF ARCHIMEDES, edited by T. L. Heath. All the known works of the great Greek mathematician, including the recently discovered Method of Archimedes. Contains: On Sphere and Cylinder, Measurement of a Circle, Spirals, Conoids, Spheroids, etc. Definitive edition of greatest mathematical intellect of ancient work. 186 page study by Heath discusses Archimedes and history of Greek mathematics. 563pp. 5⅜ x 8. S9 Paperbound **$2.00**

COLLECTED WORKS OF BERNARD RIEMANN. Important sourcebook, first to contain complete text of 1892 "Werke" and the 1902 supplement, unabridged. 31 monographs, 3 complete lecture courses, 15 miscellaneous papers which have been of enormous importance in relativity, topology, theory of complex variables, other areas of mathematics. Edited by R. Dedekind, H. Weber, M. Noether, W. Wirtinger. German text; English introduction by Hans Lewy. 690pp. 5⅜ x 8. S226 Paperbound **$2.85**

THE THIRTEEN BOOKS OF EUCLID'S ELEMENTS, edited by Sir Thomas Heath. Definitive edition of one of very greatest classics of Western world. Complete translation of Heiberg text, plus spurious Book XIV. 150 page introduction on Greek, Medieval mathematics, Euclid, texts, commentators, etc. Elaborate critical apparatus parallels text, analyzing each definition, postulate, proposition, covering textual matters, refutations, supports, extrapolations, etc. This is the full Euclid. Unabridged reproduction of Cambridge U. 2nd edition. 3 volumes. 995 figures. 1426pp. 5⅜ x 8. S88, 89, 90, 3 volume set, paperbound **$6.00**

AN INTRODUCTION TO GEOMETRY OF N DIMENSIONS, D. M. Y. Sommerville. Presupposes no previous knowledge of field. Only book in English devoted exclusively to higher dimensional geometry. Discusses fundamental ideas of incidence, parallelism, perpendicularity, angles between linear space, enumerative geometry, analytical geometry from projective and metric views, polytopes, elementary ideas in analysis situs, content of hyperspacial figures. 60 diagrams. 196pp. 5⅜ x 8. S494 Paperbound **$1.50**

ELEMENTS OF NON-EUCLIDEAN GEOMETRY, D. M. Y. Sommerville. Unique in proceeding step-by-step. Requires only good knowledge of high-school geometry and algebra, to grasp elementary hyperbolic, elliptic, analytic non-Euclidean Geometries; space curvature and its implications; radical axes; homopethic centres and systems of circles; parataxy and parallelism; Gauss' proof of defect area theorem; much more, with exceptional clarity. 126 problems at chapter ends. 133 figures. xvi + 274pp. 5⅜ x 8. S460 Paperbound **$1.50**

THE FOUNDATIONS OF EUCLIDEAN GEOMETRY, H. G. Forder. First connected, rigorous account in light of modern analysis, establishing propositions without recourse to empiricism, without multiplying hypotheses. Based on tools of 19th and 20th century mathematicians, who made it possible to remedy gaps and complexities, recognize problems not earlier discerned. Begins with important relationship of number systems in geometrical figures. Considers classes, relations, linear order, natural numbers, axioms for magnitudes, groups, quasi-fields, fields, non-Archimedian systems, the axiom system (at length), particular axioms (two chapters on the Parallel Axioms), constructions, congruence, similarity, etc. Lists: axioms employed, constructions, symbols in frequent use. 295pp. 5⅜ x 8. S481 Paperbound **$2.00**

CALCULUS, FUNCTION THEORY (REAL AND COMPLEX), FOURIER THEORY

FIVE VOLUME "THEORY OF FUNCTIONS" SET BY KONRAD KNOPP. Provides complete, readily followed account of theory of functions. Proofs given concisely, yet without sacrifice of completeness or rigor. These volumes used as texts by such universities as M.I.T., Chicago, N.Y. City College, many others. "Excellent introduction . . . remarkably readable, concise, clear, rigorous," J. of the American Statistical Association.

ELEMENTS OF THE THEORY OF FUNCTIONS, Konrad Knopp. Provides background for further volumes in this set, or texts on similar level. Partial contents: Foundations, system of complex numbers and Gaussian plane of numbers, Riemann sphere of numbers, mapping by linear functions, normal forms, the logarithm, cyclometric functions, binomial series. "Not only for the young student, but also for the student who knows all about what is in it," Mathematical Journal. 140pp. 5⅜ x 8. S154 Paperbound **$1.35**

THEORY OF FUNCTIONS, PART I, Konrad Knopp. With volume II, provides coverage of basic concepts and theorems. Partial contents: numbers and points, functions of a complex variable, integral of a continuous function, Cauchy's intergral theorem, Cauchy's integral formulae, series with variable terms, expansion and analytic function in a power series, analytic continuation and complete definition of analytic functions, Laurent expansion, types of singularities. vii + 146pp. 5⅜ x 8. S156 Paperbound **$1.35**

THEORY OF FUNCTIONS, PART II, Konrad Knopp. Application and further development of general theory, special topics. Single valued functions, entire, Weierstrass. Meromorphic functions: Mittag-Leffler. Periodic functions. Multiple valued functions. Riemann surfaces. Algebraic functions. Analytical configurations, Riemann surface. x + 150pp. 5⅜ x 8. S157 Paperbound **$1.35**

PROBLEM BOOK IN THE THEORY OF FUNCTIONS, VOLUME I, Konrad Knopp. Problems in elementary theory, for use with Knopp's "Theory of Functions," or any other text. Arranged according to increasing difficulty. Fundamental concepts, sequences of numbers and infinite series, complex variable, integral theorems, development in series, conformal mapping. Answers. viii + 126pp. 5⅜ x 8.
S 158 **Paperbound $1.35**

PROBLEM BOOK IN THE THEORY OF FUNCTIONS, VOLUME II, Konrad Knopp. Advanced theory of functions, to be used with Knopp's "Theory of Functions," or comparable text. Singularities, entire and meromorphic functions, periodic, analytic, continuation, multiple-valued functions, Riemann surfaces, conformal mapping. Includes section of elementary problems. "The difficult task of selecting . . . problems just within the reach of the beginner is here masterfully accomplished," AM. MATH. SOC. Answers. 138pp. 5⅜ x 8.
S159 **Paperbound $1.35**

ADVANCED CALCULUS, E. B. Wilson. Still recognized as one of most comprehensive, useful texts. Immense amount of well-represented, fundamental material, including chapters on vector functions, ordinary differential equations, special functions, calculus of variations, etc., which are excellent introductions to these areas. Requires only one year of calculus. Over 1300 exercises cover both pure math and applications to engineering and physical problems. Ideal reference, refresher. 54 page introductory review. ix + 566pp. 5⅜ x 8.
S504 **Paperbound $2.45**

LECTURES ON THE THEORY OF ELLIPTIC FUNCTIONS, H. Hancock. Reissue of only book in English with so extensive a coverage, especially of Abel, Jacobi, Legendre, Weierstrass, Hermite, Liouville, and Riemann. Unusual fullness of treatment, plus applications as well as theory in discussing universe of elliptic integrals, originating in works of Abel and Jacobi. Use is made of Riemann to provide most general theory. 40-page table of formulas. 76 figures. xxiii + 498pp. 5⅜ x 8.
S483 **Paperbound $2.55**

THEORY OF FUNCTIONALS AND OF INTEGRAL AND INTEGRO-DIFFERENTIAL EQUATIONS, Vito Volterra. Unabridged republication of only English translation. General theory of functions depending on continuous set of values of another function. Based on author's concept of transition from finite number of variables to a continually infinite number. Includes much material on calculus of variations. Begins with fundamentals, examines generalization of analytic functions, functional derivative equations, applications, other directions of theory, etc. New introduction by G. C. Evans. Biography, criticism of Volterra's work by E. Whittaker. xxxx + 226pp. 5⅜ x 8.
S502 **Paperbound $1.75**

AN INTRODUCTION TO FOURIER METHODS AND THE LAPLACE TRANSFORMATION, Philip Franklin. Concentrates on essentials, gives broad view, suitable for most applications. Requires only knowledge of calculus. Covers complex qualities with methods of computing elementary functions for complex values of argument and finding approximations by charts; Fourier series; harmonic anaylsis; much more. Methods are related to physical problems of heat flow, vibrations, electrical transmission, electromagnetic radiation, etc. 828 problems, answers. Formerly entitled "Fourier Methods." x + 289pp. 5⅜ x 8.
S452 **Paperbound $1.75**

THE ANALYTICAL THEORY OF HEAT, Joseph Fourier. This book, which revolutionized mathematical physics, has been used by generations of mathematicians and physicists interested in heat or application of Fourier integral. Covers cause and reflection of rays of heat, radiant heating, heating of closed spaces, use of trigonometric series in theory of heat, Fourier integral, etc. Translated by Alexander Freeman. 20 figures. xxii + 466pp. 5⅜ x 8.
S93 **Paperbound $2.00**

ELLIPTIC INTEGRALS, H. Hancock. Invaluable in work involving differential equations with cubics, quatrics under root sign, where elementary calculus methods are inadequate. Practical solutions to problems in mathematics, engineering, physics; differential equations requiring integration of Lamé's, Briot's, or Bouquet's equations; determination of arc of ellipse, hyperbola, lemiscate; solutions of problems in elastics; motion of a projectile under resistance varying as the cube of the velocity; pendulums; more. Exposition in accordance with Legendre-Jacobi theory. Rigorous discussion of Legendre transformations. 20 figures. 5 place table. 104pp. 5⅜ x 8.
S484 **Paperbound $1.25**

THE TAYLOR SERIES, AN INTRODUCTION TO THE THEORY OF FUNCTIONS OF A COMPLEX VARIABLE, P. Dienes. Uses Taylor series to approach theory of functions, using ordinary calculus only, except in last 2 chapters. Starts with introduction to real variable and complex algebra, derives properties of infinite series, complex differentiation, integration, etc. Covers biuniform mapping, overconvergence and gap theorems, Taylor series on its circle of convergence, etc. Unabridged corrected reissue of first edition. 186 examples, many fully worked out. 67 figures. xii + 555pp. 5⅜ x 8.
S391 **Paperbound $2.75**

LINEAR INTEGRAL EQUATIONS, W. V. Lovitt. Systematic survey of general theory, with some application to differential equations, calculus of variations, problems of math, physics. Includes: integral equation of 2nd kind by successive substitutions; Fredholm's equation as ratio of 2 integral series in lambda, applications of the Fredholm theory, Hilbert-Schmidt theory of symmetric kernels, application, etc. Neumann, Dirichlet, vibratory problems. ix + 253pp. 5⅜ x 8.
S175 **Clothbound $3.50**
S176 **Paperbound $1.60**

12

DOVER SCIENCE BOOKS

DICTIONARY OF CONFORMAL REPRESENTATIONS, H. Kober. Developed by British Admiralty to solve Laplace's equation in 2 dimensions. Scores of geometrical forms and transformations for electrical engineers, Joukowski aerofoil for aerodynamics, Schwartz-Christoffel transformations for hydro-dynamics, transcendental functions. Contents classified according to analytical functions describing transformations with corresponding regions. Glossary. Topological index. 447 diagrams. 6⅛ x 9¼.
.S160 Paperbound **$2.00**

ELEMENTS OF THE THEORY OF REAL FUNCTIONS, J. E. Littlewood. Based on lectures at Trinity College, Cambridge, this book has proved extremely successful in introducing graduate students to modern theory of functions. Offers full and concise coverage of classes and cardinal numbers, well ordered series, other types of series, and elements of the theory of sets of points. 3rd revised edition. vii + 71pp. 5⅜ x 8.
S171 Clothbound **$2.85**
S172 Paperbound **$1.25**

INFINITE SEQUENCES AND SERIES, Konrad Knopp. 1st publication in any language. Excellent introduction to 2 topics of modern mathematics, designed to give student background to penetrate further alone. Sequences and sets, real and complex numbers, etc. Functions of a real and complex variable. Sequences and series. Infinite series. Convergent power series. Expansion of elementary functions. Numerical evaluation of series. v + 186pp. 5⅜ x 8.
S152 Clothbound **$3.50**
S153 Paperbound **$1.75**

THE THEORY AND FUNCTIONS OF A REAL VARIABLE AND THE THEORY OF FOURIER'S SERIES, E. W .Hobson. One of the best introductions to set theory and various aspects of functions and Fourier's series. Requires only a good background in calculus. Exhaustive coverage of: metric and descriptive properties of sets of points; transfinite numbers and order types; functions of a real variable; the Riemann and Lebesgue integrals; sequences and series of numbers; power-series; functions representable by series sequences of continuous functions; trigonometrical series; representation of functions by Fourier's series; and much more. "The best possible guide," Nature. Vol. I: 88 detailed examples, 10 figures. Index. xv + 736pp. Vol. II: 117 detailed examples, 13 figures. x + 780pp. 6⅛ x 9¼.
Vol. I: S387 Paperbound **$3.00**
Vol. II: S388 Paperbound **$3.00**

ALMOST PERIODIC FUNCTIONS, A. S. Besicovitch. Unique and important summary by a well known mathematician covers in detail the two stages of development in Bohr's theory of almost periodic functions: (1) as a generalization of pure periodicity, with results and proofs; (2) the work done by Stepanof, Wiener, Weyl, and Bohr in generalizing the theory. xi + 180pp. 5⅜ x 8.
S18 Paperbound **$1.75**

INTRODUCTION TO THE THEORY OF FOURIER'S SERIES AND INTEGRALS, H. S. Carslaw. 3rd revised edition, an outgrowth of author's courses at Cambridge. Historical introduction, rational, irrational numbers, infinite sequences and series, functions of a single variable, definite integral, Fourier series, and similar topics. Appendices discuss practical harmonic analysis, periodogram analysis, Lebesgue's theory. 84 examples. xiii + 368pp. 5⅜ x 8.
S48 Paperbound **$2.00**

SYMBOLIC LOGIC

THE ELEMENTS OF MATHEMATICAL LOGIC, Paul Rosenbloom. First publication in any language. For mathematically mature readers with no training in symbolic logic. Development of lectures given at Lund Univ., Sweden, 1948. Partial contents: Logic of classes, fundamental theorems, Boolean algebra, logic of propositions, of propositional functions, expressive languages, combinatory logics, development of math within an object language, paradoxes, theorems of Post, Goedel, Church, and similar topics. iv + 214pp. 5⅜ x 8.
S227 Paperbound **$1.45**

INTRODUCTION TO SYMBOLIC LOGIC AND ITS APPLICATION, R. Carnap. Clear, comprehensive, rigorous, by perhaps greatest living master. Symbolic languages analyzed, one constructed. Applications to math (axiom systems for set theory, real, natural numbers), topology (Dedekind, Cantor continuity explanations), physics (general analysis of determination, causality, space-time topology), biology (axiom system for basic concepts). "A masterpiece," Zentralblatt für Mathematik und Ihre Grenzgebiete. Over 300 exercises. 5 figures. xvi + 241pp. 5⅜ x 8.
S453 Paperbound **$1.85**

AN INTRODUCTION TO SYMBOLIC LOGIC, Susanne K. Langer. Probably clearest book for the philosopher, scientist, layman—no special knowledge of math required. Starts with simplest symbols, goes on to give remarkable grasp of Boole-Schroeder, Russell-Whitehead systems, clearly, quickly. Partial Contents: Forms, Generalization, Classes, Deductive System of Classes, Algebra of Logic, Assumptions of Principia Mathematica, Logistics, Proofs of Theorems, etc. "Clearest . . . simplest introduction . . . the intelligent non-mathematician should have no difficulty," MATHEMATICS GAZETTE. Revised, expanded 2nd edition. Truth-value tables. 368pp. 5⅜ 8.
S164 Paperbound **$1.75**

TRIGONOMETRICAL SERIES, Antoni Zygmund. On modern advanced level. Contains carefully organized analyses of trigonometric, orthogonal, Fourier systems of functions, with clear adequate descriptions of summability of Fourier series, proximation theory, conjugate series, convergence, divergence of Fourier series. Especially valuable for Russian, Eastern European coverage. 329pp. 5⅜ x 8.
S290 Paperbound **$1.50**

THE LAWS OF THOUGHT, George Boole. This book founded symbolic logic some 100 years ago. It is the 1st significant attempt to apply logic to all aspects of human endeavour. Partial contents: derivation of laws, signs and laws, interpretations, eliminations, conditions of a perfect method, analysis, Aristotelian logic, probability, and similar topics. xvii + 424pp. 5⅜ x 8.
S28 Paperbound **$2.00**

SYMBOLIC LOGIC, C. I. Lewis, C. H. Langford. 2nd revised edition of probably most cited book in symbolic logic. Wide coverage of entire field; one of fullest treatments of paradoxes; plus much material not available elsewhere. Basic to volume is distinction between logic of extensions and intensions. Considerable emphasis on converse substitution, while matrix system presents supposition of variety of non-Aristotelian logics. Especially valuable sections on strict limitations, existence theorems. Partial contents: Boole-Schroeder algebra; truth value systems, the matrix method; implication and deductibility; general theory of propositions; etc. "Most valuable," Times, London. 506pp. 5⅜ x 8.   S170 Paperbound **$2.00**

GROUP THEORY AND LINEAR ALGEBRA, SETS, ETC.

LECTURES ON THE ICOSAHEDRON AND THE SOLUTION OF EQUATIONS OF THE FIFTH DEGREE, Felix Klein. Solution of quintics in terms of rotations of regular icosahedron around its axes of symmetry. A classic, indispensable source for those interested in higher algebra, geometry, crystallography. Considerable explanatory material included. 230 footnotes, mostly bibliography. "Classical monograph . . . detailed, readable book," Math. Gazette. 2nd edition. xvi + 289pp. 5⅜ x 8.
S314 Paperbound **$1.85**

INTRODUCTION TO THE THEORY OF GROUPS OF FINITE ORDER, R. Carmichael. Examines fundamental theorems and their applications. Beginning with sets, systems, permutations, etc., progresses in easy stages through important types of groups: Abelian, prime power, permutation, etc. Except 1 chapter where matrices are desirable, no higher math is needed. 783 exercises, problems. xvi + 447pp. 5⅜ x 8.
S299 Clothbound **$3.95**
S300 Paperbound **$2.00**

THEORY OF GROUPS OF FINITE ORDER, W. Burnside. First published some 40 years ago, still one of clearest introductions. Partial contents: permutations, groups independent of representation, composition series of a group, isomorphism of a group with itself, Abelian groups, prime power groups, permutation groups, invariants of groups of linear substitution, graphical representation, etc. "Clear and detailed discussion . . . numerous problems which are instructive," Design News. xxiv + 512pp. 5⅜ x 8.   S38 Paperbound **$2.45**

COMPUTATIONAL METHODS OF LINEAR ALGEBRA, V. N. Faddeeva, translated by C. D. Benster. 1st English translation of unique, valuable work, only one in English presenting systematic exposition of most important methods of linear algebra—classical, contemporary. Details of deriving numerical solutions of problems in mathematical physics. Theory and practice. Includes survey of necessary background, most important methods of solution, for exact, iterative groups. One of most valuable features is 23 tables, triple checked for accuracy, unavailable elsewhere. Translator's note. x + 252pp. 5⅜ x 8.   S424 Paperbound **$1.95**

THE CONTINUUM AND OTHER TYPES OF SERIAL ORDER, E. V. Huntington. This famous book gives a systematic elementary account of the modern theory of the continuum as a type of serial order. Based on the Cantor-Dedekind ordinal theory, which requires no technical knowledge of higher mathematics, it offers an easily followed analysis of ordered classes, discrete and dense series, continuous series, Cantor's transfinite numbers. "Admirable introduction to the rigorous theory of the continuum . . . reading easy," Science Progress. 2nd edition. viii + 82pp. 5⅜ x 8.
S129 Clothbound **$2.75**
S130 Paperbound **$1.00**

THEORY OF SETS, E. Kamke. Clearest, amplest introduction in English, well suited for independent study. Subdivisions of main theory, such as theory of sets of points, are discussed, but emphasis is on general theory. Partial contents: rudiments of set theory, arbitrary sets, their cardinal numbers, ordered sets, their order types, well-ordered sets, their cardinal numbers. vii + 144pp. 5⅜ x 8.
S141 Paperbound **$1.35**

CONTRIBUTIONS TO THE FOUNDING OF THE THEORY OF TRANSFINITE NUMBERS, Georg Cantor. These papers founded a new branch of mathematics. The famous articles of 1895-7 are translated, with an 82-page introduction by P. E. B. Jourdain dealing with Cantor, the background of his discoveries, their results, future possibiilties. ix + 211pp. 5⅜ x 8.
S45 Paperbound **$1.25**

14

DOVER SCIENCE BOOKS

NUMERICAL AND GRAPHICAL METHODS, TABLES

JACOBIAN ELLIPTIC FUNCTION TABLES, L. M. Milne-Thomson. Easy-to-follow, practical, not only useful numerical tables, but complete elementary sketch of application of elliptic functions. Covers description of principle properties; complete elliptic integrals; Fourier series, expansions; periods, zeros, poles, residues, formulas for special values of argument; cubic, quartic polynomials; pendulum problem; etc. Tables, graphs form body of book: Graph, 5 figure table of elliptic function sn (u m); cn (u m); dn (u m). 8 figure table of complete elliptic integrals K, K', E, E', nome q. 7 figure table of Jacobian zeta-function Z(u). 3 figures. xi + 123pp. 5⅜ x 8. S194 Paperbound **$1.35**

TABLES OF FUNCTIONS WITH FORMULAE AND CURVES, E. Jahnke, F. Emde. Most comprehensive 1-volume English text collection of tables, formulae, curves of transcendent functions. 4th corrected edition, new 76-page section giving tables, formulae for elementary functions not in other English editions. Partial contents: sine, cosine, logarithmic integral; error integral; elliptic integrals; theta functions; Legendre, Bessel, Riemann, Mathieu, hypergeometric functions; etc. "Out-of-the-way functions for which we know no other source." Scientific Computing Service, Ltd. 212 figures. 400pp. 5⅝ x 8⅜. S133 Paperbound **$2.00**

MATHEMATICAL TABLES, H. B. Dwight. Covers in one volume almost every function of importance in applied mathematics, engineering, physical sciences. Three extremely fine tables of the three trig functions, inverses, to 1000th of radian; natural, common logs; squares, cubes; hyperbolic functions, inverses; $(a^2 + b^2)$ exp: ½a; complete elliptical integrals of 1st, 2nd kind; sine, cosine integrals; exponential integrals; Ei(x) and Ei(−x); binomial coefficients; factorials to 250; surface zonal harmonics, first derivatives; Bernoulli, Euler numbers, their logs to base of 10; Gamma function; normal probability integral; over 60pp. Bessel functions; Riemann zeta function. Each table with formulae generally used, sources of more extensive tables, interpolation data, etc. Over half have columns of differences, to facilitate interpolation. viii + 231pp. 5⅜ x 8. S445 Paperbound **$1.75**

PRACTICAL ANALYSIS, GRAPHICAL AND NUMERICAL METHODS, F. A. Willers. Immensely practical hand-book for engineers. How to interpolate, use various methods of numerical differentiation and integration, determine roots of a single algebraic equation, system of linear equations, use empirical formulas, integrate differential equations, etc. Hundreds of shortcuts for arriving at numerical solutions. Special section on American calculating machines, by T. W. Simpson. Translation by R. T. Beyer. 132 illustrations. 422pp. 5⅜ x 8.
S273 Paperbound **$2.00**

NUMERICAL SOLUTIONS OF DIFFERENTIAL EQUATIONS, H. Levy, E. A. Baggott. Comprehensive collection of methods for solving ordinary differential equations of first and higher order. 2 requirements: practical, easy to grasp; more rapid than school methods. Partial contents: graphical integration of differential equations, graphical methods for detailed solution. Numerical solution. Simultaneous equations and equations of 2nd and higher orders. "Should be in the hands of all in research and applied mathematics, teaching," Nature. 21 figures. viii + 238pp. 5⅜ x 8. S168 Paperbound **$1.75**

NUMERICAL INTEGRATION OF DIFFERENTIAL EQUATIONS, Bennet, Milne, Bateman. Unabridged republication of original prepared for National Research Council. New methods of integration by 3 leading mathematicians: "The Interpolational Polynomial," "Successive Approximation," A. A. Bennett, "Step-by-step Methods of Integration," W. W. Milne. "Methods for Partial Differential Equations," H. Bateman. Methods for partial differential equations, solution of differential equations to non-integral values of a parameter will interest mathematicians, physicists. 288 footnotes, mostly bibliographical. 235 item classified bibliography. 108pp. 5⅜ x 8. S305 Paperbound **$1.35**